Fifty Years of POPULAR MECHANICS *1902-1952*

An album of American progress containing the most fascinating articles, predictions, pictures and inventions that have appeared since the first issue of Popular Mechanics

EDITED BY
Edward L. Throm

SIMON AND SCHUSTER
New York

PUBLISHED BY SIMON AND SCHUSTER, INC.
ROCKEFELLER CENTER, 1230 SIXTH AVENUE,
NEW YORK 20, N. Y.

FIRST PRINTING

MANUFACTURED IN THE UNITED STATES OF AMERICA
PRINTED BY THE ACWELTONE CORPORATION
BOUND BY AMERICAN BOOK-KNICKERBOCKER PRESS, INC.

To the Readers of

POPULAR MECHANICS MAGAZINE

ACKNOWLEDGMENTS

FOR GUIDANCE in the preparation of this book, the editor is deeply indebted to William Harrison Fetridge, Roderick M. Grant, Wayne Whittaker and Clifford B. Hicks; for editorial assistance: James S. Crenshaw, Betty M. Kanameishi and George A. Uskali.

CONTENTS

INTRODUCTION

*THIS is the story of fifty fabulous years. It is a nostalgic album that will bring pangs of reminiscence as vivid as the first orange-winged biplane you watched buzzing and wheeling overhead, the first family auto that was proudly yours—fire-engine red, it was, with a broom handle for steering and a crank that kicked like a mule. In these pages you will live again the exciting, the terrifying, the amusing, the stimulating years from 1902 until now. It seems fitting to tell a little of the story of the storyteller itself—*POPULAR MECHANICS MAGAZINE*, fifty years old now and still growing as it moves into its second half-century.*

Its beginnings were modest. It was started largely on borrowed money in a rented loft on Chicago's West Washington Street and it was generally one man's show. The man: Henry Haven Windsor, forty-one, son of an Iowa minister, a graduate of Grinnell College, editor of two trade magazines and a firm believer way back at the turn of the century that the age of mechanics and science had arrived and needed him to report it to the world.

From the first, POPULAR MECHANICS *displayed the individual flavor that its pages maintain to this day. It started a new style with its pictorial presentation of the mechanical world. It looked at the present and future of science, mechanics and invention, with rarely a backward glance. Its approach was international and cosmopolitan but its language was that which the common man could understand.*

The first issue, dated January 11, 1902, went out bravely to five subscribers and a few hundred persons who paid five cents a copy at the newsstands. Every word was written by the resourceful Mr. Windsor himself, and each of the advertisements had been sold by his personal solicitation. He hired only a bookkeeper and a mail clerk at the start and it was to be many months before either was effectively occupied.

Those first years were lean years of barely met payrolls, of successive bank loans, of opening the mail each day with prayers for an advertising order. But the new magazine caught on. In September, 1903, the 16-page weekly became a 100-page monthly and its format began to mold into the shape that would be familiar to millions: a section devoted to news and general feature articles, a section for shop mechanics, and a section for home craftsmen that pioneered a brand-new reader relationship. Then, as now, POPULAR MECHANICS *was filled with things to do and make—things as simple as a footstool or as complex as a cabin cruiser. Every step was clearly explained and illustrated by scale drawings and photographs. It was a new technique in journalism, and it found an enthusiastic reception.*

The years and decades marched, and POPULAR MECHANICS *marched too. The First World War came, and then the dreary depression. It took its toll of American periodicals, but* POPULAR MECHANICS *helped thousands of readers to weather the economic storm with its useful ideas for small family enterprises and hobbies that could turn a profit. The Second World War precipitated a fresh crisis, but* POPULAR MECHANICS *reached further through its specially printed Overseas Edition.*

There is no word of politics as it portrays the achievements of the American way of doing things, and thus it wins friends for America wherever it is read.

Now what of POPULAR MECHANICS *as it enters upon its second half-century? Henry Haven Windsor died in 1924 after seeing his magazine become a household word in America. His only son, Henry H. Windsor, Jr., now editor and publisher, has carried the magazine to greater heights than his father ever dreamed possible. Of the third generation of the family, Henry Windsor III is now an officer of the company. The magazine with such an obscure beginning now has a circulation well in excess of 1,000,000 copies every month; an estimated readership of 4,500,000. Several foreign editions have been established—in French, Swedish, Danish and Spanish—and bear such familiar-sounding names as* MÉCANIQUE POPULAIRE, POPULÄR MEKANIK, POPULAER MEKANIK *and* MECANICA POPULAR.

Curiously enough, although they are numbered in the millions, the readers of POPULAR MECHANICS *are readily identified. They are men of a particular stamp. They are the men who have become custodians of an American heritage—craftsmanship. They know, as did the colonists and pioneers, the satisfaction of seeing wood and metal take shape under the cutting edges of skillfully guided tools. They are the men who look beyond the brick of a building to see the steel beneath; who know why airplanes fly and vacuum cleaners sweep; how images appear upon your TV screen; how ships float and atoms react. They may be industrialists or farmers or workmen, with a costly array of power tools or only a simple basement workshop. They may be scientists, students or artisans with a passion for probing, inventing, learning. All are practical men, with one thing in common: pride of workmanship.*

Looking back, one might say that a magazine dedicated as was POPULAR MECHANICS *to reporting civilization's technological advance in a fresh, simple, pictorial fashion could not help but succeed, for its beginning almost precisely paralleled the awakening of America to the benefits of science. The period of the magazine's growth coincided with the development of the automobile, the airplane, radio and television, motion pictures, X-ray, nuclear energy . . . with the creation of a vast array of machines, engines, appliances, gadgets to lighten labor and make for better living.*

But it is of the future that its editors are thinking now . . . and of the far greater story they will be telling to you and your children in the half-century just beginning.

Fifty Years of

POPULAR MECHANICS

1902-1952

1902-1911

THE first issue of *Popular Mechanics* Magazine, an entirely new development in its own right, came at a period rich in important discoveries and technological progress. It was, of course, the unprecedented interest of the man in the street toward the marvels of his age that led H. H. Windsor, Sr., to risk the adventure of such a magazine aimed at the popular market. It was apparent to him, as it was to many others, that America stood on the threshold of an age of mechanical miracles.

Because of the inevitable lag between the invention of something new and its entrance into everyday life, the new magazine was to record the development of many things which had actually been invented earlier. Charles Duryea built the first American automobile in 1893; Henry Ford's first car ran on Detroit streets in 1895, and Ransom Olds set up the first plant for the mass production of cars in 1899.

Henry Ford's first car

But the automobile was still a curiosity to the first readers of 1902 issues of *Popular Mechanics.* Ford's second company failed in the same year, and his third and finally successful venture was not begun until 1903. In all, there were only 8,000 automobiles in the United States—most of these were steam or electrically driven.

In a feeble sense, man had already conquered the air in 1902, when the Wright brothers sailed their glider over the sand dunes of Kitty Hawk a thousand times for flights that sometimes lasted a full minute. Their historic first flight in a gasoline-powered plane at Kitty Hawk followed on Dec. 17, 1903. That flight, frankly, seemed of little importance to the editors of *Popular Mechanics.* Like most of their contemporaries, they were watching the cigar-shaped balloons called "sky cycles," most of them pedal-operated, but a few of which were propelled by one-cylinder motorcycle engines. But before the publication's first decade had ended, it had reported Blériot's flight across the English channel (1909) and the flight of Galbraith P. Rodgers from New York to California in 1911 (3,390 miles in 82 hours and 4 minutes flying time, in 68 hops).

Cross-country flight at forty-one miles an hour

It was a decade of progress in other directions. Discovery of the nitrogen fixation process (1902) opened the way for cheap fertilizers, greatest spur to farm production. The first gasoline-powered tractor (1902) and the first caterpillar tractor (1903) were other new tools for America's farmers. The acetylene welding process (1905) was a great forward step in metal fabrication. Other developments of the decade included Einstein's advancement of his theory of relativity (1905), the tungsten filament light (1906), De Forest's radio vacuum tube (1907), the electric iron (1909) and bakelite (1909). Scientists conducted endless experiments with radium and X-rays during the period.

While all this was going on, however, there was little change in the American scene from what it had been before the turn of the century. It was still a rare sight to see an auto chug up to a hitching post—the buggy and the bicycle were still the most common forms of private transportation. The polite art of conversation was still the principal recreation. On summer evenings people gossiped on wide front porches or during the intermission at Saturday night band concerts; in winter in parlors illuminated by gas mantles, heated by "base burners" and made comfortable by Morris chairs, mission furniture and pillows labeled "Souvenir of Niagara Falls."

Gas lights, base-burners and Morris chairs

They talked about bicycle "scorchers" and "bloomer girls"; argued heatedly about the practicality of the Panama Canal; discussed the millionaires —Rockefeller, Morgan, Carnegie, Vanderbilt, Gould, McCormick and Harriman; talked about the "newfangled" notions of some of their neighbors sporting the first electric lights, hot-air furnaces, gas stoves, iceboxes, aluminum kitchenware, window screens and sanitary plumbing. This was the golden age of vaudeville—Weber and Fields, Montgomery and Stone, Lillian Russell, George M. Cohan, Eddie Cantor, Nora Bayes, Fritzie Scheff and Belle Baker—these were some of the household names. And everyone had heard of, if they had not seen, Sarah Bernhardt, Ellen Terry, Richard Mansfield and Henry Irving. Baseball, following the first World Series in 1902, was firmly the favorite sport, and the barbershop talk was of "Pop" Anson, Johnnie Evers and "Iron Man" McGinnity.

The phonograph was still in the awkward stage, so most of the music was homemade. Parlor songs were "The Bowery," "Sidewalks of New

York," "After the Ball," "In My Flying Machine," "Ida" and "Peg of My Heart." There were some who preferred the new "jazz"—introduced by the original Dixieland band, organized in 1905, which toured the larger cities. Nickelodeons quickly became popular after *The Great Train Robbery,* America's first story film, was produced in 1903. By 1908 there were 10,000 of these 5-cent movie houses. The "fast set" played progressive euchre, or danced the one-step and the fox trot. "Mashers" tipped small-brimmed derbies and smiled over high-banded collars at demure ladies in the high-necked, full-skirted, lacy costumes typified by the Gibson Girl. Sarsaparilla, chewing gum and Milwaukee beer were the reigning minor vices.

Jazz and Western movies get started

Frank Norris died in 1902, unable to enjoy the success of his last book, *The Pit,* published a year later. Jack London was closing his long and productive writing career; Theodore Dreiser was just beginning his, and Upton Sinclair was gaining recognition as a writer. Eleven per cent of the people could not read or write, but a new high school was being opened somewhere in the nation every day.

Theodore Roosevelt wielded his "big stick" at home and abroad during most of this decade (1901-1909). These were the years that saw Oklahoma admitted to the Union (1907); the passage of the pure food laws, federal meat inspection and the Reclamation Act; creation of the Army General Staff, the Bureau of Immigration and the Departments of Commerce and Labor. America was just winning recognition as a world power, having established the Caribbean as a "United States lake," extended the Monroe Doctrine in Venezuela and the Dominican Republic, put down the Cuban revolution, gained control of the Panama Canal Zone and begun digging the "big ditch."

The big stick and the big ditch

By 1910 the population of the country was nearly 76 million. There were 19 cities with more than 200,000 people, but two of every three Americans lived on a farm or in a small village. More than 5 million workers were employed in half a million factories. The average wage was between $500 and $600 a year. A few industries had the 8-hour day, but this was quite rare.

Vol 1, No. 18. CHICAGO, MAY, 10, 1902. PRICE 5 CENTS.

TINY TORPEDO BOAT ALARMS NAVIES

The Latest Terror of the Deep

A new terror of the deep has made its appearance in the form of a tiny torpedo boat, only 11 feet long, built for one man only, the invention of Thomas J. Moriarty, of the Newport Manufacturing Company, Newport, R. I. It can dart about on top of the water, under the water, and defy the most tempestuous seas.

The greatest war vessels of the earth's powers would be at its mercy in the event of war. With no danger of detection the little boat can slip down, plant a torpedo on the bottom of the largest man of war, make its escape and rise to the surface again in time to see the monster iron clad be blown into fragments.

Looking like a fish as it glides about on the surface, like a fish it can drop down into the ocean's depths and change its course at the operator's will. It will open up anew to man the mysteries of the deep and make him at home in the realm of the fishes. To the water it is what the perfected flying machine will be to the air.

Almost as long as man has been trying to invent a flying machine he has been trying to invent a one-man sub-marine boat, but this is the first time he has succeeded in devising such a boat—one that will delve into the mysterious deep, rise and sink at the will of the operator. "The boat is guided, submerged and controlled

There is no record that this "terror of the deep" ever terrorized anyone except, perhaps, its operator. This was by no means the first submarine. The earliest was built for James I in England in 1620 and was propelled by twelve rowers. And then in 1776 David Bushnell built one, driven by a propeller and a hand crank, with which he tried to sink an English warship in New York Harbor. The idea was to fasten a time charge to the bottom by means of a screw thread. He couldn't pierce the ship's copper sheathing, however, so he released it and hastily paddled away, allowing the powder charge to explode on time but without damage. During the Civil War the Housatonic, *while blockading Charleston, was attacked by a submarine armed with a spar torpedo fixed to its bow. The* Housatonic *was sunk and the submarine swamped through an open hatch. It went down and her crew of nine men was lost*

Europe was well ahead of the Unted States in the development of vending machines. In London, sandwiches and beverages were dispensed by machines in railroad stations as early as 1895. A Rush, Pa., man patented a machine to vend hot peanuts in 1897

by one person only," says the American Shipbuilder, "and is provided with a conning tower about the size of a bucket. The operator rests in an inclined position in a padded frame. This position gives free play to his legs in operating the pedals connected with the propeller shaft. The man keeps his head in the conning tower, which is provided with a glass front through which he can observe his course and objects about him. Two handles, connected with the propeller shaft, are in easy reach of his hands."

DESPERATE FIGHT WITH A PIANO.

Paderewski Has a Narrow Escape in His State Room During a Storm.

A fight with a piano that came near proving disastrous to the greatest of pianists, occurred on shipboard while Paderewski was on his way to New York a short time ago. Paderewski in his state room had a small upright piano on which to practice. It was fastened to the floor by means of bolts. On the opposite side of the room was the bed. In a heavy storm the piano was loosened by the rolling of the vessel. Straight it made for the pianist and crashed into his bed, nearly pinning him to the wall. Paderewski on reaching the floor rushed to the opposite side of the room. Instantly the piano followed, coming at him with great force. He dodged it, but it came at him again, being hurled about in the room by the rolling of the boat. The pianist tried to get out the door, but could not loosen the bolt and he was thus hemmed in with the tumbling piano which threatened to crush him to death every second. There was nothing to do but wrestle with the instrument. He grasped it as it came toward him again and after lengthy struggle in which he was nearly exhausted, succeeded in binding it to the wall.

Alberto Santos-Dumont was a household name in 1902. This daring, 110-pound pioneer of flight was better known than our native Wright brothers, especially after his appearances at the St. Louis World's Fair in 1903. Santos-Dumont was a wealthy and extremely personable Brazilian who lived in Paris

SANTOS DUMONT COMING TO AMERICA.

Santos Dumont expects to visit America early next summer and here continue his experiments. He will probably make several ascensions around New York. He will bring with him two of his latest air ships, the Santos Dumonts Nos. 6 and 7, the former being the one with which the famous aeronaut won the Grand Prix de Paris by encircling the Eiffel tower and returning to his starting point in 29 minutes and 30 seconds. The Santos Dumont No. 7 has just been completed and never tried.

MILK SLOT MACHINE TO REDUCE DRUNKENNESS.

Temperance workers of Stockholm, Sweden, have placed milk slot machines on the corners in that city as a means of reducing drunkenness among people who are forced to spend much of their time on the streets. A coin equivalent to 1½ cents is placed

in the slot and the machine gives in return a cup of milk. In summer the milk is ice cold and in winter it is heated by means of a small gas stove which is placed under the supply tank inside.

ROCK AND KEEP COOL.

For people who are too old to travel under the bicycle canopy, L. M. Sartrain of Tracy City, Tenn., has invented a summer breeze attachment to the ordinary rocking chair. An air pump is fastened to the back of the chair and is worked by rocking back and forth. The air is discharged through a pipe which can be adjusted in any direction desired.

ELECTRIC AUTO MAKING ONE MILE IN 63 SECONDS.

Here was a race where gasoline, electric and steam powered vehicles were all represented

BREAKS ALL RECORDS OF ELECTRIC AUTOS.

All records of electric machines were broken by A. L. Riker's low-rigged racing frame in a contest between members of the Long Island Automobile Club, on Coney Island Boulevard, in Brooklyn. Mr. Riker finished a mile in 63 seconds. The machine was stripped down as far as was possible and presented the appearance of a mere frame. Onlookers thought it made much better time than it really did, because it was so low and there was so little display and noise. It was in striking contrast to the ponderous looking machines of other of the contestants.

The three fastest machines in the race were those of Henry Fournier, Foxhall P. Keene and A. C. Bostwick, all gasoline. The best time was 51⅘ seconds.

"The performance of the three fastest machines," says the Automobile Magazine, from which the accompanying illustration is taken, "were very even." Each driver had several trials, and several had to take more than their allotted number on account of the timers being confused.

"Mr. Riker went back for a start only about 200 yards from the point time would be taken, he being towed there. He gathered headway with surprising alacrity. All others, especially the heaviest class, went back to distances varying from ¼ to the full mile allowed them. Mr. Davis brought out a racing locomobile, having steaming capacity which should satisfy any one. The vehicle looked as though it would do something great and under Mr. Davis' control it went faster than any steam automobile has yet traveled in America."

TELEPHONES IN THE UNITED STATES.

The Electrical Review for December 14 has a valuable article on the growth and magnitude of telephones in this country. The telephone was invented by Professor Alexander Graham Bell in 1875 and patented by him the next year. At that time good business men considered it would never be of practical use. By January, 1878, some 5,000 instruments were in use on private lines. The same year a test conversation was had between New York and Philadelphia, and Philadelphia and Washington. The first exchange was established in 1879. The fundamental patent on the speaking telephone expired in 1893. There are now many concerns manufacturing telephones.

Of independent companies there are now 2811 with 708,717 subscribers, and having $125,000,000 invested. Farmers' and other private lines number 490,000 instruments. The Bell company has 1,500 exchanges with 1,080,000 telephones and an investment of $320,000,000.

Total in United States: Exchanges, 4,311; telephones, 2,278,717; investment, $470,000,000.

At the present time the manufacturers are turning out over 3,000 telephone instruments daily or over 1,000,000 sets a year, valued at $30,000,000. Wire, poles and other material used to install these phones is $25,000,000 a year.

Popular Mechanics is "written so you can understand it."

Total telephones in U.S. today: some 40,000,000 of the world's 65,800,000

The road engine was simply a small locomotive on tractor wheels. At this time, the future of steam "wagon trains" seemed assured. It was not expected that gasoline engines would ever do heavy hauling. Refinement of the automobile and the building of "farm-to-market" roads quickly overwhelmed the usefulness of wagon trains

The Beginning of The Horseless Age.

Large Cash Prizes Offered for Improvements in Road Engines.

We have already crossed the threshold of the horseless age. Not that the time will ever come when the inborn love which man possesses for the horse will cease, nor horses entirely disappear from boulevard, and town and farm; but henceforth machinery will perform the heavy work now done by animal power, just as the harvesting machine has taken the place of the sickle. The largest displacement of horses thus far was when street railways adopted electricity to operate their cars. To do the work performed by the trolley cars of the United States today, would require not less than 300,000 horses or mules, and these would have to be replaced every four years.

Automobiles propelled by steam, gasoline and electricity are already in use by thousands, and that village is far remote where at least one of these flying roadsters has not been seen. This week we illustrate several types of machines built for practical work.

California is a state of magnificent distances. Its railroads are few and far between as yet. To reach the nearest shipping point hundreds of farmers must team the grain and other products of thousand-acre farms many miles. This has resulted in the construction of thousands of miles of the finest highway in the country. Many of these roads are kept sprinkled at public expense for seven months in the year. The common method of hauling is in wagon trains of six or more big wagons, fastened one behind the other, and drawn by 16 to 20 horses. Two men constitute the crew. Travel is mostly by night when the air is cool. One of these trains carry upwards of 25 tons, and make three to four miles an hour.

To save time, expense and to travel night and day, road engines weighing 10 tons each and capable of drawing 40 tons at five miles an hour are being made. The California wagon train illustrated herewith is drawn by one of these engines built by the Best Manufacturing Co., at San Leandro. It burns coal, carries its own supplies of coal and water and is controlled by an engineer who steers the train from a high seat. The fireman stands on a lower platform, stokes the fire and keeps plenty of water in the boiler. By using two engine crews the

IOWA FNGINE ON HIGHWAY.

CALIFORNIA WAGON TRAINS READY TO LOAD.

train can be in motion night and day and make 120 miles in 24 hours. The direction the train will take is determined by turning the single front wheel to the right or left.

An Iowa builder, J. A. Wicke, at Van Horne, is also working along the same lines and is building a road engine of a somewhat different type. It also burns coal but carries supplies in a tender. This engine runs on four wheels, the front pair for steering and the large pair for traction. The machinery is housed in a cab very like a locomotive, which with its headlight and smoke stack it somewhat resembles.

HAT THAT TIPS ITSELF.

Inventor Comes to the Rescue of That Much-Abused, Over-Popular Gentleman.

"Swell" automobilists, naval and military officials of high distinction and the leisure class of nobility often find their most arduous duties to consist in tipping their hats to lay acquaintances and others. To save this very aggravating physical exertion a Frenchman has invented a hat that will tip itself.

The crown of this curious headpiece contains a sort of clockwork arrangement that operates a set of springs. This machinery is wound up before the wearer starts out on his walk or ride. When he wants to salute some one instead of carrying his hand to the brim of his hat he merely finds it necessary to incline his head slightly, that movement serving to put the springs in the crown of his hat in operation. His brow displaces a small brake, and the springs lift the hat gracefully from his head. He can keep on saluting until the machinery is run down.

RAILWAY BICYCLE.

Latest Invention Has Two Small Guide Wheels, is Light and Attains High Speed.

Several types of bicycle for use on steam railroad tracks have already been built. We illustrate the latest, the invention of Chas. Gorneman of Cedar Valley, Utah. He has improved on previous wheels by the addi-

tion of two small guide wheels to run on the inside of the rail which supports the bicycle wheels proper. The machine is capable of very high speed, and being light can be instantly removed from the track upon the unexpected approach of a train.

RED IS DANGER EVERYWHERE.

Even in the far-away Society Islands, red is used as a danger signal. It is made from burning a dried sea weed which gives forth a bright cherry red, somewhat like Bengal's fire. The moment any emergency arises a heap of the weed is set on fire and every native in sight of the signal is in duty bound to rush to the rescue.

Bicycles like this were in wide use for several years. They were fine for cross-country jaunts, but their presence on the right of way made railroadmen nervous, and the vehicles finally were banned

HOUSE MOVING AT SHELBYVILLE, IND.

House moving up to this time had been a "20-mule-team" job

The impact of this article on the reader of 1902 must have been strong, since most autos of the time had little grade-climbing ability. It was common for motorists to alight and push their gas buggies up slight grades

The Ferocious Automobile Is Tamed.

Roaring and Pitching Inhabitant of the City's Wilderness of Walls Submits to Complete Control.

The automobile is becoming tamed. It was formerly believed to be something like the zebra, the lion or other wild animals of the dark continent that defied the efforts of man to effect its subjugation. Like a wild bronco of the Texas plains it would buck, and lunge and pitch until few had the nerve to tempt its ferocity. Sometimes it would charge backward when the chauffeur tried to make it go forward and sometimes it darted forward when he wanted it to go back. It would switch around sideways, jump upward and endways and in fact it was a hard matter to tell which way the "mechanical beast" would go when the lever was touched.

But now all these troubles of the automobilists are over. Automobile trainers have become expert in their work. They have so completely subjugated the former wild, rearing, untame thing that it is now as docile as a work horse. No longer does it tear down a crowded street, despite the chauffeur's efforts to stop it; nor does it plunge into street cars at the crossings or suddenly take a notion to make a speed test run when the chauffeur has left it to stand for a while. To demonstrate the abject submission this once proud, ferocious creature has undergone, it is but necessary to glance at the front page illustration. Here is a chauffeur making his automobile climb on top of a house. He is running up an inclined track, 42 78-100 per cent grade, the wheels on either side being supported by wooden rails but little wider than those of a railroad. This feat was performed in Chicago and is considered the most remarkable ever attempted by a motor vehicle in any country. It was done by its manufacturers to demonstrate its complete control, wonderful power and grade climbing ability.

Newark, N. J., is credited as the first U.S. town to have an asphalt street—in 1870. Few communities followed suit until after the turn of the century

COVERS BRICK STREET WITH ASPHALT.

Covering brick streets with asphalt is a new departure which has been successfully accomplished at Decatur, Ill. The old brick pavement was first cleaned, dried and especially prepared for the coat of asphalt. The brick made a good foundation. A good contour and pleasing grade was secured and the appearance of the surface after completion was like that of other asphalt streets.

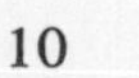

The Old Century and the New.

THE AUTOMOBILE KING OF VEHICLES.

Extremes in style of vehicles are represented in the illustration below. The one-horse chaise is now seen only in the rural districts and will soon be a thing of the past. The automobile is the vehicle of the new century and while it has been the conveyance of fashionable people for several years past it seems to have only begun its successful career. The day of the chaise has ended; that of the automobile has just begun. The Motor Age, a recognized American authority, says: The rapid increase in the automobile business is strikingly illustrated by the present crowded condition of the prominent factories. Business was increasing rapidly before the late show, but the army of purchasers that made its appearance at that time, and since, pile up orders to such an extent that few makers are in a position to do anything but make promises of future deliveries, a condition not at all satisfactory to the people who are willing and anxious to spend their money.

TRACKLESS TROLLEY CARS FOR NEW ENGLAND.

Will all the street cars give way to easy-riding autos, and the car tracks be removed and leave a smooth, unbroken surface to the pavement? This is a question many are asking. The trackless trolley car is attracting a great deal of attention these days. Since the publication in Popular Mechanics of Aug. 23 of the remarkable system now in operation in Europe, it has been announced that an American company is about to establish a similar line at Lowell, Mass., with extensions in the near future to various parts of New England. Our readers will recall the system as that of a spacious vehicle, on rubber-tired wheels, propelled by an electric motor like a street car and taking current from overhead trolley wires.

The Lowell cars or carriages will each seat twenty passengers. Instead of the cumbersome trolley apparatus used abroad, the American line will have two trolley poles with horizontal trolley wheels in place of the vertical wheels on our street cars. Two wires are necessary, as one is required to carry the return current back to the power-house, which passes through the track rails of our street car lines.

Only two overhead wires are necessary, as cars can pass by one pulling down its trolley while the other goes around, the trolley poles being arranged to swing around in any direction. On a large city line two sets of overhead wires would be desirable. The small expense of constructing these trackless lines will doubtless lead to many being built where costly tracks could never be made to pay.

This was the first trackless trolley system in the United States. It was not successful because of the erratic performance of the double trolley poles, particularly in bad weather. Not until the 1930's were trackless trolleys put into service in appreciable numbers in the larger cities

The big trees no longer dwarf the world's tallest building as they did in 1902. The Empire State Building's height of 1250 feet is taller than any three sequoias. Popular Mechanics' *indignation over the desecration of the big tree was shared by other conservation-minded people. Now most groves of these magnificent trees are protected by National Parks. It appears that in this case editorial enthusiasm was the better part of discretion; the best estimates now give the age of the largest as somewhat over 3000 years, not 8000 as the article states*

Giant Trees Have Stood For 8,000 Years.

Monarchs of the World's Flora That Have Outlived All Ages of Mankind and Are Yet Young.

Survivors of the era of mammoth tropical growth, probably eight thousand years of age, the big trees of California are the oldest and the largest living things upon the earth. Could they but talk our language the secrets and mysteries of ages unknown to human history might be truthfully revealed. They witnessed the flood; they stood when, according to history, mankind first made his appearance on the earth. These same living trees, seemingly unnatural in their gigantic size, the source of amazement and bewilderment to travelers, have outlived all the nations of the earth up to the present time and many of them now seem to be but enjoying the prime of life.

California Big Tree
Masonic Temple, Chicago

The tallest of these great trees is 405 feet high; the largest trunk measures 110 feet base circumference. The wood of the big trees might be put to many valuable usages from a mechanical standpoint, but they are considered too sacred for such degradation. Already they have been mutilated to a degree that is a stigma on American sense of reverence. Great gates have been cut in them for horses and vehicles to drive through. Houses have been built on their stumps. They have been hollowed out for liquor inns, in this irreverent day of commercialism. One was exhibited at the world's fair in Chicago by a wine dealer. Part of the tree's trunk was made hollow by chopping away the interior and thus transformed into a two-story wine house. The exterior of the trunk remained in its natural state, while the interior was equipped with counters, shelves, mirrors and other furniture to best exhibit the wines of California. Ornamented stairs inside led from the first to the second floor.

It has been said: "A famous writer scientist spent 15 years excavation and calculation and determined that Cheops built the great pyramids of Jeezeh in 2170 before Christ. There are trees now alive in California that had bark on them a foot thick when Cheop's army of 100,000 began their 30 years' task."

Beards were the badge of professional men in the early 1900's, although the mustache was preferred by ordinary folk. Most young doctors hid their inexperience behind the bushiest beards they were capable of growing before graduation

SAY WHISKERS DISSEMINATE DISEASE GERMS.

Whiskers are collectors of dangerous disease germs, according to New York scientists and their wearing should be prohibited. The Milk Commission of New York has, in consequence, taken steps to force milkmen to shave off their beards lest they convey germs to the milk. Nothing is more detrimental to public health, it is claimed, than the wearing of beards by doctors, and every municipality should force its practicing physicians and surgeons to be clean shaven and wear skull caps when attending patients. Long whiskers, according to this latest sensational discovery, are more to be feared in the dissemination of contagion than the rat, which has been known to carry plague from the country to another. Germs of divers degrees of danger are said to cling to the whisking whiskers as fragments of loadstone would cling to a needle.

The Great American Canal.

Merits Panama and Nicaragua Hold Out to Uncle Sam.

Shall it be Nicaragua or Panama? The great ditch which it is proposed to dig to divide the two Americas is a subject that is interesting every American. The French company which has failed in its efforts to construct the Panama canal is now trying to sell the partially completed channel to the United States. At first the company wanted $109,141,500, but now, according to report, they are willing to sell for $40,000,000. They say they were forced to this step to avoid ruin, which is inevitable should the United States decide to build the Nicaragua canal.

It is the current belief that it will take eight years to finish the Panama canal, besides two years for preparation. The Nicaragua canal can be finished in six years after the two-year preparatory period is over. The Panama canal is 49 miles long; the Nicaragua is 183.66. The Panama route would also have a lower summit elevation and less curvature. It would cost $1,350,000 less a year to maintain the Nicaragua canal. It would take a draught vessel 12 hours to pass through the Panama canal and 33 hours to pass through the Nicaragua. Winds for sailing vessels and hygienic conditions favor Nicaragua. The Panama would be a shorter route for commerce to our Atlantic ports and to the west coast of South America. The Nicaragua would save a day between the Pacific coast and any port on the Atlantic. It would make the same saving between our Atlantic ports and China, Japan and the Philippines. It costs from $250 to $3,000 a day to operate an ocean vessel. Making the average $1,500 for each vessel, the Nicaragua canal would mean a saving of $15,000 a day to vessels bound going to and from these ports, on the supposition that only ten should pass through each day. This would amount to more than $5,000,000 a year.

The cost of building the Nicaragua canal from the beginning is estimated at $189,964,062. The cost of finishing the Panama canal is estimated at $144,233,358. Already about $300,000,000 has been spent on the Panama. The Panama route would carry with it little or no commercial development, but would be simply a means of communication between the two oceans.

THE NICARAGUA ROUTE.

WORLD IS GOING CRAZY, SAYS DR. HOYT.

Present Rate of Insanity and Criminality Gives Cause for Alarm.

Dr. Benjamin R. Hoyt of Detroit has figured out that the world will be mad within three centuries at the present rate of increase of insanity. He says:

"During the past fifty years the number of insane persons and fools has increased 300 per cent. During the last decade the increase of population has been 30 per cent, and the apparent increase in the defective classes has been a little more than 155 per cent.

"The United States census of 1890 showed the total number of persons in prisons to be 82,329; number in juvenile reformatories, 14,846; number in almshouses, 73,045; inmates of benevolent institutions, 111,900; number of insane, 106,445. Total number belonging to defective classes, 403,615.

"In 1850 one person in every 3,500 was a criminal. In 1890 there was one criminal for every 786 of population, an increase of 445 per cent, while the population increased only 170 per cent.

This was the "great debate" at the turn of the century. Nicaragua was chosen first, but the French, who had been working off and on since 1881 in Panama, later converted Theodore Roosevelt to that route. A revolution and a new republic friendly to the U.S. clinched the decision. In 1904 the U.S. bought the French holdings and started work. Although the first ship went through on schedule in 1914, slides delayed the formal opening until some years later. The total cost to us including payments to the French company and Panama was some $366,000,000. During a busy year over 6000 ships travel its 40-mile length

Christened the Thomas W. Lawson, *this huge ship was the last major attempt of sail to compete with steam in commercial shipping. The steel seven-master dashed all hopes of her builders on the rocks of the Cornwall coast. She turned turtle and sank on Dec. 13, 1908, after a three-week battle with Atlantic gales. Only three of the 18-man crew were rescued*

Seven-Masted Schooner Amazes Seamen.

She is to be the Largest Sailing Vessel in the World, and is Watched with Interest.

The first and only seven-masted schooner in the world is being built by the Fore River Ship and Engine Company, at Quincy Point, in Boston harbor. It was designed by B. B. Crowninshield for Captain J. G. Crowley of Taunton, Mass. Such a strange looking craft is it that the boat is attracting attention from all over the world, and there is intense interest in the speculation as to whether the builders can make a success of what old-time seamen have long considered an impossibility.

The vessel is built of steel, which makes it possible for her to carry the seven masts and the enormous weight. She is not only the largest fore-and-after ever built, but is the largest sailing vessel of any kind in the world. There is a picturesque significance in the fact that she is being built, not on the Maine coast, where wooden schooners have mostly come from, but in a modern steel "battleship yard."

Dr. Gatling's steam plow was not the first such implement. A similar tractor was made in 1886 by Daniel Best of San Leandro, Calif.

THE AUTOMOBILE PLOW IS HERE.

At last the automobile plow has come: but it was invented by Dr. Richard J. Gatling, of St. Louis, and so is called the "Gatling" Motor Disc plow. It is expected to revolutionize the science of farming, says the Age of Steel, as much as the Gatling gun revolutionized the methods of warfare. The plow is operated by steam. It may use coal, wood, oil or gasoline for fuel. A wheat drill may be attached and the grain sown as the soil is turned. The motor may be separated from the plow and used for all kinds of heavy hauling. The plow, which is a huge, many pointed device, and operated by one man can accomplish as much in a day as 40 men with 80 horses using old-fashioned plows.

HE AIN'T WENT YIT.

By S. E. Kiser.

Every little while they tell us that the
horse has got to go;
First the trolley was invented, 'cause the
horses went so slow,
And they told us that we'd better not keep
raisin' colts no more;
When the street cars got to noting that
the horses pulled before;
I thought it was all over for old Fan and
Doll and Kit,
S'posed the horse was up and done for,
But
he
ain't
went
yit.

The First Real Ship of The Desert.

Strange Craft That Terrified Natives May Do Away With the Camel in Sahara.

(Copyright, 1902, by John L. Von Blon, Los Angeles.)

Preoccupation with wind machines was a sign of these times. Small boys made "sidewalk sailers," and here and there adults tried "sail wagons" on the public roads, getting fewer laughs from onlookers than the early motorists. There was little indication that the automobile would ever become, for ordinary travel, both speedy and thoroughly dependable. This soaring prophecy for the future of sail cars somehow never bore fruit

It remained for America to construct a real "ship of the desert." It is doubtless destined to work an innovation in the methods of transportation across the great Sahara. The device ilustrated on the front page is used for traffic on the once dreaded desert of Majava in Southern California. It is called the "Desert Queen" and is the first sailing vessel for service on the land ever built. It makes a speed of from 50 to 80 miles an hour and has obliterated all the perils and horrors formerly attended with the crossing of this lonely waste. A whole fleet of such craft will probably be put in operation on this desert and the one in New Mexico. With their aid traffic across the lifeless plains will be made pleasant, sure and speedy. Faster than the fastest train the Desert Queen glides ghostlike over the hard sands, reminding one of traveling in an air ship. The sailing trucks may result in populating those weird parts of the earth that have hitherto been regarded uninhabitable.

This "mechanical dromedary," the strangest vehicle ever propelled by the wind, was built by two miners, Charles S. and Carl L. Hoyt, of Cleveland, O., just six months ago. It has been in use ever since, covering thousands of miles. The Hoyts have a gold mine in the buttes near Rosamond, Cal. They live nine miles away at the other end of a peculiar dry lake, which is hard as concrete and swept smooth as a tennis court by the sands forever driven over it by the fierce winds rushing through Tehachepi pass.

Those who have ridden on the Desert Queen claim it to be the most exciting of experiences.

Nostalgia strikes the pocketbook as well as the memory. Ten dollars would dress you from head to foot, and one could buy a book on telegraphy by none other than Thomas A. Edison. In 1902 the used car you bought for $275 couldn't have been used long or driven far

Telegraphy Self Taught

A Complete Manual of Instruction by Thomas A. Edison, M. A.

Railroad corporations, telegraph companies, newspaper offices are always looking for first-class operators and this book will teach you how to rank among the top-notchers. Everything is treated in a clear, concise manner; batteries, operating keys, Morse code signals, commercial messages, order of transmission, provision, grain and stock abbreviations all fully explained and "written so you can understand it." Fully illustrated with diagrams of line connections, circuits, etc.

Price, Durable Cloth Binding, $1.00 Postpaid

Popular Mechanics Co., Journal Bldg., Chicago

SEWING MACHINE MOTOR.

An electric motor for running a sewing machine is illustrated below. The motor is attached to the table and a starting rod connects with the treadle, allowing the machine to be controlled by the feet of the operator. Various speeds are secured according to the position of the foot treadle.

SEWING MACHINE MOTOR.

The motor and attaching device are made by the Diehl Mfg. Co., Elizabethport, N. J. Where a residence is not wired for electric light, power can be had from a storage battery.

INSTANTANEOUS SHOE FASTENER.

A Jersey City man who found great difficulty in trying to lace his shoe with one hand while fighting mosquitoes with the other has invented a lightning shoe fastener. The cut shows how it works. The fastener draws up with a telescope slide.

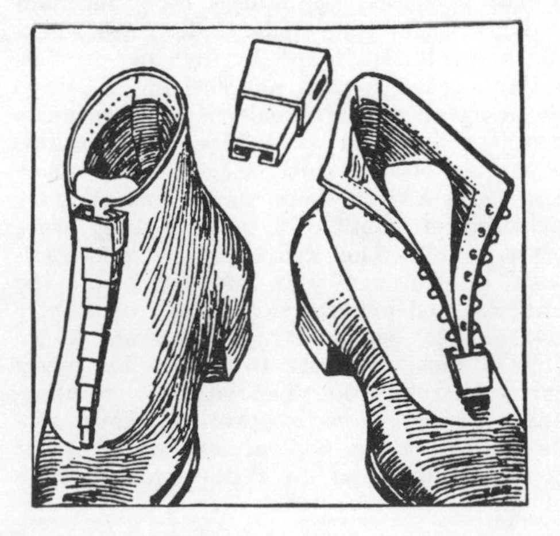

ONLY ONE PAIR OF THESE SHOES EVER MADE.

A style of foot gear, unlike anything ever worn before in the history of the world, has just appeared in the shape of what is called "twenty-strap sandals," a pair of which were made especially for Anna Held. They cost the actress $50, and are the only pair ever produced of the kind. Hervey E. Guptill, Haverhill, Mass., were the manufacturers. The sandals were cut from Corona kid, which the manufacturers say was the only patent leather found with sufficient strength, light weight, spread and luster to give satisfaction. The exact size and measurements of the boot are as follows: No. 3½, D width, ankle 8½ inches, calf 14½ inches, knee, 13½ inches, top 23 inches, height 26 inches.

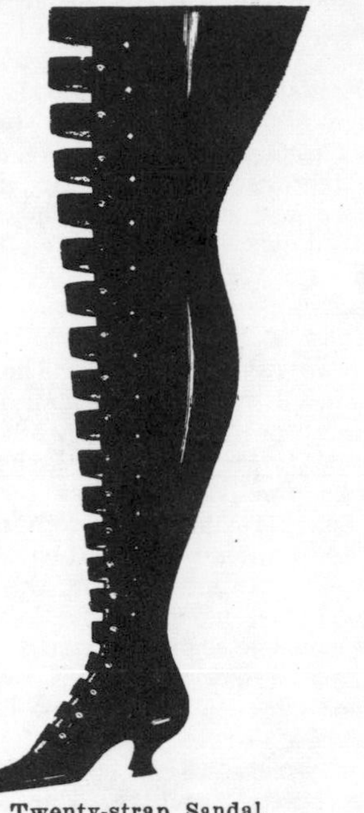

Twenty-strap Sandal.

KING EDWARD LIKES AUTOS.

It is to be hoped that King Edward will be able to use his new automobile, which will soon be completed. He has taken a great interest in the development and progress of the horseless carriage and has watched the progress of his new tonneau closely. It is a gasoline machine of 22 horse-power and has room for six passengers, besides the operator. There are four forward speeds controlled by a lever while the reverse is accomplished by a pedal.

The electric sewing machine is an interesting example of "production lag." Almost 20 years passed before such machines became commonplace

Shoes like this . . . "milk baths" for her complexion . . . a marriage to Florenz Ziegfeld . . . all these conspired to make Anna Held a darling of her age. She was born in France, came to the United States in 1896 and starred in plays like The Parisian Model, Papa's Wife *and* A Parlor Match. *Divorced from Ziegfeld in 1915, she returned to Paris, where she died in 1918*

The Jersey City inventor just missed the principle of the zipper. In 1906, in nearby Hoboken, Gideon Sundback patented a true hookless fastening. A crude fastener already had been invented by Whitcomb L. Judson of Chicago in 1896

This was one of the earliest practical applications of X-rays, discovered in 1895 by Wilhelm Konrad Roentgen. New uses of the principle continued to be found. The betatron, for example, used in the liberation of atomic energy, is a product of modern X-ray research

The X-Ray a Wonderful Aid to Science.

How the Photographs Are Taken—New Method of Illuminating the Body.

The ordinary light that we are accustomed to, makes glass, water and air transparent. But there is another light which does not make glass transparent, but which renders diaphanous every other substance except lead. This is the X-ray. It has been a wonderful revelation to surgical science in that it makes the human body pervious to light, enabling the surgeon to see and locate any foreign substance. We give herewith the picture of a little girl showing a hat pin she had swallowed. She resides in Indiana and her life was saved by means of the X-ray.

It is easier to take the picture of a thin person than a fleshy one with an X-ray machine. To take the picture the negative plate is placed under the patient instead of in the camera. The plate, which in size corresponds to the portion of the body to be photographed, is laid flat on a board and the board rests on a common surgical chair. The person whose interior is to be photographed is laid flat on the negative plate, the board being placed between the the plate and the chair cushion to keep the former from breaking. An X-ray tube is then placed over the part of the body to be photographed. From this is extended the leading-in wires, which connect the tube with the static machine, the source of electrical energy. Thus the X-ray light is produced in the X-ray tube and to this light the patient is exposed from one-half to three minutes according to the density of the part of the body to be photographed. After the exposure the negative plate is developed by the ordinary photographic process.

Looking into the interior of a person with the eye, aided by a spy-glass, was made possible by the invention of W. C. Fuchs, manager of the Chicago X-ray laboratory. This is accomplished with the aid of salts, which when taken internally has a peculiar effect on the X-ray, causing it to brightly illuminate the stomach. The salts are by scientists called tongstate of calcium, barium platinum cyanide and uranium. The patient is made to drink a full glass of these salts dissolved in water. An X-ray machine is so placed as to cast its rays on the stomach. This causes the liquid to light up the interior of the stomach. An instrument called a cystoscope, which is a sort of telescope, fitted with a small mirror so that a person can see out at right angles to the end, is then pushed down the patient's throat into his stomach and the physician makes his examination. Formerly the cystoscope was used with a small electric light attached to its end, but the light grew so hot that the patient suffered great torture.

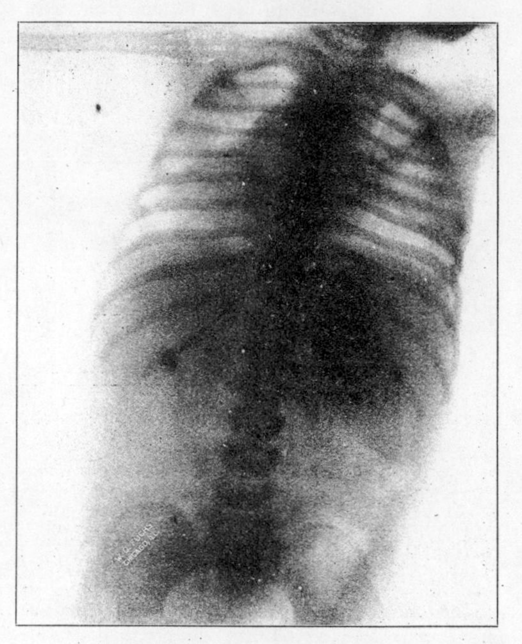

X-RAY PHOTOGRAPH OF 6-INCH HAT PIN IN STOMACH.

THE HAREM AS IT IS TODAY.

Mechanical Inventions Work an Innovation in the Home of the Sultan and His 300 Beautiful Wives.

Late electrical appliances, other mechanical inventions and modern ideas are working a revolution in the Turkish harem. The sultan's mind is thus not entirely absorbed in thoughts of the hundreds of Circassian beauties that surround him. The sultan's wives are called sultanas. There are now but about 300 of them, as he has recently disposed of about 100 because they were growing old. The apartment of each sultana is equipped with electric bells; the imperial and private harems are brilliantly lighted with electricity. The sultan, Abdul Hamid, may now talk to any of his wives over the telephone. The edifices are thoroughly equipped with speaking tubes, servant's call bells and almost every other convenience known to a modern American or European mansion.

Popular Mechanics *became a monthly magazine with the issue of September, 1903. Its cover fittingly bore the head of Vulcan, god of fire and patron of the blacksmith and metalworker. Also on the cover, as it is today, was the famous slogan of simplicity: "Written so you can understand it." The paid circulation had jumped from the five subscribers for the first issue to about 35,000 monthly.*

Arthur Brisbane, one of America's most widely read columnists, lived to see this prediction come true. And before his career ended, he made practically the same prediction for the future of the airplane. Brisbane's column, "Today," was printed in newspapers throughout the nation for more than 25 years

Future of the Automobile.

Soon Its Position Will be Reversed and it Will Be the Conveyance of the Laborer.

By Arthur Brisbane, of the New York Evening Journal.

In less than fifty years from now the working man, the mechanic and the laborer will go to their work from their cottages in the country in automobiles.

You smile at this?

Don't smile too confidently.

Do you remember when the present model of bicycles first came into fashion?

Who used and paid for the first bicycles, at one hundred dollars or more each?

The rich men and women.

Who made fun of the first bicycle riders, laughing at their sensible costumes, throwing tacks on bicycle paths, doing everything to delay the manufacture of the cheap bicycle by discouraging those who paid for the first experiments?

You did, you who now laugh, or throw tin cans at the fast automobile did the same for the bicycle, not so many years ago.

And who uses the bicycle now? Get up early in the morning, especially in the country, and you will see the bicycle carrying the mechanic to his work. The cheap bicycle is almost exclusively used by working men. It is used exclusively by people of moderate means.

The rich have long since tired of it. The bicycle at Newport used to fill the foolish "society" columns. It now carries the butcher boy to and from work. It enables the workman to save his carfare, to get cheaper rent and fresh country air for his children by living far from his task. It gives these advantages, in addition to fresh air and daily exercise to thousands of clerks with small salaries.

Suppose that public jeering, sprinkling of tacks, etc., had prevented the development of the bicycle. The rich would simply have been deprived of one toy. They would never have missed it. The great loss would have fallen upon the poor, to whom the bicycle now offers many economical advantages, and their sole chance of reaching the country and of knowing nature's beauties.

Then, as now, hotel fires were a problem. And their aftermath, even as now, was a rash of "foolproof" devices for escaping the blaze

Rescuing Herself From Fire

MAKES ESCAPE FROM FIRES EASY.

New Patent Device Appears in Chicago That Will Result in Saving Many Lives.

Escaping from a fire in a flat building or hotel is made as easy and simple as swinging in a swing by a new device that has just been patented and placed on the market in Chicago. It is a mechanical contrivance, that is light, always ready and cannot get out of order. Had the inventor conceived the idea sooner it might have been the means of saving many lives lost through the need of just such a contrivance. Its field of usefulness for the future, however, is without limit. All a person has to do in escaping from a burning building is to slip the end of the rope over any solid projection, sit in a swing and ride down at any speed he desires and with the speed always under perfect and easy control. The device is known as the O. & L. reversible fire escape, deriving its name from Orr & Lockett, the well-known Chicago hardware firm, who placed it on the market. A woman or child can operate it as well as a man. The illustration is from a photograph of a woman descending in the escape showing the manner of its operation.

Aerial Picnic on Myers' Balloon Farm

Novel Social Event Where Riding in Balloons and Airships is as Common as Traveling in Electric Cars at a Trolley Party

At this time a heavier-than-air craft capable of carrying a man on a sustained flight was still a dream. Just about the only method of controlled flight was a lemon-shaped, gas-lifted bag operated by pedal power. Carl Myers (or Meyers; the spelling varied in periodicals of the time) called his version of this airship the "Sky Cycle." One may be seen in the corner of this early photograph

While scientists are discussing the problem of airships in Europe, and debating as to whether the navigation of the air will ever be an accomplished fact, there is a man in the United States who is quietly building airships in wholesale lots and sailing them about as he desires for his profit and amusement. Foreign nations have often wondered where the great balloons employed by the United States during the Spanish-American war came from. They were made by this same man who is now engaged in building a fleet of balloons and airships. This man is Carl Meyers and in the secluded little town of Frankfort, N.Y., he has a balloon farm where nearly every kind of vehicle for navigating the air is produced. Often friends of the professor come down from Utica, nine miles away and have an aerial picnic and then riding in the air is as common as trolley rides in the city.

The balloon farm is an unique institution, devoted to producing hydrogen gas balloons, airships and other aerial creations. Within a brief period it has produced for the United States government, 108 hydrogen gas balloons, 21 during our late war with Spain, and 11 during the season of 1902 for use in the army and navy manoeuvres off the Atlantic coast last September, previous to which a detachment of the United States Signal service balloon corps under Major Rebur and Lieut. Clifton from the Signal Post at Fort Myer, Va., near Washington, D. C., visited the balloon farm to inspect balloons under construction and become adept in their operation.

MANIA FOR PULLING TEETH.

The "tooth-pulling" mania is the latest infection and it has proven worse than the "hair-cutting," kissing, hugging, or other manias. A man by the name of Johnson went on a tooth-pulling expedition at Duluth, Minn., a few days ago and tried to "de-tooth" the town before he stopped. He started in by pulling the teeth of four men who were found intoxicated in a saloon. An hour later he accosted an old man on the street, knocked him down, and pulled two teeth. Fifteen minutes later he entered the residence of Mrs. Ellison, knocked her down, and extracted two teeth. The police in the meantime had been called and arrested him.

The man said he was a dentist, and when he was asked to show his license produced a contract to saw wood. He appears sane, but his actions indicate that he is mad.

The Louisiana Purchase Centennial Exposition attracted more than 19 million visitors to St. Louis in 1903. Forty-two states and 53 countries had exhibits. About 100 automobiles were shown, including one which had performed the then remarkable feat of coming from New York City under its own power. Airships raced a triangular course over the crowds, and the snake charmers and the dancing girls—Belle Fatima and Little Sheba—held sway on the "Pike"

$55,000 Go Up in Fireworks.

Magnificent Display of World's Fair Dedication—Good Work of Gas Balloons.

Brilliant Pyrotechnic Display at St. Louis

Fifty-five thousand dollars went up in noise and smoke to please visitors to the World's Fair dedicatory services at St. Louis on the night of May 1. It was declared by many to be the most magnificent pyrotechnic display ever witnessed. It required just three hours to burn the tons of powder Henry Pain, the fireworks king, had piled on the ground. The sensation of the evening was the ascension of seven great gas balloons controlled by experienced aeronauts. At a great altitude the operators fired a salute of aerial guns. The largest vessel dropped a huge flaming American flag in pyrotechnics, 400 feet long by 200 feet wide. An aerial salute of 20 guns greeted the appearance of the stars and stripes. This was the signal for the dropping from the six other balloons the pyrotechnic flags of the six other greatest powers. Each flag was 150 feet by 100 feet.

The festival hall and the Cascade gardens of the fair were done in fire on a set piece 600 feet long by 60 feet high, the exact vertical height of the genuine cascades. Streams of opalescent fire fell over the cascades. Other numbers, including about everything that is known to pyrotechnics.

THE WORKMAN OF TODAY.

Notwithstanding the great number of strikes and loud labor agitations the workingman is in better condition today than he ever was before. The skilled mechanic of 50 years ago was paid $1.50 a day. Now he gets from $3 to $4.50. He used to work from daylight until dark and his labors were the most toilsome. Now he works eight hours and his duties are comparatively light. The cost of living has increased, it is true, but not in proportion to the increase in wages. The Metal Worker says:

"The twentieth century workman lives better, dresses better and has many more comforts and luxuries, with more time to enjoy them, than this predecessor in the middle of the last century. The wants of the workingman today are certainly greater than they were in the early fifties, but that is because he has risen in the scale of life. Whether, under the strain of modern methods and the limitations of his labor unions, he is happier than the mechanic of fifty years ago was, as Kipling would say, "another story."

WHY FLIRTING STENOGRAPHERS FAIL.

They Are Rewarded With Candy, But Never With Promotion.

By Mrs. Juliet Shumaker, Principal of the Lancaster School, St. Paul, Minn.

The stenographer who, in the mildest and most harmless way flirts with her employer, her fellow clerks, or callers at the office, who is called to the telephone on an average of five times a day by some one to whom she talks in a honeyed voice, and whose giggle is a well known sound in the office, need not be surprised if she is pushed to one side and a man preferred when a responsible duty is to be performed.

Feminine graces will be rewarded with candy and compliments, never with promotion or confidence.

The stenographer who goes into an office expecting to win recognition and compensation on an equality with men must remember first and distinctly that she is not a woman, but a stenographer.

It is all well to talk about a woman's presence inculcating gentleness and courtesy in an office, but a busy man has no time for an extra word; he has no time for the effort to make that word a pleasant one when he does not feel pleasant.

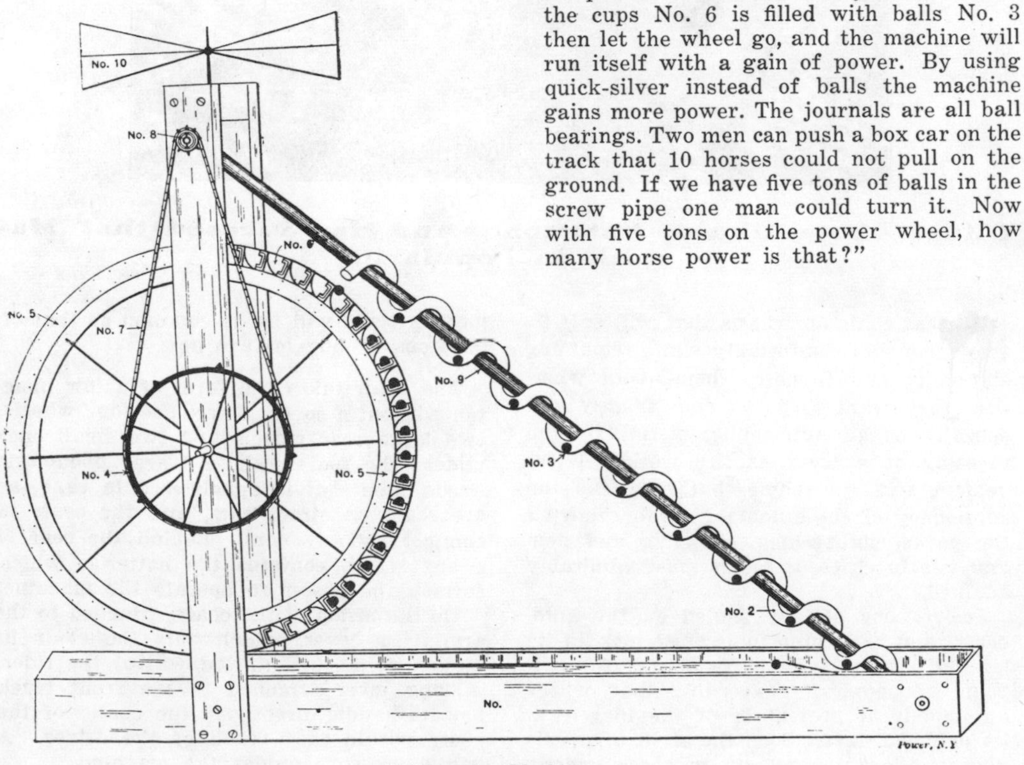

Self-Running Machine

PROGRESS IN CIGARETTE MAKING.

A few years ago, when cigarettes were made by hand, a smart girl could manipulate six pounds of tobacco in a ten-hour day, and roll 2,000 cigarettes. Then came the invention of the cigarette-making machine, which a single operator manages with ease. In a day it makes 200,000 cigarettes, thus saving the wages of ninety-nine girls—a sum of very nearly $15,000 a year.

RESEMBLES PERPETUAL MOTION.

William L. Dayton, of Austin, Texas, Rural Free Delivery Route No. 7, writes to Power:

"I have invented a self-running machine with a gain of power; two balls will pull three balls. See sketch.

No. 1 shows trough for ball to roll in. No. 2 shows screw pipe. No. 3 shows the balls. No. 4 shows the driven wheel. No. 5 shows the main power wheel. No. 6 shows cups on power wheels. No. 7 shows driven chain. No. 8 shows sprocket wheel. No. 9 shows shaft to revolve screw pipe. No. 10 shows fan or governor to regulate speed. Now we will take all the balls No. 2 and put in the trough No. 1, then begin to turn the power wheel No. 5 with your hand until the cups No. 6 is filled with balls No. 3 then let the wheel go, and the machine will run itself with a gain of power. By using quick-silver instead of balls the machine gains more power. The journals are all ball bearings. Two men can push a box car on the track that 10 horses could not pull on the ground. If we have five tons of balls in the screw pipe one man could turn it. Now with five tons on the power wheel, how many horse power is that?"

Women, managing somehow to look individually pretty despite their skirt-and-shirtwaist uniformity of dress, began to appear in large numbers in the offices and factories of the nation after 1900. Demonstrating superior skills over men for certain tasks, they brought new opportunities—and new problems—for management

Plans for perpetual-motion machines still come to the editors of Popular Mechanics, *but not as frequently as they did in the early 1900's. Then many competent inventors had not yet given up the ancient and foolish dream of overcoming friction and gravity*

Many people of the early 1900's never really expected the automobile to be a success. Some die-hards proclaimed it would "never take the place of the horse," while others, consciously or unconsciously, looked for a "successor" to the automobile. Few realized that it would "succeed" itself by constant improvements in mechanical engineering and design

The Automobile's Successor is Here

Glides About Like an Automobile and May Succeed that Machine in Popularity

A great chair on wheels that will seat its two occupants comfortably while remaining stationary or will carry them about wherever they want to go as conveniently and speedily as an automobile, merely by the pressing of a lever, is the world's latest vehicle, and a machine that threatens the supremacy of the automobile. For viewing the parks, sight-seeing, shopping and general use in cities, it seems most admirably adapted.

Society has already smiled on the autochair, and the automobile must look to its laurels. Its manufacturers predict for it a reign of popularity exceeding that of the automobile at present or of the bicycle in its palmiest days. Soon the sight of people gliding about the streets in these swiftly moving seats will be as common as that of phaetons or buggies are now.

The chair takes the form of a low phaeton without a cover. There are four wheels, two large rear wheels and two small ones under the foot rest. All are pneumatic tired. The seat is upholstered in cane, as are seats on street cars, and the seats in summer railway cars. Behind the seat is a box which contains the batteries which furnish the power to operate the machine.

On the inside of the chair, attached to the arm, is a lever, which puts the chair in motion or stops it at the will of the rider. A long lever attached to the front truck has its handle directly in the center of the chair within easy reach of the driver. A gentle pressure guides the machine

Airship Versus Passenger Engine.

World's Fastest Train Would Race Across the Continent With Swiftest of Aerial Craft.

Imaginary Race Between the World's Fastest Train and a Fleet of Airships—Copyrighted 1892 by George H. Daniels, Gen'l Passenger Agent New York Central.

The race never took place, since the performance of airships at the time never equaled the enthusiasm of their builders. These dirigible balloons actually were quite sluggish. The pilot controlled ascent and descent, after a fashion, by shifting the position of sandbags hung along the keel, and he felt that he was zipping right along when a speed of ten miles an hour was attained. Even the early airplanes flew at only forty-five or so. It was not until the World War stimulated the advance of aviation that speeds of over 100 miles an hour were common even to the fastest planes

An airship race from New York to St. Louis during the coming world's fair has been proposed by a New York aeronaut. This, it is claimed, would give the entire country lying on the route between the two cities an opportunity of witnessing the ships in flight and would prove the most sensational race in the history. Of course there is no airship at present that would undertake the long journey, but Santos Dumont claims that he will have a craft in readiness by the time of the world's fair that can safely fly across the American continent. The same claim is made by Prof. Stanley, who is building the monster aluminum airship in San Francisco, and by a Chicago aeronaut.

While some of the inventors say that their ships will be able to double the speed of a passenger train in the race, the New York Central officials say they have no fears of anything that flies, walks or rolls, making better time than the 20th Century Limited, the fastest long-distance train in the world. The suggestion has been made to enter the "Limited" in the race.

Billiards was a popular pastime of the first decade of the 1900's. Tables were in many homes. Since public billiard parlors often were in the back room of a saloon, manufacturers based advertising of home tables on such appeals as, "My Boy Is Home Nights Now." Another novelty was a combination davenport and billiard table, the table folding over to become the back of the davenport

Wonderful Combination Table Has Appeared

Used for Dining, Billiards, Pool, Ping Pong and Reading--Keeps Husbands at Home in "The City of Clubs"

To keep husbands at home an ingenius contrivance has made its apearance in Indianapolis, a city said to have more men's clubs than any other municipality in America in proportion to it size. The device is a dining table, a billiard table, pool table, ping pong table, card table and library table all in one. In fact on this one piece of furniture may be afforded nearly every amusement that so entices the man in the club. Besides it gives a wonderful amount of amusement to the women of the house, and since this combination board has arrived the society women of Indianapolis are becoming wonderfully expert with the billiard cue.

Combination Dining, Billiard, Pool, Library and Ping Pong Table

It Amuses the Women

As a Ping Pong Table.

The table offers a multitude of advantages. When the family has religious visitors the oak top is allowed to remain over the billiard cushion and there is no indication that there is anything more present than a very reverend piece of oak.

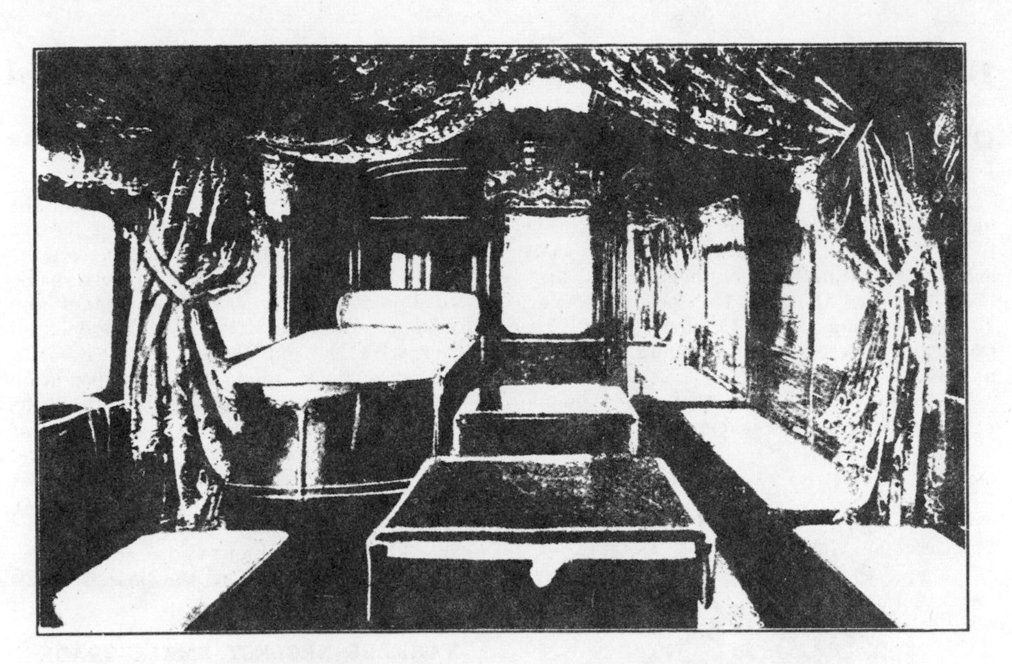

Interior View of House Car Showing Bed, Bunks, Tables and Seats

Automobile House Car The Latest

In This Novel Conveyance One May Live in Comfort and Tour the World

The automobile house has come; in it one may ride, eat, sleep, and entertain his friends by speeding over the country at 60 miles an hour. What the sleeping and dining car is on steam railroads the automobile house, "Motor caravan," is to automobile travel.

This unique and costly conveyance is the property of M. Jules, Secretary of the Bordeaux Automobile Club.

The House Car – Twenty Feet Long

Even at this early date, the automobile trailer would have been practical except for the lack of good roads. With pavements stopping at the city's edge, the solid-tired cars of the day were not likely to get far enough to make sleeping quarters necessary, not at sixty miles an hour anyhow. The constantly exaggerated speed claims of the day—such as in this article and in the one on page 15—no doubt sprang from the fact that up until a few years before, the speed of vehicles other than steam trains was limited to the rate of the animals which pulled them. With the development of the automobile and the airplane there followed a general intoxication with the knowledge that for the first time in history the speed potential of a personal conveyance was infinite

Although this is one of the most unusual feats of its kind on record, kites have been used for many other odd purposes. The United States Weather Bureau, which now employs balloons, once used kites to carry recording instruments three or four miles into the air. A kite pulled steel cables across Niagara Falls during construction of the suspension bridge across the falls. In World War II huge kites were used as targets for aerial gunnery, and others carried radio antennas upward for emergency signaling

Kite Hauls a Boat Across The English Channel

Queerest Craft that Ever Sailed Successfully Crosses the Turbulent Water

Hauling a boat by kite is a new feat that has been successfully performed in Europe by S. F. Cody. After several attempts Cody crossed the English Channel in his. kite-boat, leaving Calais at 11 o'clock p. m. Nov. 7 and reaching Dover 13 hours later. Mr. Cody encountered much shipping and some narrow escapes.

The kite employed was on the principle of a box-kite and was capable of hauling quite a load. The boat weighed four tons and was decked with canvas. It somewhat resembled a miniature submarine boat. A combined steering gear manipulated the kite and the boat's rudder alike and enabled Cody to guide the craft with comparative ease.

Experimenting with the Man Lifting Kite that Hauled the Cody Boat

Launching the Cody Boat

Mr. Cody has a scheme to reach the North pole by means of this kite. He says that Nansen's progress toward the pole was stopped by a huge wall of ice 125 feet high. He could not surmount an obstacle of that size and had to turn back. With this kite, Cody says, the sledges and provisions could be lifted over the ice, together with the explorers.

Nansen's dogs died and transportation became almost impossible. With the kite, Cody says, Nansen would be independent of dogs, for in favorable wind the kite would draw the sledges along. Three or four kites would drag a ton weight of material, including three men.

The kite with which Cody crossed the channel was connected to the boat by 3,600 feet of piano wire.

YANKEES NEGLECT SMALL TRADE.

South African Exports says: "The Yanees do not appear to be making much headway in the engineering line as far as Cape Town is concerned. The 500-horsepower generating set lately installed by the corporation is entirely of British manufacture, while the machinery for the new electric light stations at Claremont and Wynberg was also made in Great Britain.

"In Johannesbarg, where there is a wider field for this class of work, there is a different tale to tell. Most of the big American houses have branches or agents in the Golden City, and are making desperate efforts to capture the trade by cutting prices. When it comes to a question of prompt delivery it is not unlikely that the British manufacturer may feel the pressure, though so far few contracts have been missed through this cause. Just now both parties are merely marking time, as until the labor question is settled there will be little demand for machinery. Owing to the deadlock in the mining industry many tenders for big orders have remained unopened, and will not be considered until an improvement sets in."

Claus Neelson, whose farm near Omaha, Neb., is a general landing place for balloons after exhibition ascensions, has obtained an injunction restraining balloons from "descending on his farm or property, from destroying his crops or frightening his live stock."

"HOME-MADE" AUTOMOBILES THE RAGING FAD.

Not Hard to Build. All Parts Can be Bought Separately, and the Enjoyments in Its Possession are Tenfold.

Why not make your own automobile? It is not difficult; it is much cheaper; you can make it any size or design you fancy, and when completed you have the tenfold satisfaction of viewing and enjoying the pleasures of a construction that you know is

A "Home-Made" Automobile

entirely the product of your own mechanism. "Home-made" automobiles are now all the fad. Popular Mechanics told in a previous issue of a boy who made a motor car in its entirety, the machine being just large enough to accommodate the boy and his sweetheart. Those who have not the facilities for making all the parts necessary to a first class machine, can now buy them separately. An establishment—the Automobile Supply Co., 2108 Olive street, St. Louis,—will sell any or all parts for any design of automobile the amateur builder may desire and ship them to any address.

SPLENDID WORLD'S FAIR BUILDING.

With its elegant statuary, colonnade and pavilions there will be no more beautiful structure at the St. Louis World's Fair than the Textiles building. It is to occupy 525 feet on the main thoroughfare of the exposition and this and the Electricity are the only two buildings facing the Grand Basins with the cascades and approaches to the terrace.

GRAMOPHONE AT A FUNERAL SERVICE.

Minister Who Used It Advocates the Talking Machine for Funerals, Weddings, Lodges and Other Ceremonies.

By the Rev. Samuel Pearson of the First Congregational Church, Leavenworth, Kan., the first minister to use the gramophone for music at a funeral service.

The use of the gramophone at the funeral of Daniel P. Williams, in Leavenworth, came about in this way. It was a question of economy from the doctor to undertaker—one of those cases where a poor man can not afford to die. The clergyman was donating his services willingly. It was a dull day and the roads muddy. The residence was on the outskirts of the city and difficult to reach without a conveyance. As a soloist or choir would involve carriage-hire even if the singers donated their services, the idea of using the gramophone suggested itself.

No objections were proferred when the clergyman reached the residence and explained that he would like to test its utility. So the service was opened by the selection, "The Holy City," and concluded with "My Jesus as Thou Wilt." It was the first time the clergyman had handled such an instrument as doubtless it was the first use of the gramophone at such a service. There were about thirty people present and the innovation did not appear to provoke surprise, or unfavorable comment. On the contrary, the possibility of this substitute rendering a useful service under similar circumstances was apparent, and the clergyman in this instance received the cordial thanks of those interested for so doing.

MODERN TUG OF WAR.

Even at this early date, the automobile trailer would have been practical except for the lack of good roads. With pavements stopping at the city's edge, the solid-tired cars of the day were not likely to get far enough to make sleeping quarters necessary, not at sixty miles an hour anyhow. The constantly exaggerated speed claims of the day—such as in this article and in the one on page 15—no doubt sprang from the fact that up until a few years before, the speed of vehicles other than steam trains was limited to the rate of the animals which pulled them. With the development of the automobile and the airplane there followed a general intoxication with the knowledge that for the first time in history the speed potential *of a personal conveyance was infinite*

Barney Oldfield made the phrase "a mile a minute" a semantic symbol of speed that endured in American speech long after 60 miles an hour became commonplace. Famous as a bicycle racer before he was 20, Oldfield's first auto race was in 1902. He blew pressure into the gas tank through a rubber hose with his mouth as "Spider" Huff drove. By 1904 Oldfield held all world dirt track speed records, appeared in every major racing event, and was hailed as the "Speed King of the World." There seems to be a typographic error where the article states his speed for the five-mile run

LOWERS AMERICA'S TRACK RECORD.

Barney Oldfield at the recent automobile races in Indianapolis lowered the American track record, clipping two seconds off the one mile record and 23⅗ off the five mile record. The mile was run in 59⅗ seconds and the five miles in 58 minutes and 28 seconds. The previous American records were 1:1⅗ for the mile and 5:28 for the 5 miles. Oldfield performed the feat in a contest with Tom Cooper. The performance was witnessed by 5,000 cheering spectators.

A SKY-CYCLE.

There is a rapidly growing interest in navigation of the air and it is by no means improbable that within the next ten years vehicles for aerial travel will be as common as automobiles today.

Carl E. Meyers, who has a balloon farm at Frankfort, N. Y., writes in the Automobile Review of some of his experiments. He calls his strange craft a "sky-cycle," or gas kite, which is a combination of balloon and bicycle. The gas bag is made in the shape of an inverted boat from which is suspended a frame fitted with bicycle saddle and pedals to drive the propeller. It is steered by the inclination of the body; leaning forward to descend, backward to ascend, and to the right or left as on a bicycle. He has made several hundred voyages and without any accident to himself or air ship. Such a machine complete ready to sail can be built for $500, and weighs only 75 pounds. He is now at work perfecting a light gasoline engine, which he expects to introduce the coming summer.

He also exhibited at St. Louis in 1900 an air ship 13 feet long driven by a small electric motor current, to which power was supplied by wires leading to the ground. This ship was called the Electrical Aerial Torpedo, and was steered by electric devices controlled through wires. It carried no passengers, but was built to demonstrate its ability to carry and drop dynamite in military operations. It travelled in all over 600 miles while on exhibition at a speed of from 5 to 15 miles per hour.

Telephone Without Wires a Success

Prof. Collins Sending the First Message from one Ferryboat to Another in the North River, New York.

Today, by means of the wireless telephone, or radiotelephony, any of the approximately 40 million telephones in the United States can be connected to almost any one of the more than 65 million telephones in about 70 foreign countries. Radio telephones connect aircraft, ships, trains, police cars, taxis and military units with each other and with their respective headquarters

Tests recently made by A. Frederick Collins, in the North River, New York, almost in the same waters where nearly one hundred years ago Robert Fulton proved his steamboat to be a success, showed that the wireless telephone is perfectly practicable for commercial use. The tests were made from two moving ferryboats going in opposite directions with the vessels several hundred feet apart. The apparatus used was very simple. It consisted of wires attached to the top of the flagstaff of the boat, a wire running from the receiver and transmitter in the pilot house and connecting with a copper plate held under water, and ordinary electric batteries. The 'phone was just like the one in common use, with a bell for ringing up and microphones for talking and listening.

The only means of communication between the boats was through the water and the air. All the scientists present were convinced of the success of the test. The words of Prof. Collins were distinctly heard by his brother in the other boat and there was an absence of the scratchy sound heard in the ordinary telephone. On account of the crude apparatus used and the moving about of the submerged copper plates by the waves, the messages were not as distinct as they can be made. This part of the apparatus will be developed into more perfect form, overcoming this difficulty.

Prof. Collins is of the opinion that his invention will prove of the greatest service at a distance of one thousand or two thousand feet. It will be put to immediate use to warn vessels of their approach to each other in a dense fog.

While wireless telephony is not new it remained for Prof. Collins to show that it may be adapted to commercial use.

WHAT HE SAW IN A STREET CAR.

This joke is still current—possibly because it still has its core of truth

I saw a woman in a street car open a satchel and take out a purse, close the satchel and open the purse, take out a dime and close the purse, open the satchel and put in the purse, close the satchel and lock both ends. Then she gave the dime to the conductor and took a nickel in exchange. Then she opened the satchel, took out the purse, closed the satchel and opened the purse, put in the nickel and closed the purse, opened the satchel and put in the purse, closed the satchel and locked both ends. Then she felt to see if her back hair was all right, and it was all right, and she was all right, and just as sweet!

Marconi's optimistic prophecy of "full and efficient service between Great Britain and the United States" within a year actually was fulfilled only four years later, thanks in part to his own development of the rotary spark gap. In 1907 the British Marconi Company opened limited public service between Newfoundland and Ireland, and in 1908 made this service general. By 1912 the wireless branch of the Bureau of International Telegraph Union had 1000 members, and the great nations had agreed upon wave lengths, for already they were filling the air with their messages

Wireless Telegraphy For 1904

Signor Marconi Talks of His Plans and Improvements Being Made

BY GUGLIELMO MARCONI.

What are the prospects of wireless telegraphy for the ensuing year? It is a big question and an indefinite one. It must be remembered that wireless telegraphy is yet only in its infancy. To some extent it has emerged from the experimental stage—that is, over certain distances it is an actual practical working system—scientifically and commercially perfect. In overcoming long distances its practical utility has also been demonstrated, but it has not been able so far to justify itself on commercial grounds. That is what I mean when I say it is only in its infancy.

I know from my own experience, from my own positive knowledge gained by incessant labor, that the transmission of signals across the Atlantic is thoroughly practicable. It has been done and it is being done and in the approaching year I have every reason to believe that I shall be able to maintain a full and efficient service between Great Britain and the United States.

My continuous experiments and the improvements I have made in my apparatus warrant me fully in making that prophecy, and I do not usually prophesy unless I know. There are many doubters and skeptics, rivals and others who have poo-poohed its practicability for trans-Atlantic messages—well, before 1904 is out they will be sorry they spoke.

At the present moment we are negotiating with the United States government for the establishment of wireless communication between the American continent and the Philippines and in the event of the United States acquiring new colonies—for you are an expanding power now, you know—we shall hope to be permitted to establish our wireless system there also.

Not only do we work forward with confidence to establishing wireless communication on a commercial basis between Great Britain and the United States, but also between the United States and the continent of Europe. I do not want to expatiate on the advantages it will be to the world's commerce and thought when this cheap and perfectly reliable, if invisible, method of communication is established between the new world and the old. Its results cannot fail to be great. I might be justified in using a bigger word, but prefer to await the justification of events.

Our next important experiment will be the connection of Italy and South America by the wireless system. It is a distance of 6,500 miles, nearly double that to America from London, and I may say we are as certain of success in this as over the shorter distance. The Italian government is offering us every assistance, facility and encouragement in setting up this installation and is perfectly satisfied, moreover, with the proofs we have furnished of the progress we are making.

At present we are working for the British admiralty on wireless communication between London and Gibraltar. It is proving most successful and of the 1,000 miles 500 is over sea, while 500 is across the Spanish peninsula. There is no interference with our signals over that distance, and one of the most important developments of the near future will be the absolute security with which we can transmit over any distance without any possibility of interception or interruption, whether accidental or designed.

I need not dilate on the uses to which our system has been adapted on ships. Over 100 ships are now equipped with the Marconi apparatus, sixty of them warships, the others being trans-Atlantic and other liners. I know that the installation is immensely appreciated by the ships using it, and before long the big vessels of the White Star line, including the Cedric, following the example of Cunarders, will be fitted with our apparatus.

AMERICANS DRINK 910,000,000 GLASSES OF SODA WATER.

The soda water season is closing. A simple statement, but few know all that it means, or how great a commercial feature the soda water season is. In the United States alone, says the Soda Fountain, 75,000 merchants sell soda water, averaging sales of $730 a year, or a total of $54,750,000 per annum. The average price of drinks is six cents, giving the number of drinks as 910,000,000. Could the glasses required to serve this many drinks be placed side by side they would reach to within a day's travel of once around the world. These figures do not include pop, ginger ale, root beer, etc., but only sales made at the fountain.

The Future of Radium

By M. Pierre Curie

It is quite difficult to predict the future of radium, but I believe its field will be in the domain of medicine, rather than of warfare and commerce. A physician with a tenth of a grain of radium could receive an unlimited number of patients and probably effect cure after cure in cases of lupus and cancerous affections. The scope of radium is naturally affected by its enormous cost, as an ounce is worth a king's ransom. Recently, however, I received a communication from a firm in Buffalo, N. Y., claiming to have a new process of extracting radium from uranium, which may cheapen the article.

Radium might be a factor in warfare in the way of producing explosives in a magazine, causing the disappearance of the ship and the entire ship's company. But radium is dangerous against individuals rather than objects. A tenth of a grain left contiguous to a person is capable of producing complete paralysis. For this reason it would prove a dangerous medium in causing crime which would defy detection, if it ever become as easily obtainable as other chemicals. It is also dangerous to bring a tenth grain in contact with a highly charged electric battery, because an immediate explosion is certain. At first we hoped that the blind would be benefited by it, for a particle of radium inclosed in a box, placed on the forehead, conveys a sensation of light to the eye. But we found it did not enable the blind person to distinguish objects.

A man entering a room where there is a pound of pure radium would perish, but there is no fear of this, as only radium salts are yet obtainable from the barium found in Bohemia called pitchblende, of which a ton often yields less than a gram of radium salts. Already the mineral of Jachimsthal, which gave my wife and myself our first material, is exhausted, and only the discovery of a veritable Klondike of radium will demonstrate the wonderful force of this chemical so little understood even by its most ardent investigators.

Before doing what Prof. Gustav Lebon has suggested, the blowing up of magazines, forts and arsenals in the enemy's country by using a small tube of radium, we shall have to find the requisite amount of pure radium. Its potentiality is wonderful.

Few scientists saw as clearly the future uses of their work as Pierre Curie does here. Radium is still used almost exclusively in medicine, and while the price has gone down somewhat since the Curies extracted their first few grains from a ton of pitchblende in 1898, it still costs more than $25 a milligram, and the world's supply is two pounds or less. Curie, a physics teacher at the Paris Sorbonne, won the Nobel Prize in 1903 for the discovery. Two years after this article appeared in Popular Mechanics, *Curie was run down and killed by a wagon, and Madame Curie carried on his work*

FIRST AUTOMOBILE IN THE UNITED STATES.

What is claimed to be the first automobile built in the United States, is still in operation and is owned by Achille Philion, of Akron, Ohio. It was fourteen years ago that he had the machine built under his direction. The picture affords a very fair idea of the construction. The motive power is steam; the upright boiler burns coal; the engine is one horsepower; and the wheels are wire-spoke with flat metal tire. The steering wheel is quite similar to present practice, while the whistle is something of a novelty. Two persons find comfortable seats in front, and the rear seat is for the engineer who is also fireman, and who controls the operation of the engine.

Claimed to Be the First Auto

Cross-country auto runs, testing performance under ordinary travel conditions, were highly popular. The first such run on record was held on Thanksgiving Day, 1895, on a snow-covered road from Chicago to Waukegan. It was won by James F. Duryea at an average speed of 7½ miles per hour. When the Vanderbilt Cup Race was held over the same course in 1904, the winner averaged better than 52 miles per hour

An Endurance Run in Truth Was This

Terrible Experiences of Men and Machines in the Remarkable 1,000 Mile New York to Pittsburg Test

Narrow escapes from drowning, thrice barely saved from being dashed down slippery mountain sides, exhaustion from hunger, sleepless nights and inhuman exposure—this is the story of the 1,000-mile automobile endurance run given by the National Association of Manufacturers. It was "endurance" almost beyond "endurance" throughout the remarkable expedition. Such another was never experienced before, and will never be experienced again by those who escaped the hazards, so they declare.

Two Cars Caught in the Susquehanna River Flood

The run was from New York to Cleveland and thence to Pittsburg, over a route specially selected by the promoters for its perils. Floods, thunder storms, washouts and numerous unlooked for catastrophes added to the distress of the men and vehicles. The automobiles at times were forced to abandon the road and take to the railroad tracks; they had to be hauled out of flooded districts by horses. Often the automobilists were up to their necks in water. The men proved to possess more endurance than the automobiles, as when the perils were at their height the automobiles stalled in the middle of streams, and the men had to wade out in the water and pilot them across. In one of the cars a can of carbide was ignited in a flood which nearly swept the vehicles from their path near Binghamton. The flames burst all over the car, creating almost a panic and seriously injuring the operator, who in consequence was forced to abandon the run.

These extracts from the Automobile's description of the run may give an idea of some of the other "endurances" encountered: "The jolting over the railroad tracks had loosened every electrical connection. Again our engine stopped, and for four hours we were looking for a spark. During this four hours the writer availed himself of the first opportunity in the last 48 hours to lie down by the side of the road under a tree and get nearly two hours' sleep. We covered 447 miles in 47 hours, with only six hours' sleep on the part of the operator, and no sleep from Saturday until Friday night on the part of either passenger or observer in our wagon, except such as we gained while sitting in the wagon.

"Horses refused to draw in our efforts to get out of the flood near Binghamton. For an hour and a quarter the operator, in water up to his waist, and sometimes above his shoulders, tugged away with the second horse. A rope 200 feet long was secured, and finally bystanders on the railroad track succeeded in pulling the car back to its original starting place. From there it was towed back five miles to Binghamton. There new batteries and new coil were secured, and we obtained dry clothing, having traveled in wet clothes for 96 hours."

Future of the Submarine

Author of the Nautilus Says Its Use Will Be Confined to War and It Will Bring Peace

By Jules Verne

For some inexplicable reason many people insist upon regarding me as the inventor, or the imaginer, of the submarine. I am not in any way the inventor of submarine navigation, and reference to the authorities will show that many years—fully fifty, I should say, before I wrote about the Nautilus—the Italians were at work upon submarine war vessels, and other nations were busied with them, too. All that I did was to avail myself of the great privileges of the fiction writer, spring over every scientific difficulty with fancy's seven-leagued boots, and create on paper what other men were planning out in steel and other metals.

The future of the submarine, as I regard it—and let me here disclaim all gift of prophecy—is to be wholly a war future. The Nautilus, as I have written of it, will never be, I think, an actual fact, and I do not believe that under-sea ships will be built in future years to carry traffic across the ocean's bed to America and to Australia. Even if the air difficulty were successfully encountered (and I have my grave doubts as to the possibility of that), what would be gained by any such sub-ocean traffic except freedom from sea-sickness? No submarine would ever cross the bed of the Atlantic faster than a ship upon the waves would traverse it.

I am an old man now, and working, as well as my deficient eyesight will allow me, upon my one hundred and second volume of boys' stories, and as I look back on the years which have passed since I first wrote the life-story of the Nautilus, and of its owner, I see no progress in the submarine which makes me hope for its use as a commercial medium. It has been wonderfully improved, I grant you—miraculously improved almost—but the improvements have all tended to one point—its efficacy as a war weapon; and that will be its one use in the future, I believe. I even think that in the distant future the submarine may be the cause of bringing battle to a stoppage altogether, for fleets will become useless, and as other war material continues to improve, war will become impossible.

First Test of Submarines in a Gale.—Portsmouth Flotilla Navigating the Surface in a Wild Sea

"For the last 20 years the advance of peoples is merely living the novels of Jules Verne." Marshal Lyautey, a French administrator, paid that tribute to this early writer of science fiction. In more than 100 books like Twenty Thousand Leagues Under the Sea, The Nautilus *and* Around The World in Eighty Days, *Verne anticipated some of the inventions to come, including the submarine, the airplane and television. He was born in Nantes, France, in 1828; died a year after this article appeared*

A potpourri of advertising that reflects the perennial interests of nearly everybody—food, comfort, love, independence and politics

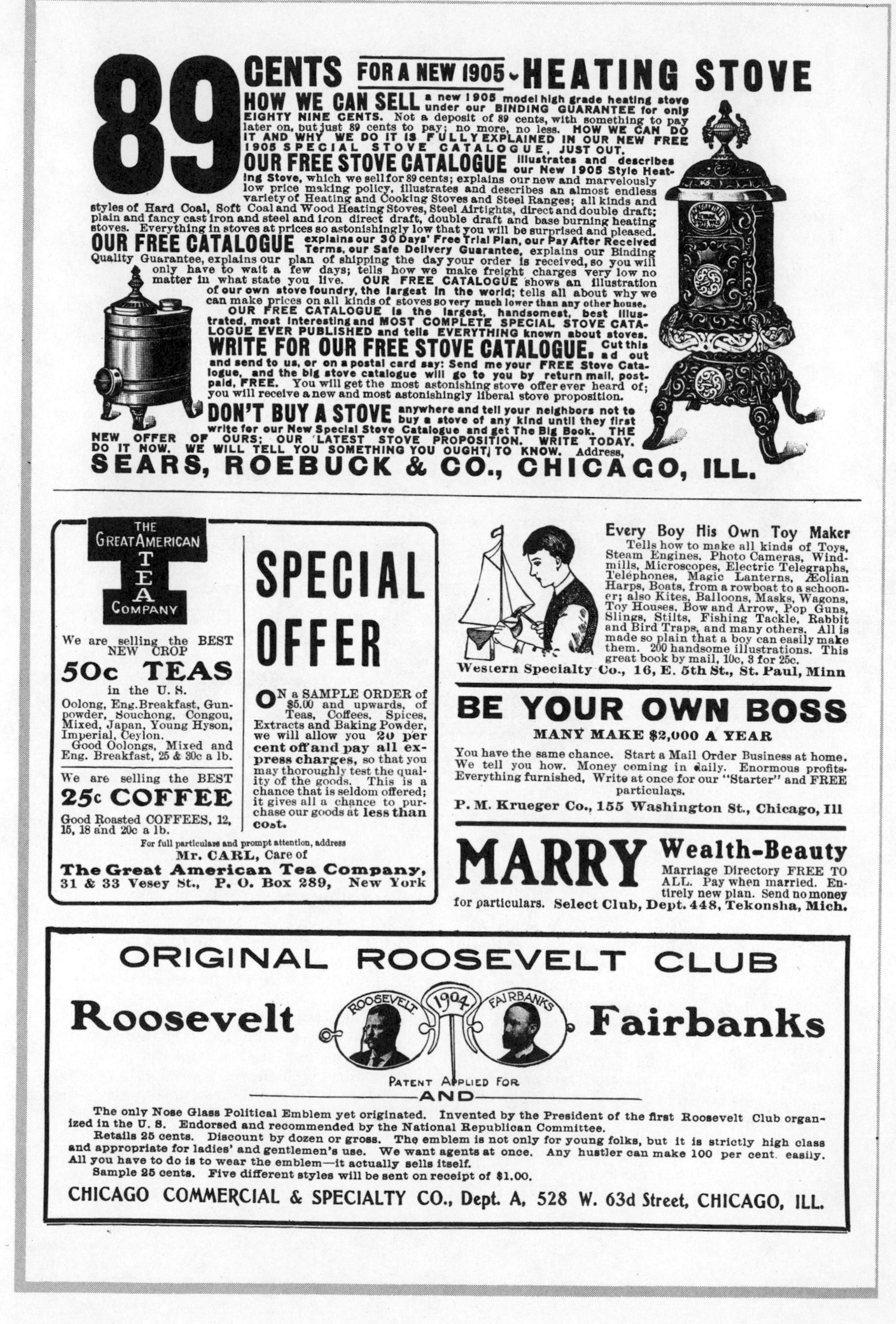

Largest Automobile in the World

Has 400 Horsepower -- Is Expected To Run 100 Miles An Hour -- Cost $35,000.

The Touring Body.

The largest automobile in the world, costing $35,000, of 408 horsepower, and capable of a speed of 100 miles, has lately been built at Cleveland, Ohio.

This machine, which was built for Louis D. Schoenburg, will accommodate ten persons with separate sleeping apartments for long distance trips, besides which they may have their meals served in the vehicle, as it is provided with a kitchen and dining-room. It also carries a dynamo for electric lighting and heating. Besides being so commodious the interior appointments and decorations are rich, beautiful and luxurious.

The car has three bodies: The Pullman body described, a touring body and a racing body. It certainly surpasses anything yet attempted in automobile construction and will probably stimulate a number of competitive efforts.

With a 400 horsepower engine this one probably would actually go 100 miles an hour—if it would hang together and stay on the road. Some of the steamers of the day had amazing power and pickup, far in excess of what was safe, considering the general engineering of the car other than the engine

FIVE HUNDRED DOLLARS POPULAR PRICE FOR AUTOMOBILES.

Where there is one person who can afford to pay $5,000 for a luxurious automobile there are fifty who cannot pay more than $500, and these are waiting for the manufacturers to bring their prices down. Thus far the demand for high-priced machines has been sufficient to keep the factories busy on machines ranging from $700 up, but if autos drive horses from the streets it will be when present prices are very greatly reduced.

That $500 is a popular price was demonstrated a few days ago in this city. A dealer had a job lot to dispose of, and advertised them at the usual price, $750. No sales resulting, he tried them at $700, then $600, but without satisfactory results. Then he came out with an offer to close them out at an even $500 each, and they were sold in no time.

The masses want a safe, strong car, reasonably fast, and plain and simple in finish, and with the least possible number of contraptions. Before many years such machines will be available and will find ready buyers.

AUTOMOBILE DRAWS STREET CAR.

The owner of an auto in Detroit was boasting about the pulling abilities of his machine, and to make good his claims hitched on to a street car that was crowded with passengers. The auto turned out to be a first-class locomotive and drew the car along at its usual rate of speed.

Popular Mechanics *pleaded for a $500 automobile, but not until 1911 did any manufacturer succeed in coming near this. Then the Brush Runabout Company produced an open two-seater that sold for $485. There also were chain-driven "cycle cars," some only three-wheeled, that sold for less, but these were not regarded as true autos.*

Inventors, professional and amateur, tinkered and refined endlessly through the "age of marvels." This stenophile was neither the first nor the last in many stages of improvement, but it was very close to the modern stenotype. It actually had fewer keys. John Zachos of New York patented the first stenotype in 1876

Machine for Writing Shorthand

French Invention Which May Revolutionize Present System of Learning Shorthand

Shorthand can now be written on a machine. For many years there have been attempts made to construct a machine for this purpose, and while several inventions have been made and put upon trial they have not come into general use. However, a Frenchman, M. Bivort by name, has recently brought out a machine which he calls the stenophile and which promises to be of the greatest value, inasmuch as it is capable of practical use for all business purposes and is qualified to supplant the present method of writing shorthand by hand.

Taking Notes in Shorthand by Machine

Recognizing the necessity of having a rational alphabet which would contain the greatest number of sounds in the fewest signs, M. Bivort has designed an alphabet in which all similar consonant sounds are consolidated, and has constructed a system of syllabic writing by means of which the operator is enabled to attain the speed of shorthand writers of to-day. Following the phonetic principles used in present systems he has combined several of the consonants, such as B and P, F and V, T and D, etc., thus reducing the number of keys necessary to twenty, ten for each hand. There are two intermediate keys, one for the aspirate H, while the other moves the paper forward.

Tremendous activity was going on at this time to develop color photography. Although F. E. Ives is generally conceded to be the man from whom modern color photography stems, an astonishingly complete book on its principles was published back in 1868 by Ducos du Hauron. Practical application of his ideas was delayed for many years because none of the photographic emulsions of the day were sensitive to other than blue or ultraviolet light

Wonderful Discovery in Photography

Portraits in Colors by a Purely Photographic Process--Negative Partly Developed Under Sunlight

Among all of the investigations and discoveries that have recently been made relative to the phenomena of light in connection with photography, the experiments of Mr. J. Ellsworth Hare, a Chicago photographer, are showing some of the most promising practical results. While photographers all over the world have been attempting to discover methods of photographing in colors or of producing colored photographs by one process or another, this young man has actually succeeded in producing portraits in colors by a purely photographic process. These portraits bear a distinctively poster character in appearance and, although the process has only been perfected within the past few weeks, the new style colored photographs are already commanding high prices among the members of Chicago's four hundred.

The process of making the "poster portraits in colors," as the inventor calls them, is a printing process, the result being brought about by a double exposure to the light and a triple manipulation of the chemicals. The photograph is made on a thin metallic plate, very light in weight, which is prepared by a complicated system of coating before it is ready for printing.

The first coat is of a collodion nature, containing the double salts of silver. After this coating has been allowed to dry over night in a dark room, it is recoated with a heavy coat of specially prepared and sensitized bicromate solution, in which enough black carbon pigment has been added to make the solution perfectly opaque. The plate, when thoroughly dry, is ready for printing.

An ordinary portrait negative such as is used by all photographers is used to print from. Although the operation of placing the sensitized metallic plate in contact with the negative must be done in the dark room, the printing is done in the sunlight. The first exposure is determined by time.

THE AERIAL ROWBOAT

New Air Boat Propelled by Oars which Imitate Motion of a Bird

By Alva L. Reynolds, Los Angeles, Cal.

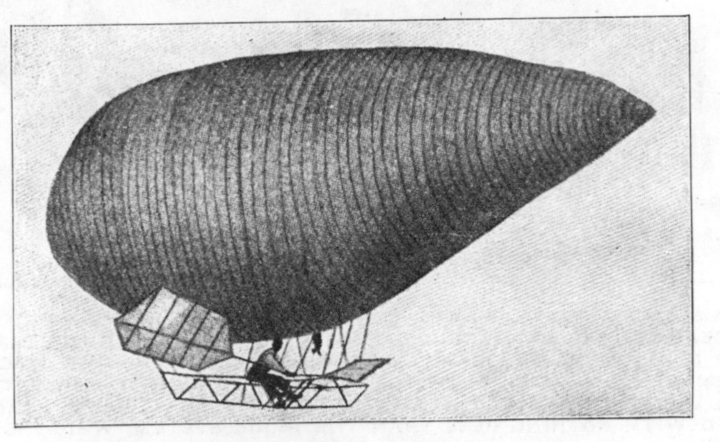

Fig. 1--Rowing in the Air

Although Samuel Langley and the Wright brothers had demonstrated clearly the principles of airplane flight, many early designers of flying machines clung tenaciously to the idea that the wings should imitate those of birds—either in their shape or in mechanical action.

I am happy to comply with your request and tell the readers of Popular Mechanics something of my aircraft. The illustration shown in Fig. 1 is a fair representation of my "Man Angel" flying-machine in the act of flight. It has been given the name of "Aerial Rowboat" by those who have judged it simply from the standpoint of appearances. I have been frequently asked why I gave my invention the name "Man-Angel," many people seeming to think it bordered on the sacrilegious. I gave it that name as symbolical of my home city, Los Angeles.

It is the only machine in the world that flies heavier than air, or lighter at the will of the operator, and can ascend or descend without discharging ballast or gas. My gas-bag is an ovoid in form and has its equator forward of the middle. This is not a matter of taste as may be supposed, but is one of the scientific and essential features of my machine. Any object of this form if thrown through the air will always go *big end first.* It is this feature that renders my machine self-dirigible and self-balanced, and is one of the reasons why it requires no rudder.

FLYING AUTO THE LATEST MOTOR CAR

A new Paris aeroplane and automobile combined has the aeroplane mounted on a chassis motor worked by liquid gas. When the apparatus is well launched on its way, the force of propulsion and the resistance of the wind to the aeroplane, causes it to rise. The machine was designed by M. Vina of Paris.

M. Vina's machine may have risen, but certainly not very high or under any control

This was the period of the "muckrakers"—Lincoln Steffens, Upton Sinclair and other writers of the day were exposing shocking conditions in meat packing, steel, textile mills and other large industries. Sinclair's novel The Jungle, *set in the Chicago stockyards, is believed to have influenced Theodore Roosevelt in his decision to give his full support to the controversial Pure Food Act*

THIS IS A SCENE IN PARIS, WHERE CONDEMNED MEAT STAYS CONDEMNED AND ACTUALLY REACHES THE RENDERING TANKS INSTEAD OF BEING SIDETRACKED AND WORKED UP INTO CANNED GOODS FOR HUMAN CONSUMPTION. THE WAGON IN THE PICTURE REMOVES DISEASED MEAT, BUT FIRST THE INSPECTOR INJECTS IT WITH KEROSENE CARRIED IN THE CAN NEXT THE DRIVER'S SEAT. AMERICANS SHOULD BE SATISFIED WITH NOTHING LESS THAN THE PARIS SYSTEM, WHICH IS THE BEST IN THE WORLD.

REVOLUTIONIZE PACKING SYSTEM

"Kitchen of the Nation" Indescribably Filthy--Packers Have Now Cleaned Up a Few Rooms to Show Visitors

It begins to look as if the people were to have relief. The Pure Food bill, which was on the verge of failure in the Senate, has been revived, and under pressure of an awakened and outraged public may yet amount to something. For years new mechanical methods and applied chemistry have been made use of in a constantly increasing degree, until few of the articles of food are genuine, and many of them, while palatable, are unfit for food. Preservatives of all kinds are used in milk and meats, vinegar is made of deadly acids, butter and lard is made of "grease" and much of the grease is unfit even for soap. Much of the potted and canned meats and sausages are made of unspeakable things and by processes indescribably filthy. Even these when "spoiled" have been "recovered" by mechanical and chemical processes, and sent out again wrapped in a bright, fresh label, which gives the package a new appearance. Smoked meats by thousands of tons never saw any smoke, but are given the smoked flavor by a preparation of creosote, which is quicker and cheaper.

The lust for profit has grown to such an extent, and has been unchecked, until through immunity what was first an experiment soon became an established practice.

Much the larger proportion of meat killed by the Chicago and other large packers is healthy, and hence wholesome, but an almost incredible amount of diseased meat, absolutely unfit for human use in any form, has been going out. When cut up into steaks or roasts only a highly trained expert can detect disease.

That portion of the Reynolds-Neill report which has been given the public is true, every word of it, and conditions immeasurably worse have long existed. Just now the big packing houses in Chicago are receiving the first general house cleaning since they were established, and in full page advertisements the public is invited to call and see. But what the packers choose to allow the visitor to see is selected departments, which are not now and never were, specially offensive. In the hundreds of great buildings and pens covering a space equivalent to several hundred city blocks there are more places the visitor cannot find and enter than those he will be allowed to see.

The packers righteously deny the accusations, but men who will deliberately deceive the public with false brands and sell diseased meat as good meat, naturally would not hesitate to deny having done so.

London is experiencing an awakening as to its own slaughter houses, and points to Paris as having the most perfect large system in the world. There they have an inspection which means something, and once a carcass is condemned it is used only for fertilizer or fed to wild animals in captivity.

THE MOTOR SKATE

The newspaper reports from Paris of a motor skate prove to be true, so far as the skate itself is concerned. A small gasoline motor is attached to a miniature chassis, and a speed of 25 miles an hour is claimed. The motor is directly connected to the rear axle. The gasoline tank is strapped to the body of the operator. Just what would happen if the skater should chance to "interfere" can be imagined.

The Latest Roller Skates

THRILLING RESCUE AT NIAGARA FALLS

The most sensational rescue ever made at Niagara Falls was accomplished recently, by the fire and police department. Annis Sweitzer, demented and escaped from an asylum, plunged into the rapids and was carried down until within 15 ft. of the brink of the American fall, where he landed on a small rock 35 ft. from shore. He refused to be rescued. Ropes thrown to him were cast aside and efforts to lasso him failed.

The hook and ladder company was finally called, which loaded the truck with heavy weights and ran the extension ladder out 40 ft. over the water. Fireman Conroy and Policeman Butts crawled out on the ladder and after a furious struggle with the maniac, in which they several times narrowly escaped going over the falls, he was finally secured, bound and brought ashore. The incident was the most thrilling rescue ever made by a ladder company.

Paris Police Inspector Stamping Good Meat--It Can Now Be Sold

National magazines also participated in the "muckraking." In Collier's Weekly *a series of articles on patent medicines by Samuel Hopkins Adams created a sensation. Backed by public opinion, sponsors of federal food and drug regulation and meat inspection finally succeeded in having such legislation adopted in 1907. No penalties were provided until later, however*

No invention hit the age with greater impact than King Camp Gillette's safety razor, patented in 1895. This advertisement appeared during Gillette's first successful year since incorporating his company in 1901. In 1903 he sold only 51 of his "newfangled" razors, but in 1906 paid out more than $100,000 in dividends

The manufacturers of straight razors fought back hard. After all, men had been shaving with straight razors for some 4000 years—at least since the court of ancient Egypt. There was constraint, too, between a man and his barber when the customer bought a "Safety." But economy and convenience won in the end

The San Francisco earthquake and the fire that followed it in 1906 killed 452 persons and destroyed 28,000 buildings. The total property damage was estimated at a billion dollars, which was a devastating loss to a city in those days Although horrible in its consequences, the earthquake did serve one purpose—it convinced builders that steel structures were safest for modern cities

MODERN STEEL STRUCTURES RESIST EARTHQUAKE

Astonishing Demonstration at San Francisco--Modern Skyscrapers Stand While Old-Style Three-Story Buildings Fall

By J. M. Baltimore, San Francisco

No. 1.--City and County Building: A Total Wreck

(The following from our staff correspondent in San Francisco is in response to our request for information specially concerning the condition of the modern steel constructed skyscrapers, and will correct the general impression that this type of construction failed under earthquake shock. The announcement that more steel-frame buildings will be erected at once will now be better understood.—Editor.)

The chaotic condition of affairs here, which is simply indescribable, together with having lost all my own personal effects in the fire, has made it difficult for me to send a report with as full details as you expect. Practically everyone has a new address, and the engineers and architects I had to seek out were no exception to the rule. They are working night and day, and will grant an interview of only a few minutes.

The modern steel construction, including the skyscrapers of twelve or more stories, apparently stood the shock in a manner which astounded even their most enthusiastic advocates. Even the conflagration which followed, and whose mass of heat and flame

No. 2.--Post Office: Unharmed

No. 3.--Call Building, 300 Ft. High--Interior Burned Out, but no Visible Cracks in Outer Walls

Like Chicago after its own great fire, San Francisco came back stronger than ever. Within three years some 20,000 structures had been rebuilt. This time all public buildings were fireproofed and equipped with fire extinguishers

was simply a great gulf of roaring, boiling fire, failed in several cases to destroy the steel structure while burning out everything combustible in its interior. The following is compiled from the first examinations of the experts; a minute investigation will take weeks and perhaps months, and may possibly reveal strains which are not apparent or easily discovered.

Photograph No. 1 shows the once magnificent City Hall, including the Court House, Hall of Records, City Prison, Hospital, Police Courts, etc., after the dreadful earthquake and fire. It must have been the very center of the seismic disturbance, for no building in all San Francisco was one-tenth as badly damaged by the quake as was it. It was practically wrecked; then the fire, some 30 hours later, completed the work of ruin. The shock knocked off all the stone and metal covering all around the huge and towering dome, one of the finest in the United States, leaving the top standing. The network of steel structural part standing comparatively intact. This magnificent structure originally cost $5,000,000, and was several years in process of construction. It is deemed past all repair.

No. 4.--Flood Building--12 Stories--Interior Burned--
Can be Restored for $100,000

Lincoln Beachey, hero of the exploit pictured here and described on the opposite page, was the daredevil of the early airmen. He was flying balloons at 17, took up dirigibles next, and switched to airplanes in 1911. He was one of the first "barnstormers" touring the country first in his balloon, The Rubber Cow, *and later in the company of Barney Oldfield, another stunt man of the decade*

Views of the Flight

The Airship Motor

AIRSHIP CIRCLES WASHINGTON MONUMENT

Sails Around the Dome of the Capitol and Makes a Call at the White House--Flight Covers 20 Miles

Stately senators and eloquent congressmen are no more immune to the sensation of a real airship overhead than the average small boy at a county fair. Business at the Capitol was suspended for a full half-hour, while the entire city gazed skyward. There was good reason for it all, too, for a young American from California was demonstrating in a way never accomplished by even Santos Dumont. An airship sailing around the great dome of the Capitol, like some mammoth bird, and later circling around the Washington monument in a graceful ascending spiral, was something never before witnessed.

From the monument the ship sailed straight for the White House and gently came to rest on the lawn, where the President's wife, in his absence, acknowledged this, the most novel call ever made at the executive mansion.

The captain of the airship is a young Californian—Lincoln Beachy—who is a mere youth. He became interested in the work while helping a balloon man in San Francisco a few months ago. His ship is 66 ft. long, 16 ft. in diameter, with a two-bladed propeller in front and a large rudder. The flight described was of nearly 20 miles. The construction of the gas engine will readily be understood from the illustration.

A German lad has invented a device for controlling and changing the direction of a torpedo after it has been fired. His machine is being tested by German naval officials.

Lincoln Beachey's call at the White House was only one of a series of sensational aerial stunts. One week after soloing at Glen Curtiss' flying school, Beachey electrified the flying world by a straight dive of 400 feet. Later he stunted over Niagara Falls, skimming within 30 feet of the falls at one point. Beachey was the first flier to loop the loop, to fly a plane upside down and to go into a deliberate spin. He was universally considered the greatest precision pilot of the era, and soon was in such demand that he received $1000 a day for exhibition flying. He was killed while stunting in a new monoplane of his own design when a wing collapsed as he dived over the San Francisco Exposition in 1915

PHOTOGRAPHS ON FINGER NAILS

The latest London fad is to have the portrait of lover or favorite relative photographed on a finger nail. Young brides select the nail of the wedding ring finger. The process of picture making is best done by what is known as the carbon process. A photograph of the subject is first made in the ordinary way, and reduced to a size suitable for the finger nail. A print is then made from the negative on carbon paper, which is made in substantially every color. After the print has been fixed and toned, it is transferred to what is known as transfer paper. At this stage the finger nail must be rubbed with pumice powder, to render it quite smooth. Then the wet transfer paper is placed with the photograph on the finger nail. When dry, the transfer paper is stripped off and a finished photograph is left on the finger nail. Finally, a fine coat of transparent enamel is brushed over the photograph, rendering it perfectly safe to wash the hand without damaging the picture.

1906 STYLE AUTO

Some of the new styles of autos which will be brought out next year will lose much of the accustomed resemblance to a motor car and will easily pass for a horse-drawn vehicle. The running side board is omitted and the rear seat is higher than the other. The room required for machinery is greatly reduced and the lines throughout are much more graceful. The style illustrated will be known as the phaeton auto.

Phaeton Auto for 1906

The Atlantic steamship record was lowered 10 minutes by the new French liner "La Provence" on her maiden trip from Havre to New York. Time was 5 days 9 hours and 10 minutes.

Men now who were boys then will recall the thrill of the secret club, whose members were bound by rituals including awesome oaths and minor blood rites. A secret clubhouse, maybe underground like this one, perhaps in the branches of a tall tree, or just a shack on a vacant lot, was a necessary adjunct. The boys' clubhouse was immortalized in American literature first by Mark Twain and later by Booth Tarkington

MECHANICS FOR YOUNG AMERICA

AN UNDERGROUND CLUB-HOUSE

Nearly every boys' club wants a place to meet and it was for this purpose that the underground house here shown was constructed. The house is built in a hill which was first excavated, as shown in Fig. 1, the dirt being thrown on each side, to be used later for banking and covering the roof.

The house consists of two principal parts: the entry, Fig. 2, and the club room, Fig. 3. This may be made any length desired, but should not be more than 5 or 6 ft. wide, as a greater width would require cross beams to support the roof and would thereby make the construction much more complicated.

The lumber used should be about 1 in. thick and should be fastened together in a good workmanlike manner. This is especially true of the roof, which is required to support the weight of the earth above in addition to the weight of any possible intruder and which, if too weak, will endanger the occupants of the house. The boards should be nailed across the short way to give greater strength and it is well to nail a long board along the middle the entire length of the roof.

In Figs. 4 and 5 are shown the articles of furniture that are usually required. These may be either home-made, as shown, or may be obtained from the old furniture discarded from the home. The door, Fig. 6, is provided with a secret lock which consists of a latch, A, supported on a strong frame, B, and swinging on a pivot near the center.

A string, C, is fastened to the latch and terminates in a ring, D, which is placed in a location known only to the members of the club. A light spring or rubber band may be used to make the latch spring over in front of the door, and when the door is closed it will lock itself.

Details of Construction and Equipment of Underground Club-House

The longitudinal section of the complete house is shown in Fig. 7. The ventilator, A, can be made of either wood or stove pipe and if desired can have a small cover over the top to prevent rain coming in. If a stove is used, a pile of burnt wood can be placed around the stack, as shown at B, so that the suspicions of passers-by will not be aroused in any way. Also a bush, C, transplanted at the entrance, will hide the door.

An underground club-house of this kind will prove a source of mystery to those uninformed of the secret entrance.—Contributed by Charles Edwards, Jr., 2623 E. Preston St., Baltimore, Md.

STEEL PASSENGER CARS BOUND TO COME

"It is true that present passenger coaches are somewhat longer and much heavier, and will resist impacts that would have wrecked cars built ten or fifteen years ago. It is true, also, that they are operated at much higher speeds, and while it may seem a broad statement, our average passenger coach today is relatively no stronger than the cars of our forefathers. If this is doubted a perusal of the newspaper reports of a few wrecks in late years will suffice. For high-speed service it is practically essential to use a steel car, if the safety of the passengers is desired. The splinters from the old wooden warships in time of action killed more men than the cannon balls. We have been over the Spanish fleet scare for some years and do not expect anyone to fire 13-in. shells at our cars, yet in a collision the conditions are not dissimilar. The force of impact will splinter the sills, posts and side plates, and a passenger caught in the wreckage has not much chance, particularly with the addition of fire. In the steel car the passengers may suffer contusions, but these are cheaper, from a claim department standpoint than an amputated limb. Aside from the question of accidents, steel passenger cars should be a good investment. The repairs are less; the life much longer; and the cost and weight of a steel passenger coach very near that of a wooden car built to the same specifications."—J. F. MacEnulty before the New England Railway Club.

The gradual replacement of wooden cars with those of all-steel construction, begun at the turn of the century, was a great step forward in public safety. Today all interstate transportation vehicles must be of all-metal construction. But a few wooden cars still remain in service on elevated and streetcar lines in some cities

Steel Passenger Car After Wreck—Note Its Good Condition

Steel freight cars have now been in use about eight years. Of 225,000 freight cars ordered from nine of the car builders in 1895, two-thirds were steel. The steel freight car was first built to enable the carrying of loads unsafe in cars constructed of wood. Soon it was found the repairs were greatly less than on wooden cars, and that a steel car could go in a wreck and be repaired for $50 which would have absolutely destroyed a wooden car.

One instance will illustrate this point: Several cars, each containing 50 tons of ore, ran three miles down a 4 per cent grade, and with the engine jumped over the end of a switch-back, the cars and engine going by actual measurement 422 ft. before striking the ground; the point of contact was frozen ground, the drop being 53 ft. from track level. The engine and cars then rolled 516 ft. The cost of repairing the bodies of these seven cars was only $350 each.

The Morris chair for many years was the most imposing (and most comfortable) furnishing in the average American home. Few who enjoyed the padded roominess of this chair knew it was named for William Morris (1834-1896), who at various times was a clergyman, artist, poet and furniture designer. His chair made the widest impression on posterity, and there are many who regret its passing. Modern versions, none so comfortable as the original, have appeared from time to time

INGENIOUS SHOP-LIFTING APPARATUS

Book with Spaces for Jewels--Dummy Hand Bag with Secret Compartment--Garters with Goods Hung on Hooks

The art of the shop-lifter has been reduced to a science in which many mechanical devices are employed to facilitate the work and conceal the stolen goods. The London police recently made an arrest of a female expert who was literally covered from head to foot with evidences of theft, and without any one of the several dozen articles being visible to the keen-eyed store detectives.

In her hair were valuable pieces of small jewelry; under the skirt was a well filled bag easily reached through a false pocket; a book carried under the arm had been prepared with spaces to hold rings and gems; a dummy hand satchel had a trap door at one end held shut by means of a spring. Her garters were sewed with spring hooks and clasps for hanging various articles; a slit in the skirt enabled easy access, while a piece of wax attached to the sole of the shoe next the heel enabled the picking up of jewelry after it was dropped to the floor. What appeared to be an innocent cuff ornament was really a spring-clip that dexterously picked up articles on the show case while the hand was in full view. On the person of the shop-lifter described were found 47 articles having a total value of several hundred dollars—the result of one day's operations.

PUSH BUTTON OPERATES MORRIS CHAIR

No Exertion to Operate

The latest ease producer is a Morris chair which tilts backward or forward as much or little as desired without getting up to set the rod. In fact there is no rod, but instead a series of stops controlled by a push button. You simply touch the button and the weight of the body carries the back to any angle wanted, sit up straight and touch the button again and the chair straightens up at the same instant.

The steel and electric manufacturing companies have orders amounting to $1,200,000,000.

MOTORCYCLE MADE FASTEST TIME ON RECORD

The largest and most powerful motorcycle ever built has recently been completed and entered the contest in the 1907 Beach races. It is an 8-cylinder machine of 40 hp. The record for the 10-mile race is already held by the same builders who won the 10-mile race three years ago at Ormond Beach with a double cylinder machine in 8:54 2-5. Great expectations are placed on the performance of the new machine, which is driven direct with a one to one gear, with 26-in. rear wheel. The wheel base is 65 in. The entire machine weighs 300 lb. and is faster than any other mechanical motive power ever built by man.

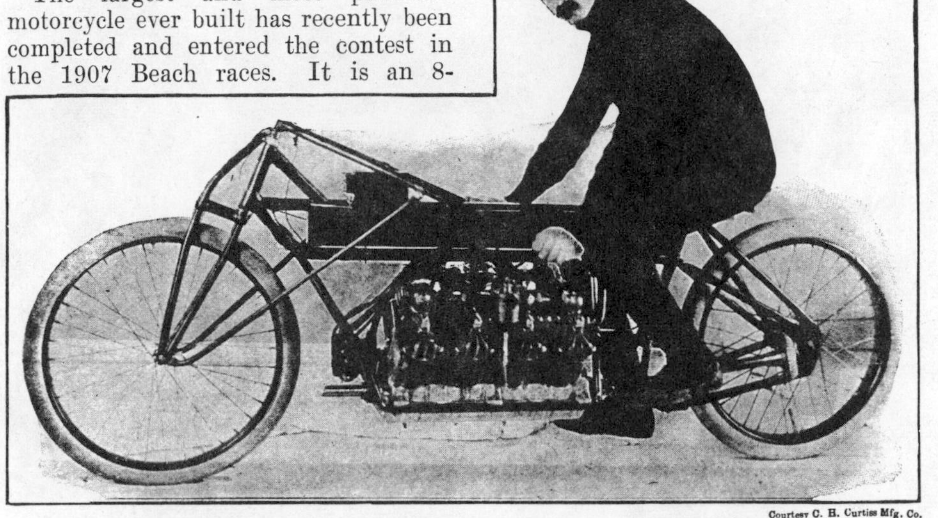

Courtesy G. H. Curtiss Mfg. Co.

40-Hp. Motorcycle Which Made a Mile in 26 2-5 Seconds

AERIAL NAVIGATION A SUCCESS, SAYS DR. BELL

"The problem of aerial navigation already is solved and America is in advance of the rest of the world in heavier-than-air flying machines." This was the emphatic statement made by Professor Alexander Graham Bell in England, recently, whither he had gone to receive the degree of doctor of science conferred upon him by Oxford. Dr. Bell declares that "there is left only the problem of improving the machine that has been invented" by the Wright brothers, and others, and that "great credit is due Mr. Octave Chanute of Chicago," who not only induced young Americans to experiment, but paid much of the expenses out of his own pocket. In regard to future developments, Dr. Bell said:

"The development of the airship, I think, will come for other than commercial reasons, for the flying machine is destined to take an important part in warfare. The war departments of different governments are watching with greatest interest whatever is being done in this direction, and once a successful airship is given to the world its growth toward perfection will be more rapid than anything ever seen.

"The airship will overturn all present methods of warfare. Then, too, wealthy men will take to airships as they have taken to automobiles, and the machines will be developed for speed. They will undoubtedly be utilized for purposes of rapid and light transportation, such as carrying the mails."

For this brief moment in the history of speed, the motorcycle was the "fastest thing on earth." A mile in 26⅖ seconds, or 136.36 miles per hour, was better than auto, airplane or train could do. The locomotive of 1907 could make 100 m.p.h., the automobile a little less, while the infant airplane ran a bad fourth in the speed sweepstakes. Today the airplane leads with speeds faster than sound, the automobile record is better than 400 m.p.h., while the locomotive and the motorcycle haven't improved their basic speeds much

Thomas Alva Edison's most original invention, the phonograph, hit the American scene with all the impact of the radio in the 1920's and of television in present times. Bringing fine music within the reach of everyone, the phonograph has held its own in competition with these new mediums, and today it is not uncommon to find all three in the family living room. Although technically refined, electrically operated and automatic in its record changing, today's phonograph operates on the same basic principles as the Edison phonograph of 1909

LOOK at this happy home scene, all enjoying the Edison Phonograph. The Edison has indeed been rightly called the king of entertainers for the home.

Why Don't YOU Get This PHONOGRAPH on

For almost four years I have been making the most liberal phonograph offer ever known! I have given hosts of people the opportunity of hearing the genuine Edison Phonograph right in their own homes without charging them a single penny.

Think of it! Thousands and thousands and thousands of people have been given the opportunity to hear in their own parlors concerts and entertainments by world famous musicians—just such entertainments as the greatest metropolitan theatres are producing.

So far you have missed all this. Why? Possibly you don't quite understand my offer yet. Listen—

I will send you this Genuine Edison Standard Outfit (the newest model), complete with one dozen **EDISON MOULDED AND AMBEROL RECORDS**, for an absolutely free trial. I don't ask any money down or in advance. There are no C. O. D. shipments; no leases or mortgages on the outfit; no papers of any sort to sign. Absolutely **nothing** but a plain out-and-out offer to ship you this phonograph together with a dozen records of your own selection on a free trial so that you can hear it and play it in your own home. I can't make this offer any plainer, any clearer, any better than it is. There is no catch about it anywhere. If you will stop and think just a moment, you will realize that the high standing of this concern would absolutely prohibit anything except a straightforward offer.

WHY I Want to Lend You This Phonograph: I know that there are thousands and thousands of people who have never heard the Genuine **Edison** Phonograph. **Nearly everyone** is familiar with the screechy, unnatural sounds produced by the imitation machines (some of which though inferior are very expensive). After hearing the old style and imitation machines people become prejudiced against all kinds of "Talking Machines." Now there's only one way to convince these people that the Edison is superior and that is to let the people actually see and hear this remarkable instrument for themselves. THAT IS WHY I AM MAKING THIS OFFER. I can't TELL you one-twentieth of the wonders of the Edison, nothing I can say or write will make you actually HEAR the grand full beauty of its tones. No words can BEGIN to describe the tender, delicate sweetness with which the genuine new style Edison reproduces the soft, pleading notes of the flute, or the thunderous, crashing harmony of a full brass band selection. The wonders of the new style Edison defy the power of any pen to describe. Neither will I try to tell you how, when you're tired, nervous and blue, the Edison will soothe you, comfort and rest you, and give you new strength to take up the burdens of life afresh. The only way to make you actually realize these things for yourself is to loan you a Genuine Edison Phonograph free and let you try it.

F. K. BABSON EDISON PHON. DISTRIBUTERS EDISON BLOCK, SUITE 1194 **CHICAGO**

Mr. Edison says:

"I want to see a Phonograph in every American home."

HERE is the "King of Entertainers," the Edison Phonograph just as you receive it for a free trial in your own home—records and all. An extremely short trial will convince you that you have been without a phonograph too long already. The *perfect* naturalness of vocal and instrumental reproduction on the *new style* 1907 model Edison Outfit has surprised and pleased even the most critical judges.

An Offer open to every responsible person.

Thomas A. Edison.

FREE TRIAL!

No Money Down—No C. O. D.—No Guarantee

While this offer lasts we will send to any reliable person living any place in the United States a Genuine Edison Phonograph and one dozen Gold-Moulded Records for a FREE TRIAL lasting two entire days. If after the free trial you do not care to keep the instrument send it back at our expense. But we are confident that this sweet toned, perfect instrument with the intensely human voice and the ringing clearness of a bell will win your heart as it has won the heart of one million (1,000,000) other people.

Entertainment for the Home!

THERE is always something to turn to for a session of fun and pleasure when an Edison Phonograph is in the house. You may have any kind of entertainment you desire right in your own parlor. You may have a piano recital with all of the wonderful technique and execution of the most renowned pianists, band recitals, orchestral selections, grand operas, vaudeville skits, black face comedy, monologues from the best known monologuists, whistling solos and selections on the violin, banjo, guitar or mandolin. There is always the most perfect harmony of sound given by the Edison. Music critics have bowed down before the marvelous Edison and have stated that they would rather hear a Sousa band selection from the horn of an Edison Phonograph than to be in the hall with the musicians.

$2.00 a Month buys the most perfect of all Phonographs—a genuine Edison. **$3.50 a month** for the fine, excellent Edison Outfit No 5.

For cash in full: Many cash buyers are taking advantage of the free trial, but we cannot allow a discount for cash as we have already allowed the *rock-bottom price* to those who buy on time.

Edison Catalogue on Request

Just cut out or tear out this coupon, sign your name and address plainly and mail to us. We will send you by return mail the elaborate Edison Phonograph catalog with a complete description of all the Edison Machines. This catalog is the most extensive booklet on phonographs issued. It tells you all about the interesting machines, about Mr. Edison and about the struggles of the inventor before he gave the perfected Edison Phonograph to the world. With the catalog we send a list of thousands of records. **Sign the coupon right now**

CUT OFF OR TEAR OFF THIS COUPON

FREE COUPON

F. K. Babson
Edison Phonograph Distribrs.
Edison Building
Suite 119Y, Chicago

Without any obligations to me please send me your complete Catalogue of Edison Gem, Edison Standard, Edison Home and Edison Triumph Phonographs, free circulars of *New Special Edison Outfits* and complete catalog of Edison gold-moulded records, all free, prepaid.

Name...

....

Address...

....

No letter necessary; just send the coupon.

The Edison phonograph pictured here, featuring the famous "morning glory" horn loud-speaker, was spring-operated and played wax cylinders instead of the disk-shaped record developed later. Edison's first crude phonograph, put together in 1870, recited the verses of "Mary Had a Little Lamb," recorded on a sheet of tinfoil wrapped around a cylinder. The first improvement was to coat the cylinder with wax. While the phonograph was being improved, other recording devices grew out of the original invention, including dictating machines, tape recorders and talking motion pictures

Publisher Windsor, earlier in his career a working newspaperman, liked to get out and "cover" things for his magazine occasionally. Here he turned in a colorful account (presented here only in part) of the 1907 International Balloon Race. These races began in 1906 and continued until the outbreak of World War II. Annual prize was the James Gordon Bennett Cup and $2500

POPULAR MECHANICS

Vol. 9. No. 12. CHICAGO, DECEMBER, 1907. 10 Cents a Copy $1.00 a Year

INTERNATIONAL BALLOON RACE OF 1907

German "Pommern" Wins with 873 Miles--Five Dirigible Airships Also Contest--Greatest of All American Aeronautical Events

By H. H. Windsor

"One, two, three, four, five, six, seven, eight, nine, ten, *go*."

It was the official starter counting off the remaining seconds of the five minute interval allowed each balloon in which to start on the International race which occurred in St. Louis, October 21.

As the moment approached for the contest, 150,000 excited spectators surged around the inclosure where the nine great gas bags were swaying at their moorings. Two hundred city police and 250 regulars from the U. S. Army were required to hold the crowd back from the wire fence which inclosed a space equal to two city blocks.

The "Pommern," the German prize-winning balloon, was the first to start; as it rose majestically, bands played and the gathered thousands shouted. From away up in the air floated back a farewell. Meanwhile a score of men were moving the next balloon to its place, for each balloon rose from identically the same spot. Exactly five minutes were allowed in which to take position and start. In each instance the starter counted aloud the last 10 seconds, and when the word "Go" was spoken, the balloon had to start or be debarred. So perfect were the arrangements there was no delay in any of the nine ascensions. The first occurred at 4.00 p. m., and 45 minutes later the last one was sailing away in the hope of winning the Bennett cup and a cash prize of $2,500.

The International Balloon race of 1907 was altogether the greatest event in aeronautics ever seen in this country and, in some respects, in all the history of

Fig. 1.—Balloons Laid Out--Inflation Just Begun

Photos by W. I. Bell, St. Louis

Fig. 2—Balloons Half Inflated--Fig. 3—Balloons Fully Inflated; Baskets Being Attached; Erbsloeh Testing Valve Ropes

Coal gas was used in these round balloons. The baskets carried—besides the crew of two men—bags of sand ballast, instruments, food, water and heavy clothing. The balance of weight was so delicate that the throwing out of a single small scoop of sand was enough to start ascension. Descent was controlled by a valve which allowed gas to escape at the will of the balloonist

ballooning. The start was made from an inland city nearly 1,000 miles from an ocean, and afforded possibilities for long flight which did not exist last year at Paris when Lieut. Lahm, U. S. A., won in a flight across the Channel and into England, a distance of 402 miles.

This year preparations were made for a several days' voyage. Not only did each balloon start with several thousand pounds of sand ballast, but provisions were taken for seven days.

Fourteen-year-old Cromwell Dixon was probably the youngest aeronaut in the world. For this exhibition the boy built his own dirigible, his mother assisting in sewing the gas bag, which was 25 feet long and 10 feet in diameter. Young Dixon, after narrowly escaping a crash into a tree, sailed over the Mississippi River and landed eight miles away, in Illinois. Today his ship would be called a blimp. Although "dirigible" simply means capable of being steered, the term has been corrupted so that it now means an airship with a rigid framework containing independent gas bags

The following table is a condensed statement of the voyage:

Balloon.	Landed at—	Time, h. m.	Miles from St. Louis.
Pommern	Asbury Park, N. J.	40:00	873.66
Isle de France	Herbertsville, N. J.	44:00	867.09
Dusseldorf	Little Creek, Del.	39:15	800.00
America	Patuxent, Md.	38:30	735.75
St. Louis	Westminster, Md.	39:00	716.50
Abercron	Manassas, Va.	37:35	689.75
Anjou	Louisa Co., Va.	39:15	674.50
United States	Caledonia, Ont., Can.	26:10	624.25
Lotus II	Memphis, Ohio	25:00	358.75

For the distance flown the balloon "United States" made the best speed, covering the 624 miles in 26 hr. The "United States" average speed was 24 miles an hour and the "Pommern's" speed 22 miles an hour.

In no previous records have so many long distances been accomplished; how many more hundreds of miles could have been made had not the Atlantic raised its threatening hand will never be known.

Fig. 4—Cromwell Dixon, 14 Years Old, Starting on His Flight

The exhibition on the second day and the race on the third day of dirigibles carried convincing proof to the tens of thousands present that the controllable airship is a thoroughly accomplished fact. It is the conviction of the writer however, that the dirigible, while a necessity in modern warfare, is extremely unlikely to become a serious problem for transportation even of passengers, although it is certain to become popular and even common as the most exciting sport. For express or passenger traffic, or even the transportation of the mails, it will not, in the writer's opinion, ever reach the efficiency and reliability of either steam or electric cars on tracks, while for carrying freight the suggestion is absurd.

A page of fascinating items for the reader of 1908—a record-breaking passenger-train run, a new auto speed record, a new nonflying flying machine design and a new type of power tool

RECORD BREAKING PASSENGER TRAIN RUN

A passenger train, composed of two 60-ft. baggage cars and two sleepers, recently carried a theatrical company from Pittsburg to Chicago in 7 hr. 42 min. The distance covered was 468 miles, so that the average speed was a fraction less than 61 miles an hour, including stops. The special was stopped four times and slowed down once by the block signals to prevent overrunning the Pennsylvania's 18-hour flyer. One of the forced stops was five minutes and the others were nearly as long.

It is claimed that never before has such a high average speed been maintained for so great a distance by a passenger train.

AUTOMOBILE RUNS TWO MILES A MINUTE

In a recent race on the famous Brooklands track in England a 4-cylinder car driven by Felice Nazzarro broke all speed records, averaging $94\frac{3}{4}$ miles

an hour for $27\frac{1}{2}$ miles, and accomplishing an officially recorded speed of 121.6 miles an hour for $2\frac{3}{4}$ miles. Although built to come within the 90-hp. standard, the car develops an actual horsepower of 157.

CITY MAIL CARRIERS MAY HAVE WAGONS

The postoffice department is considering the advisability of having the outlying districts of a number of the cities of the country covered by mail carriers with wagons.

FLYING-MACHINE WITH SPIRAL HELICES

This European flying-machine is kept afloat by a series of spiral helices, and the method is a practical realization of that forecast by Jules Verne in "The Clipper of the Clouds."

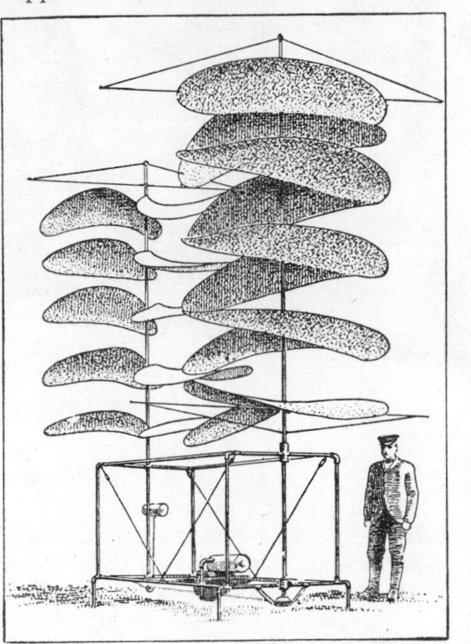

An Odd Helicopter

A FLEXIBLE SHAFT GRINDER

Attached to this hand-propelled grinder is a smaller wheel connected by a flexible shaft for use when the article to be ground is stationary or too heavy to be easily handled.

Mechanical Manicuring

Famed I.C.S. and other reputable correspondence schools have enabled thousands of Americans to jump the gap between their formal education and their native abilities. Many persons forced to leave school early because of family problems have, through home study, been able to give themselves needed background for advancement in their trade or profession. Home study is a native trait—a pattern set by Benjamin Franklin, Abraham Lincoln and other early Americans

POPULAR MECHANICS ADVERTISING SECTION

FAILURE

See them—the ***FAILURES*** and the ***SUCCESSES***—the *untrained* and the *trained* men—the "couldn't-do-it" and the "*can*-do-it" men. Be a Success. It's easier than being a Failure. It's all a matter of *training*—of being a specialist in your chosen line of work. To learn how you can secure the training that will make you successful, mark the attached coupon and mail it to the International Correspondence Schools of Scranton. Finding out costs you only a two cent stamp, and places you under no obligation. Mark the coupon.

The I. C. S. will go to you in your own home and fit you for a *better* position and a *better* salary at the work you like best—without requiring you to leave home or quit work. So long as you can read and write the I. C. S. can help you, regardless of your age, occupation or place of residence. Mark the coupon.

How Men Have

Since enrolling for my I. C. S. Course I have been advanced from stenographer to Office Manager, and my earnings have been twice increased. I have been greatly impressed with the low cost of your method compared with that of other schools where heavy tuition fees and other expenses are incurred. I assure you that my praise of the I. C. S. is most heartily given.
R. M. Gilmore, Waterville, Me.

I hardly know how to express my appreciation of the great good your School has done me. Since completing my first Course, I have advanced from Asst. Superintendent to Superintendent of the Cherry Cotton Mills, with double my former earnings. I have enrolled in another Course and expect to get as much benefit from this as I did from my first Course.
M. W. Darby, Cherry Cotton Mills, Florence, Ala.

I enrolled with the I. C. S. when I was employed as a machinist. My present position is that of Master Mechanic for the Globe Woolen Co. of Utica, and my salary has been more than doubled. I could not have secured this position had it not been for the instruction afforded by my Course.
Alfred Thomas, 255 Sunset Ave., Utica, N.Y.

When working as a cash boy in a dry goods store I enrolled for an I. C. S. Course. I heartily recommend your system of instruction. From my own personal experience I can say that it will be of great advantage to any young man who wishes to rise in his profession. I am now a Bridge Draftsman in the office of the State Engineer and my income has been increased 150 per cent. since enrolling.
Edw. G. Semon, 478 Elk St., Albany, N. Y.

When employed as a clerk in a railroad office at a salary of $65 per month, I took out my I. C. S. Course. I advanced to a position as Manager of the Portland Retail Lumber Company and my

Please Mention Popular Mechanics

POPULAR MECHANICS ADVERTISING SECTION

SUCCESS

When you consider that every month an average of 300 students ***voluntarily*** report higher salaries and better positions secured as a direct result of I. C. S. training, you can readily understand what the I. C. S. can do for ***you***. The number of successes reported in July was 310. Wouldn't you like ***your*** salary raised? Mark the coupon.

It is for ***you*** to say whether you will be a Failure or a Success. It is for ***you*** to decide your future. It is for ***you*** to mark the coupon. This done, you can leave the rest to the I. C. S. who will show you the way to a better position, a bigger salary, and independence. Take the first step ***NOW***. Mark the coupon.

Won Success

income was increased about 500 per cent. I am now a member of firm of the St. Johns Lumber Co.
W. C. Francis, Mgr. St. Johns Lumber Co.
St. Johns, Ore.

As a result of my I. C. S. Course I have changed from the work of a farmer to a position as Draftsman at double my former salary. Before I enrolled I knew practically nothing about Mechanical Drawing, but I have now undertaken and successfully completed some very difficult work in this line to the perfect satisfaction of my employer
Albert S. Cole, 14 S. Maple Ave., East Orange, N. J.

When I enrolled with the I. C. S. I was working as a helper in a machine shop at $1.50 per day. I am now Superintendent of the Municipal Lighting Plant in the city of Marquette and have, of course, very greatly increased my earnings. I consider that I owe nearly all my success to the information I have received from your Schools.
Chas. Retallic, Marquette, Mich.

Coupon NOW

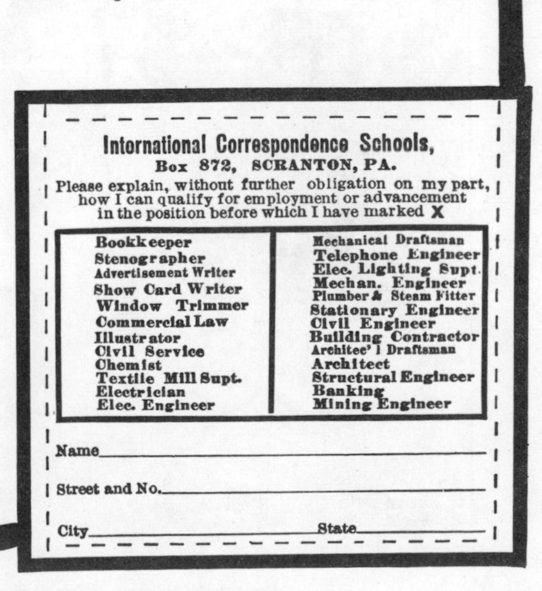

International Correspondence Schools,
Box 872, SCRANTON, PA.
Please explain, without further obligation on my part, how I can qualify for employment or advancement in the position before which I have marked X

Bookkeeper	Mechanical Draftsman
Stenographer	Telephone Engineer
Advertisement Writer	Elec. Lighting Supt.
Show Card Writer	Mechan. Engineer
Window Trimmer	Plumber & Steam Fitter
Commercial Law	Stationary Engineer
Illustrator	Civil Engineer
Civil Service	Building Contractor
Chemist	Architec'l Draftsman
Textile Mill Supt.	Architect
Electrician	Structural Engineer
Elec. Engineer	Banking
	Mining Engineer

Name____________________

Street and No.____________________

City________________State__________

Please Mention Popular Mechanics

The first advertisement of International Correspondence Schools carried in Popular Mechanics *was a tiny one in 1902. It featured the appeal: "Double Your Salary—$15/$15=$30." The idea of study at home by mail caught on, and I.C.S. was soon using double-page spreads to carry its message—a policy that I.C.S. executives say "is one of our mainstays"*

In 1908 only one in every 10 homes in the United States was wired for electricity. Not until after 1910 did the introduction of electricity become widespread in cities and towns, and for rural residents an even longer wait for electrification was in store. Even as late as 1935, the one-in-10 ratio still held true for farm homes

While Marconi has been working night and day on a system of wireless telegraphy that is this moment flashing commercial messages across 2,400 miles of ocean, scores of other as earnest inventors have been perfecting electrical devices of practical everyday domestic utility. The names of these inventors are not heard or known outside the electrical trades, but where one woman sends or receives a wireless message, thousands of others will be making use of an electric dishwasher, flatiron or kitchenette.

Household Electric Utensils Now Coming Into General Use

Machinery which has lightened the hardest labor of the farmer, miner and all other industries which were once laborious and severe, has at last been adapted to the less strenuous but exhausting household work, and electricity has proved to be the medium. To such extent have the labor-saving devices been developed, there is now scarcely anything to be done about the house which cannot be performed by turning a switch or touching a button: Cleaning, sweeping, washing, heating, cooking, chopping,—all these and many more are now done without the expenditure of any strength. The wire that brings in the light brings also a tireless, ever-ready force which instantly responds to every call by day or night.

In order to actually show the workings of electric household utensils, many electric service companies have fitted up a demonstration room at convenient places, where the public may come to see and learn. One of these exhibits is shown in the illustration below, where the practical utilities and labor-saving possibilities of electric utensils for a modern residence are seen in operation. The electric flat iron, the meat chopper, with roasters, bakers, and a great variety of other cookers are all there. No fire to wait on a tardy supply of kindling, no chimney which fails to draw, no oven which refuses to heat to the necessary temperature.

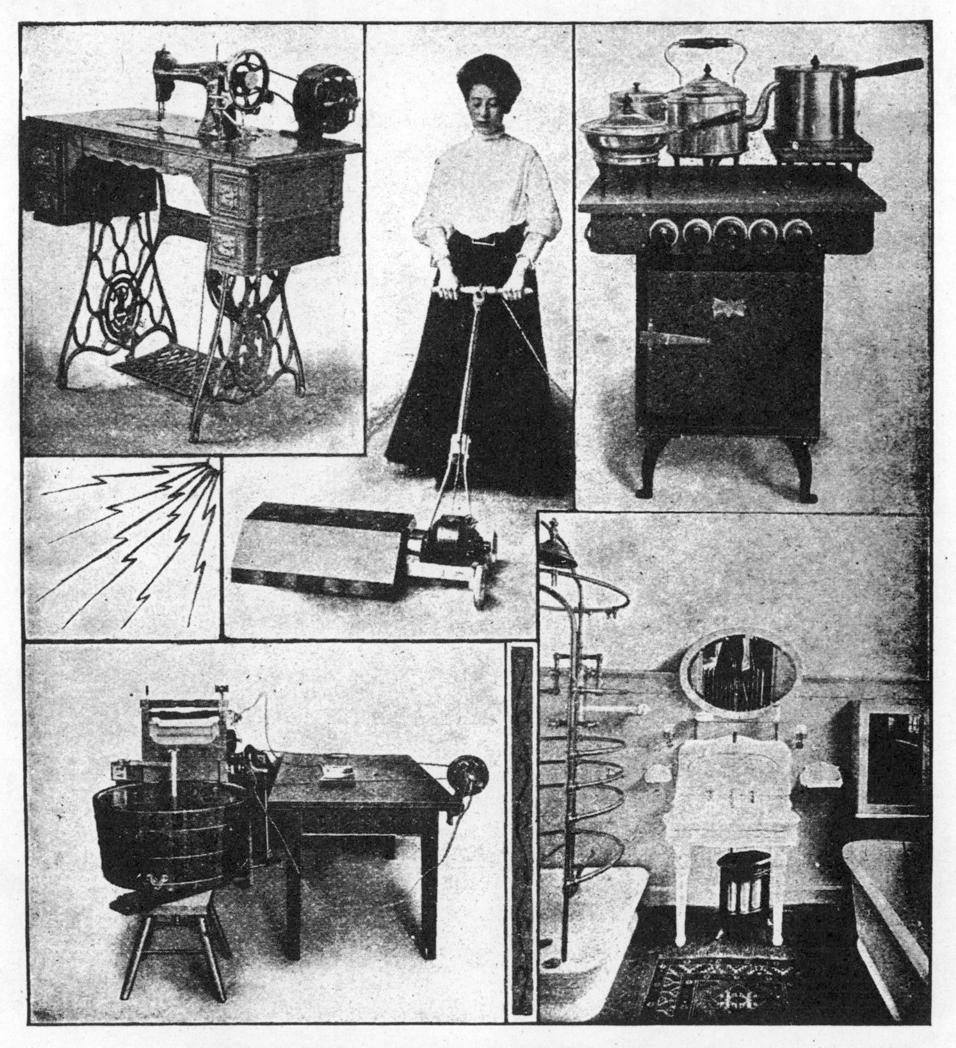

Sewing Machines, Sweepers and Wringers Run by Motors

Note that these early electrical appliances showed no radical changes in design as compared to nonelectrical models. The sewing machine with motor attached still had a foot treadle; the power-operated carpet sweeper boasted no vacuum operation and the electric washing machine was an open wooden tub with an agitator

A hand-pumped vacuum cleaner was patented by Ives McGaffey in 1869. It aroused little more than curiosity. An electrically operated vacuum cleaner like the one shown here was patented by John S. Thurmas in 1899. John H. Templin patented the first modern vacuum cleaner, combining motor-induced suction with a twirling brush, in 1910

The Ideal Christmas Present for Your Wife

is the

IDEAL VACUUM CLEANER

(FULLY PROTECTED BY PATENTS)

Operated by Hand — **"It Eats Up the Dirt"** — **or Electric Motor**

Undoubtedly your wife wishes to be considered among the progressive members of her community. Particularly as regards all that relates to cleanliness, she would not have her habits savor in the least of inferiority.

Toil as she may, urge on her servants as she may, no woman, with broom, brush or carpet sweeper, can maintain in her home the conditions of cleanliness, freshness, sweetness, purity and health now demanded by people of superior habits.

The IDEAL VACUUM CLEANER is the perfection of the modern Vacuum Cleaning System—the only system by which dirt, bad odors, vermin, germs and disease can be effectively fought and conquered.

With the IDEAL VACUUM CLEANER, your wife will truly have a Merry Christmas, and by the time, labor, strength, health and actual money it will save her, it will indeed give her a Happy New Year.

Within the Reach of All

Equipped for hand operation, the price of the IDEAL VACUUM CLEANER is **$25**
Equipped with electric motor for direct current . **$55** For alternating current **$60**
One nozzle for carpet or rug cleaning.
Special nozzles for special purposes at low prices.

The hand machine puts absolutely no tax on the strength. Compared with sweeping, it is ease itself. The motor of the electric machine is readily attached to any electric light fixture. The machine weighs only 20 pounds and is easily carried about. It is of the strongest metal construction throughout.

If you wonder how this low-priced machine can contain right within itself all the parts of a thoroughly efficient Vacuum Cleaning System, *actually doing the work better* than the big power plants, that cost from $500 up, let us enlighten you.

Our Catalogue and Illustrated Booklet give full, complete and interesting information about every phase of the cleaning problem.

Time is short. Christmas is fast approaching. Write to us at once.

THE AMERICAN VACUUM CLEANER COMPANY, 225 Fifth Ave., NEW YORK CITY

POPULAR MECHANICS ADVERTISING SECTION

The LINDSLEY $395

OTHER CARS UP TO $750

The Car that Runs the Limit

No Bother—No Fussing—No Cussing

The many superior points of this car cannot be described in this space. A snappy, stylish looking car of great simplicity. Meets every requirement demanded of it. All obstacles vanish before it. Fitted with an absolutely reliable and Powerful Engine that will send you up any hill or through any mud. YOU want this car—because it is a safe, sane, practical and durable car that gives you VALUE RECEIVED—a permanent luxury and necessity that will do all we claim, under HEAVY GUARANTEE. Money refunded if it does not do as represented under YOUR LOCAL conditions. FIVE DAYS' FREE TRIAL.

30 MILES ON 1 GALLON OF GASOLINE

10-H. P.—wheel steer—roller bearing chains—heavy steel angle iron frame—drives from both wheels—air cooled—18-inch road clearance—any color painting Same car in 14 and 16 H. P. SURREYS with removable rear seat. Write NOW for book of particulars. Place order early for quick delivery.

J. V. LINDSLEY & COMPANY
265 Dearborn Street, Chicago

The LINDSLEY $525

DELIVERY CAR—16 H. P.

Much Cheaper Than Horse Help

TIME TURNED INTO MONEY

AT LAST—here is a safe, sane, practical and highly satisfactory car, within the reach of all. Will easily do the work of 5 delivery wagons of the horse kind. Absolutely needed to meet today's competition. New customers are made as a result of quick deliveries. You will surprise yourself with your own rapidity and the money and time it will save you. Shipments to and from the depot are made as desired. Many a HERETOFORE lost moment turned into money. This car has a minimum cost of running—you can hardly figure the expense comparatively.

Fitted with POWERFUL ENGINE made to climb any hill with load f 2500 lbs. and go through any reasonable mud. Speed 20 miles an hour—splitdorf coil—roller bearing chains —cut steel sprocket—tires 2 inches—force feed oiler—heavy axles—drives from both wheels. OUR GUARANTEE—that this car will do YOUR OWN WORK as DEMANDED under YOUR LOCAL CONDITIONS or money refunded. A FREE TRIAL of 5 days will convince you that YOU need a LINDSLEY. WRITE NOW FOR BOOK OF PARTICULARS. Place early order for quick delivery. AGENTS WANTED—EXCLUSIVE TERRITORY GIVEN.

J. V. LINDSLEY & COMPANY
265 Dearborn Street, Chicago

Free Hair Food

FREE SAMPLE BOX

TO PROVE ITS WORTH

The old time theories of the medical world have been upset by the discoveries of the famous Chicago Bacteriologist, Prof. J. H. Austin, who has demonstrated that the cause of baldness and falling hair is a micro-bacillus which grows in colonies at the roots of the hair and consumes the food provided by nature for the hair itself, thus causing it to starve to death and fall out.

Prof. Austin further completely demonstrated that there are two different principal conditions of the scalp, scaly and not scaly, which characterize these troubles, so that now anyone can ascertain absolutely, his or her own trouble, and he now offers to send to every man and woman, absolutely free, a sample box of this remedy to demonstrate its power. Send your name and address, and you will get the trial box of remedy free, together with Prof. Austin's authoritative book on hair and scalp. Send today.

Address Prof. J. H. Austin, 1813 McVicker's Theatre Building, Chicago, Illinois.

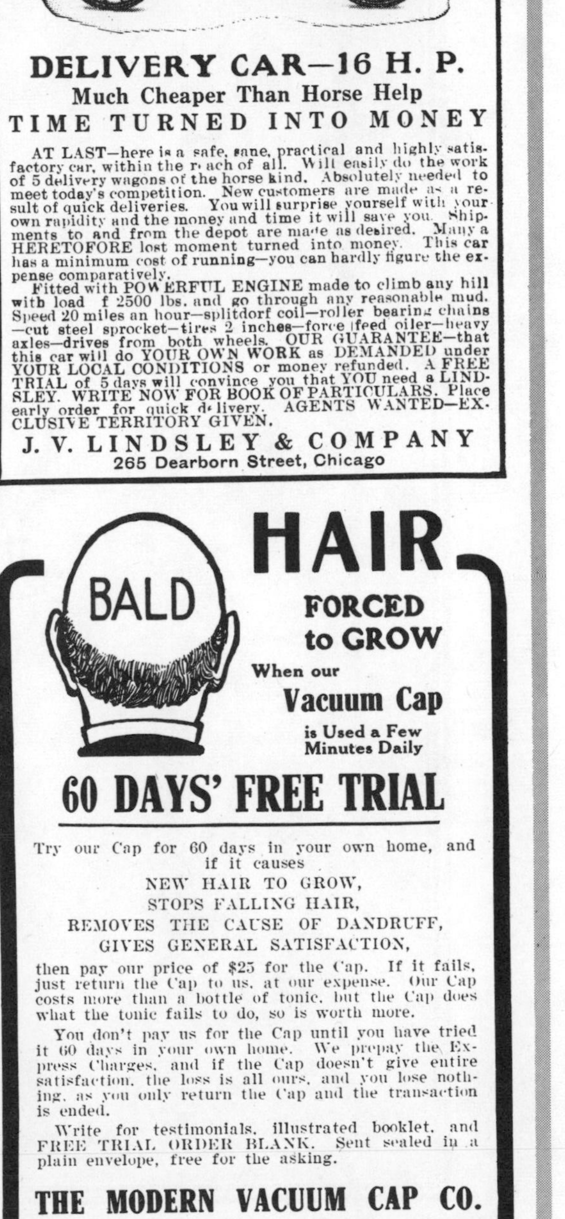

HAIR

BALD

FORCED to GROW

When our Vacuum Cap is Used a Few Minutes Daily

60 DAYS' FREE TRIAL

Try our Cap for 60 days in your own home, and if it causes
NEW HAIR TO GROW,
STOPS FALLING HAIR,
REMOVES THE CAUSE OF DANDRUFF,
GIVES GENERAL SATISFACTION,
then pay our price of $25 for the Cap. If it fails, just return the Cap to us, at our expense. Our Cap costs more than a bottle of tonic, but the Cap does what the tonic fails to do, so is worth more.

You don't pay us for the Cap until you have tried it 60 days in your own home. We prepay the Express Charges, and if the Cap doesn't give entire satisfaction, the loss is all ours, and you lose nothing, as you only return the Cap and the transaction is ended.

Write for testimonials, illustrated booklet, and FREE TRIAL ORDER BLANK. Sent sealed in a plain envelope, free for the asking.

THE MODERN VACUUM CAP CO.
563 Barclay Blk. Denver, Colo.

Then, as always, the search for miraculous hair preparations was under way. For the men, the reason was the same as now—baldness, the curse of modern man. Women had a different motive—to meet fashion's demand for a head of hair that would reach well below the waist when let down

This Channel flight from Calais to Dover by the famous French air pioneer, Louis Blériot, is generally considered the next important milestone in aviation history after the Wright brothers' success at Kitty Hawk. The year before his Channel flight he had performed a remarkable "distance" flight—17 miles overland from Chalons to Rheims. His plane was a dainty thing by modern standards. In contrast to the Thunderbolt fighter of World War II, with its 2700 horsepower engine and loaded weight of some seven tons, his ship weighed 485 pounds and was driven by a three-cylinder, 25 horsepower engine

Bleriot Flying from Calais to Dover—Distance, 21 Miles

THE FLIGHT FROM FRANCE TO ENGLAND

It was early in the morning of July 25 that Louis Bleriot crossed the English channel in his aeroplane, a date in history which will go down to the centuries to come as one full of importance in the annals of science and civilization. Bleriot arose at Calais about 2 o'clock, and, accompanied by his friend Leblanc, drove in a motor car to Baraques, where the aeroplane was housed. The weather was favorable, and at 4 o'clock Bleriot took his seat in the aeroplane and made a trial flight of about 15 minutes around Calais. His circuits totaled about 9½ miles, and at the end he descended upon the spot on the cliff from which he had determined to start. He then waited a few minutes for the sun to come out, as the conditions of the $5,000 prize required that the flight should be made between sunrise and sunset. At 4:30 the sun appeared. A light breeze from the southwest was beginning to blow. The story of the actual flight is best told by Bleriot himself:

"At 4:35 in the morning the signal was given, and in an instant I am in the air, my engine making 1,200 revolutions, almost its highest speed, in order that I may get quickly over the telegraph wires along the edge of the cliff. As soon as I am over the cliff I reduce my speed. There now is no need to force my engine. I begin my flight, steady and sure, toward the coast of England. I have no apprehensions, no sensations.

"The French torpedo boat has seen me. She is drawing ahead at full speed. She makes perhaps 26 miles an hour. What matters? I am making at least 42½ miles. Rapidly I overtake her, traveling at the height of 250 ft.

"The moment is supreme, yet I surprise myself by feeling no exultation.

"Below me is the sea, its surface disturbed by wind, which now is freshening. The motion of the waves beneath me is not pleasant. I drive on.

"Ten minutes have gone. I have passed the destroyer and I turn my head to see whether I am proceeding in the right direction. I am amazed. There is nothing to be seen, neither destroyer, nor France, nor England. I am alone. I see nothing at all. For ten minutes I am lost. It is a strange position, to be alone, unguided, without a compass, in the air over the middle of the channel.

"I touch nothing. My hands and feet rest lightly on levers. I let the aeroplane take its own course. I care not whither it goes. For ten minutes I continue, neither rising nor falling nor turning, and then, twenty minutes after I have left the French coast, I see the green cliffs of Dover, the castle, and away to the west the spot where I intended to land. What can I do? It is evident that the wind has taken me out of my course. I press a lever with my foot and turn easily toward the west, reversing the direction in which I have been traveling.

"Now, indeed, I am in difficulties, for the wind here by the cliffs is much stronger and my speed is reduced as I fight against it, yet my beautiful aeroplane responds.

"Although I am confident that I can continue for an hour and a half, and that I might, indeed, return to Calais, I cannot resist the opportunity to make my landing upon this green spot. Once more I turn my aeroplane and, describing a half circle, I enter the opening and find myself again over dry land. Avoiding the red buildings on my right, I attempt a landing, but the wind catches me and whirls me around two or three times. At once I stop the motor. Instantly my machine falls, straight upon the land, from a height of 65 ft., in two or three seconds, and my flight is safely done."

Blériot's own account of the historic flight is given here with typical French élan. *Blériot was one of the first air pioneers to see the superiority of the monoplane over the biplane. Although all American planes were biplanes, adapted from the style set by the Wrights, the French favored single-winged craft. Blériot's little ship and others, the* Antoinette *and Santos-Dumont's* Demoiselle, *have all the basic components of a modern single-engine monoplane*

The helicopter, in which the propeller also serves as the lifting wing, was a part of man's earliest dreams about flying. Leonardo da Vinci sketched helicopters as well as the bird-like wings he drew and modeled for flight. During the early 1900's, many flying machines were built which attempted to make use of the principles of modern helicopters. The great problem of overcoming the machine's own weight seems exclusively to have occupied most of the inventors. None of the designs, except this one perhaps, indicate that much thought was given to stability or directional control

THE KIMBALL HELICOPTER

"A Light Framework in Which Are 24 Small Wooden Propellers"

One of the flying machines now drawing attention of aerial enthusiasts in the United States is the helicopter built by Wilbur Kimball at a cost of $10,000. It is this type of machine that Thomas A. Edison had predicted will conquer gravitation.

The Kimball helicopter is little more than a light framework in which are 24 small wooden propellers set in a horizontal plane and run by a single motor. The air is forced downward by these propellers instead of astern, as is the case with aeroplanes.

FLYING MACHINE THAT CLIMBS THE AIR

The latest, and by no means the least promising of the flock of aerial fliers that have appeared recently, is the invention of J. E. Shearer of San Francisco. It is the result of several years of study, and was suggested by witnessing a parachute drop made by Capt. Baldwin in that city.

The machine is constructed to perform an operation just the reverse of a parachute. As Mr. Shearer says, "If a man at the end of a long rope attached to a parachute could climb the rope fast enough he would, temporarily, ascend while the parachute was dropping." The parachute form of propeller was adopted, and in practice is very simple. It is practically a case of "treading water" in the air, except that the treading is sufficiently rapid and continuous as to cause the machine and its operator to ascend. The inventor says:

"The guy rods in the picture do not belong to the operation of the machine; they are simply to hold it in an upright position while being photographed.

"The basket for the operator is, in flight, suspended below the motor. It is not shown here.

"No long flights have yet been attempted. The flier with all its equipment and engine weighs 175 lb. and the recent test was made with a young man weighing 96 lb. When the engine was started the machine gradually rose to a height of 20 ft. and remained captive there some time.

Shearer's Flying Machine "Climbs the Air"

The first true helicopter capable of carrying a man was built in 1909 by Louis Breguet, a French engineer. In 1910 a Russian, Igor Sikorsky, built one which would lift its own weight but not that of a pilot. It was not until 1939 that Sikorsky, having since come to America, built the first really successful machine. Not only was it capable of raising itself vertically into the air but of flying about in any direction at the will of the pilot. Helicopters are now used by aerial surveyors and are invaluable to both civilian and military rescue operations

THREE-HANDED SHOP LIFTERS

The tricks by which a shop-lifter succeeds in plying her profession without being caught are many and ingenious. The most successful of all tricks is the false arm and hand, shown in one of the illustrations. While the shop-lifter's hands are apparently in sight of the store clerks, one is at work stowing away articles. The false hand is, of course, gloved and thrust through one of the sleeves. The real hand works under cover of the bodice and coat. The second illustration shows one of the pockets in which stolen articles are secreted.

SLEEPING CAR BEDS INSTEAD OF BERTHS

So far as the sleeping arrangements are concerned, the new sleeping cars

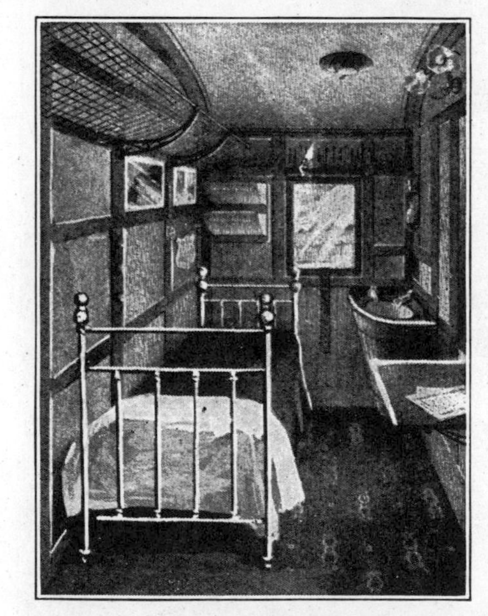

A Real Bedroom

of the L. & S. W. railroad in England are a distinct departure from the ordinary type of sleepers. Brass bedsteads take the place of the stuffy berths familiar to all who travel in this country, and heavy upholstery is eliminated.

A party of musicians sailed from New York recently as part of the government's plan to furnish wholesome amusement for the thousands of men at work on the Panama canal.

A SKYSCRAPER 62 STORIES HIGH WILL BE NEXT

Plans for a gigantic building, to be the loftiest in the world, overtopping by more than 200 ft. the Metropolitan building, were filed the latter part of June with the building superintendent of New York by the Equitable Life Assurance society.

With its tower, as now planned, the new building will have 62 stories and will reach to a height of 909 ft. above the curb. The flag pole will run up 150 ft. higher. The building will cost $10,000,000, and the plans call for a main building of 34 stories, reaching to a height of 489 ft. Above the main building the tower will rise heavenward 420 ft., having 28 stories. Its construction will be in two sections, one section extending from the 34th to the 49th story, and the other, a narrower one, rising from the 49th to the 58th story. The cupola will extend 4 stories above this.

"Tallest building in the world" statistics were revised frequently in these times. The Empire State Building (102 stories) is nearly twice as high as any skyscraper built during the latter part of this decade

The first of many attempts to get rid of a persistent character—the race track "bookie"

MECHANICAL "BOOKMAKERS"

Here is an illustration of the mechanical betting machine which is being installed at a number of race tracks to take the place of the "bookies" and to try and save the racing sport from annihilation due to the almost universal crusade against race-track gambling

The sign "Straight" means that only horses to win can be played on that particular machine. The man standing alongside takes your money, gives you a card with the number of the horse on it, pulls a little lever, and your bet is tallied on the machine. If your horse wins and you have an exclusive bet, you get all the money in the machine bet on other horses, minus the 5 per cent which the racing commission deducts as its share.

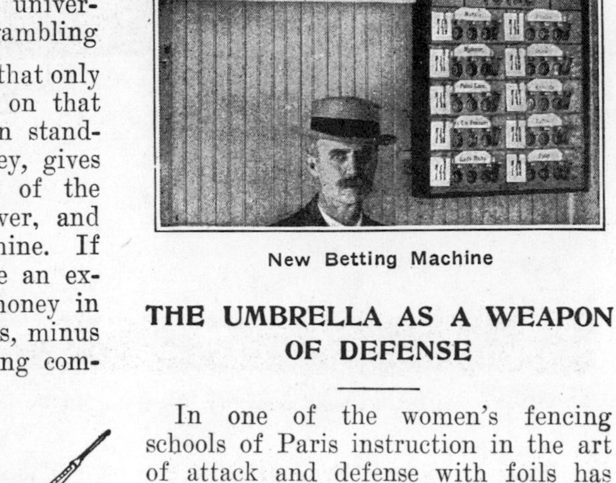

New Betting Machine

THE UMBRELLA AS A WEAPON OF DEFENSE

In one of the women's fencing schools of Paris instruction in the art of attack and defense with foils has been discontinued and umbrellas instituted.

The first lesson the pupils learn in this up-to-date means of defense from attack on the streets is to baffle the watchfulness of the aggressor by skillful blows. The most simple and at the same time most effective, consists in applying a flat stroke of the umbrella upon his headgear. Surprised by this stroke and perhaps blinded by the rim of the hat, he has not the time nor the presence of mind to seize the umbrella. The lunges which follow such a blow are not only effective, but dangerous. The first is known as the "Hors de Combat" blow. Seizing her umbrella near the handle with one hand and near the point with the other and advancing a step with the body well forward, the point if well directed against the center of the aggressor's neck will drop him to the ground senseless and probably badly hurt. The same blow aimed at the pit of the stomach will probably send the recipient to the hospital and perhaps cripple him for life.

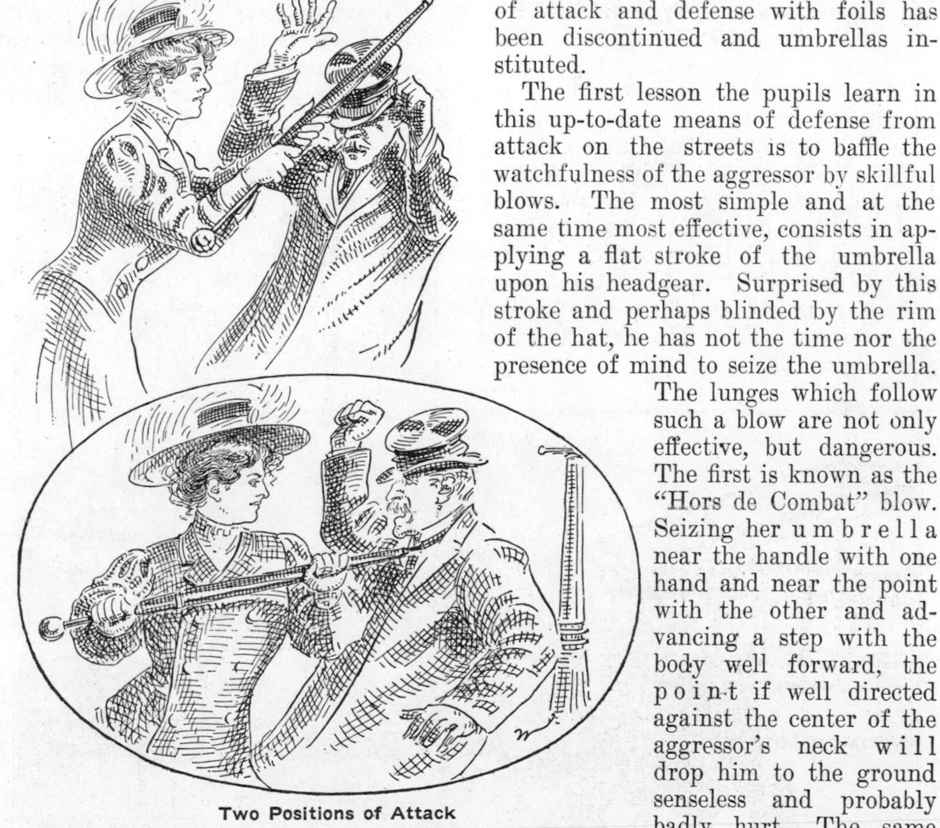

Two Positions of Attack

The great Brooklyn bridge is now 25 years old. Today it is noted not so much for its size as for stability.

This was the first of a series of blimps built by the United States Government. Thomas Baldwin, an officer of the Regular Army, built the nonrigid airship with the assistance of Glen Curtiss. The gas bag was 96 feet long and 19½ feet in diameter. Curtiss' 20-horsepower motor drove the 11-foot propellers. Of five rigid airships built by the government between 1923 and 1933, four were lost in crashes

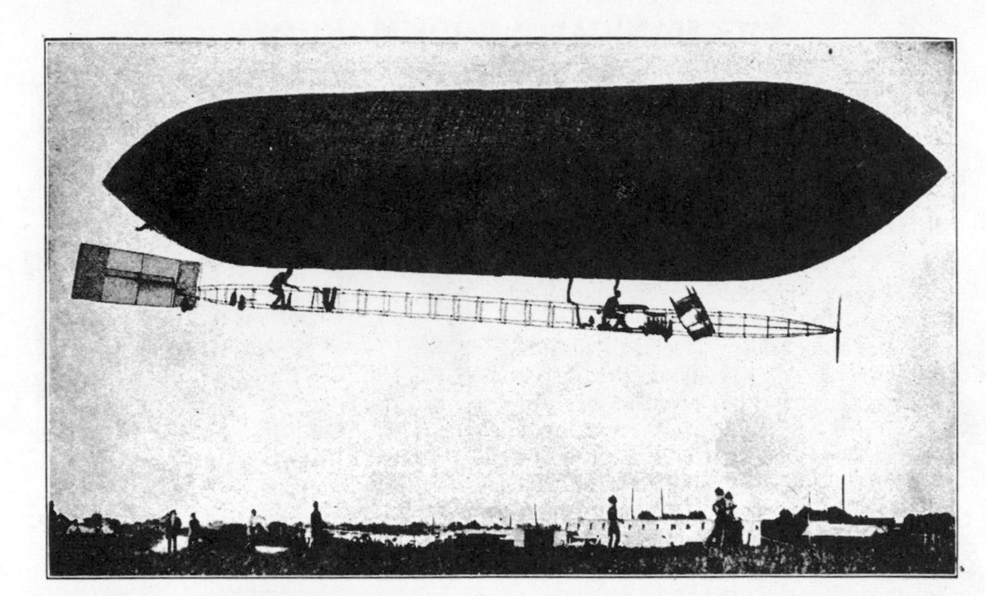

Capt. Baldwin Steering; Glen Curtiss Forward Handling Motor

THE U. S. ARMY DIRIGIBLE AIRSHIP

One of these illustrations shows the United States army dirigible airship making a turn at Fort Meyer during the official 2-hour flight in August. Captain Baldwin is in the rear handling the rudder and Glen Curtiss is forward handling the motor. It was this flight which fulfilled the last of the government specifications. The official speed of the trip was 19½ miles an hour.

The second illustration shows a close view of the propelling machinery and the air pump by which the pressure of gas under different atmospheric conditions is regulated.

THE POLAR CONTROVERSY

Sept. 1, 1909—"We have at last succeeded. The flag has been raised to the coveted breezes of the North Pole. The day was April 21, 1908."
COOK.

Sept. 6, 1909—"Have made good at last. Have the old pole. I reached it on April 6, 1909. Stars and Stripes nailed to the North Pole."
PEARY.

The Polar controversy, which has interested the entire civilized world and is destined to continue to do so for some months to come, if, indeed it is ever satisfactorily settled beyond all question of a doubt, had not developed sufficiently at the time of going to press to make advisable more than the simple recording of the claims of the two contestants.

When, with the suddenness of a flash from an aurora borealis, came the announcement, on Sept. 1, from Dr. Frederick A. Cook, that the discovery had been made by him, the world at large was disposed to accept the statement. Scientific men and bodies naturally and properly were more cautious in their expressions, but comparatively few seemed disposed to question the fact, and the general expectation was that the necessary proofs would be forthcoming.

Then on Sept. 6 came the volley from Commander Peary heralding his discovery, to be followed in a few

Commander Peary in Arctic Costume on Board the "Roosevelt"

The storm stirred up by the Peary-Cook controversy resulted in investigations by a Congressional committee and an international commission of scientists. Both groups, after careful examination of the claims of each explorer, gave Peary credit for the polar discovery. The public, meanwhile, was sharply divided between two heroes

Dr. Frederick A. Cook, a physician turned explorer, had a strange and tragic career. There appeared to be no basis for his claim, made more than a year after his 1907-08 Arctic expedition. Earlier, fellow scientists had discounted Cook's claims to have reached the top of Mt. McKinley in Alaska. In 1923 Cook was imprisoned after being convicted of mail fraud in connection with oil-land speculation

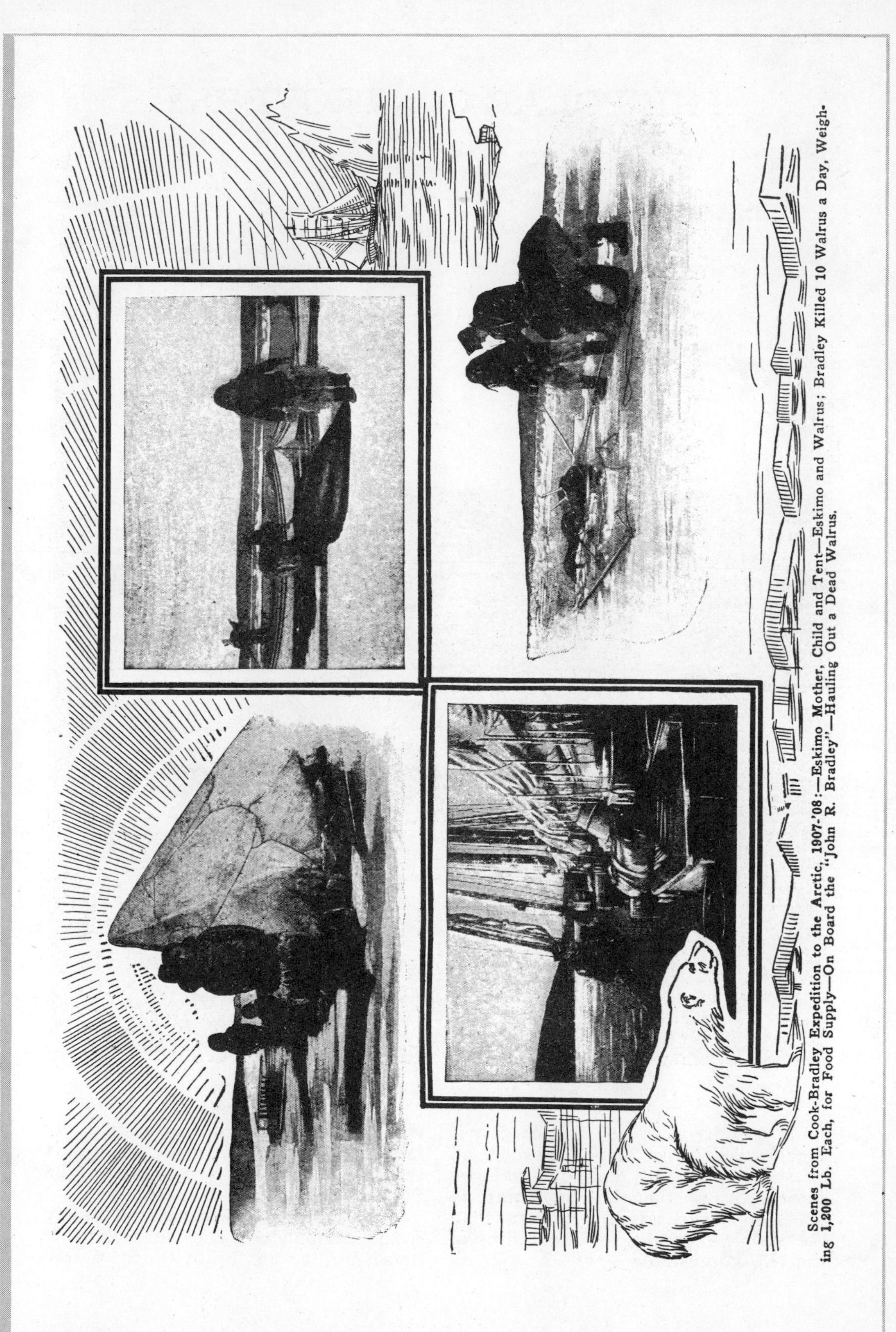

Scenes from Cook-Bradley Expedition to the Arctic, 1907-'08:—Eskimo Mother, Child and Tent—Eskimo and Walrus; Bradley Killed 10 Walrus a Day, Weighing 1,200 Lb. Each, for Food Supply—On Board the "John R. Bradley"—Hauling Out a Dead Walrus.

hours by his broadside attack on Dr. Cook.

It is a matter of regret that Cook should have for a moment parted with his original records which must ever be the most valued possessions of his life, and that Peary, even though smarting under the intense disappointment of temporary or permanent loss of first place, should have allowed himself the expressions used toward his rival.

What occurred is familiar to the reading public. Each gave his story to a newspaper as a copyrighted "scoop," and each story was criticised for its lack of scientific foundation. Peary wired that Cook's story should not be taken too seriously, as the latter had gone no great distance north, and never out of sight of land.

To this attack Cook answered that he would not degrade himself so far as to answer the message, and the battle commenced, Peary attacking and Cook remaining calm. As a result, the world, to a considerable extent, has become divided into two hostile camps, one of which resents the implications against Dr. Cook while the other discredits him, but between the two is a neutral body which takes great satisfaction that at least one, if not both, planted the American flag at a point that other flags have never reached, and whose motto is "wait."

Dr. Frederick A. Cook

The controversy so far has been more journalistic than scientific in its nature. When the two contestants have submitted their records, instruments, and what testimony they can gather, to an international commission, composed of the foremost scientists of the world, and when that body has made its decision, bestowing honor or dishonor upon both, or upon one, the world may criticise or acclaim. Until then "wait."

Robert Edwin Peary was a civil engineer for the U.S. Navy. He became interested in polar exploration after several trips to Greenland. He made one attempt to mark the pole in 1905, but was forced to turn back after coming within 200 miles of the goal. In 1908 he set out again and reached the pole, accompanied on the last leg of a desperate journey by only four Eskimos and a Negro servant

ELECTRIC STORM AFFECTS WHOLE WORLD

For the entire day of Sept. 25 a powerful electric disturbance, caused by the magnetic influence of the Northern lights, swept over practically the whole world, paralyzing all telegraphic service. The first break came early in the morning and for five hours telegraphers as far west as Chicago wrestled with the strange influence. Wires went "dead" one after another, and registers showed a pressure on the wires of 500 volts of electric current from the mysterious source. Brilliant sparks flashed when the keys were opened. San Francisco and Seattle also felt the disturbance, and the systems in England and Continental countries were also seriously affected.

PEARY'S ARCTIC SHIP

The "Roosevelt", the ship in which Peary traversed the first stages of his dash to the Pole, was built by the Peary Arctic club for his attempt in 1905. She is a 3-masted fore and aft schooner-rigged steamship, with a length of 182 ft., a depth of 16.3 ft., and a beam of 35.5 ft., built entirely of white oak, with treble frames.

The development of the airplane, of course, rapidly made these types of military observation completely obsolete

TYPES OF ARMY OBSERVATION DEVICES

Three types of the observation wagons or trucks now being experimented with in European military circles are shown in these illustrations. Two of them are formed from the front trucks of field guns, the steel shafts forming the observation posts. In one instance the shafts are fitted one upon the other, thus providing a considerable height. The ascent is made by means of a rope ladder and the observer is protected by an armored shield. The third type is a wagon constructed purely for observation. The ladder, which is of steel tubing, is made in three sections, easily erected.

It is believed by military experts that such devices will be of great assistance to artillery, as they make possible the placing of the gun under cover by providing a vantage point from which to watch the effects of the fire. One of the greatest fights at Port Arthur during the recent war was for the capture of a certain commanding position, not on which to mount guns, but from which to watch the effect of the gunfire.

Supported by an Auto Tire

NEW USE FOR AUTO TIRES

Both old and new automobile tires became very popular at continental watering places last season as swimming accessories. Rigidly inflated they make a much more satisfactory article to dive through or support oneself with than the ordinary life preserver or swimming bags.

AUTOMOBILE WATERING PLACES

That there is toleration for automobiles where automobile drivers deserve toleration is strikingly shown in this illustration. It is a watering place for steamer automobiles, voluntarily arranged in Concord, Mass. In carrying out this original idea a long hose is attached to the hydrant to make it easier for a tourist to fill his tank, and a sign calls attention to it.

Middleboro, another city of that state, has hung out banners asking automobilists for a square deal and promising one in return.

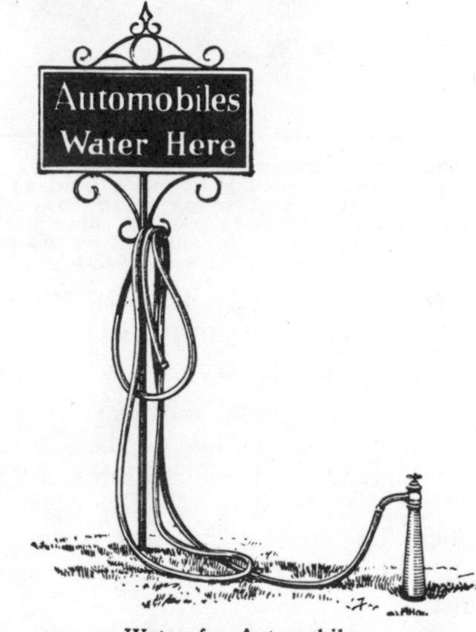

Water for Automobiles

A Police Patrol Auto

WASHINGTON'S AUTO PATROL WAGONS

The patrol wagon shown in this illustration has been adopted by the police department of Washington to take the place of the horse-drawn vehicles. Its speed is 15 miles an hour. The first couple of wagons will be given a thorough test before others are ordered. Each wagon will carry two stretchers and a first-aid-to-the-injured pack.

Fascinating new uses were being found for the auto's cast-off parts

This was an important time in the lives of the Wright brothers. A few months before Wilbur Wright made this record flight in France, brother Orville had flown for 57 minutes and 31 seconds at Fort Myer, Va., the longest flight then ever accomplished by a heavier-than-air machine

Miniature automobiles, if complete in every detail, as they must be if used as is this car, often cost much more to make than the average-sized car of the same make. This automobile was the smallest at the Savannah racing meet. It cost $2,000.

UNITED STATES PLANS BIGGEST BATTLESHIP

Plans have been outlined by the bureau of construction of the United States navy for a huge battleship of 25,000 tons, designed to carry eight 14-in. guns. The speed of the new design of battleship is figured as 24½ miles an hour.

Such a battleship would far outstrip the great "Dreadnoughts" of other nations, the largest of which is of but little more than 20,000 tons. The largest guns used on any battleship at the present time are of 12-in. caliber.

AERIAL FLIGHT POSSIBLE WITHOUT GASOLINE MOTOR

According to Wilbur Wright, the flying-machine was not dependent on the gasoline engine. "It has undoubtedly helped us, but if they had not been developed we could have flown with the steam engine. There are steam engines built now sufficiently light to enable me to fly with them."

WRIGHT MAKES NEW RECORDS

As a fitting finish of a year that raised the Wright brothers from what the world considered a pair of mere pretenders to what the world now considers its greatest aviators, Wilbur Wright established two new records at Le Mans, France, on December 18. The first of these was gained by flying through the air for 1 hour, 53 minutes and 59 seconds. The best previous record was 1 hour 31 minutes, made by Wright on September 21. This flight, as well as a number of previous flights, gave him undisputed claim to the Michelin cup, which is the prize for the longest aeroplane flight for the year 1908.

Passing Over Captive Balloon

In the afternoon Wright made another flight, notwithstanding the fact that the wind was blowing in gusts that reached a velocity of 20 miles an hour, and soaring 50 ft. above a captive line of balloons 300 ft. high, captured the height record which assured him the prize of the Sartho Aero Club.

In the evening of the day on which Wright won his double victory, the Aero Club gave a banquet in his honor.

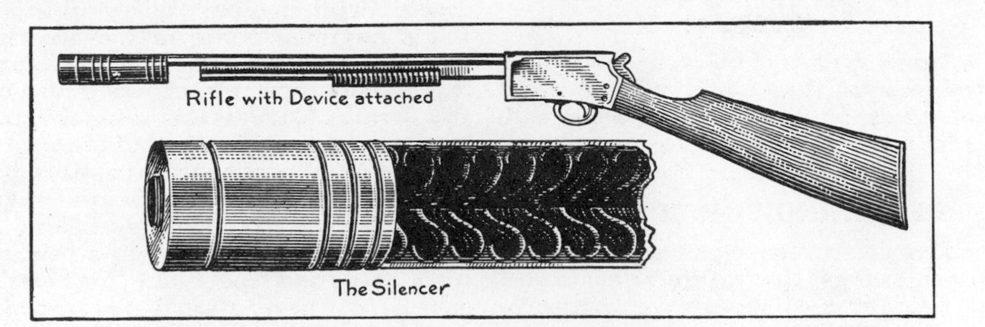

MAXIM'S NOISELESS FIREARM INVENTION

The device known as the "silencer" with which Hiram P. Maxim has succeeded in making all ordinary firearms practically noiseless appears to be nothing more intricate than a small section of highly polished gaspipe. For the ordinary army or sporting rifle the silencer is 4 in. long, $1\frac{3}{8}$ in. in diameter, and weighs about $5\frac{1}{2}$ oz. It may be carried in the waistcoat pocket like a fountain pen and can be screwed onto the end of a gun barrel in 5 seconds. To fit it to a rifle it is only necessary to cut a small screw thread at the end of the barrel.

The principle upon which the invention is based is centrifugal force. The powder gases, instead of escaping explosively from the muzzle of the gun, which produces the loud report, are caught in the silencer and whirled rapidly about through the small grooves or apartments with which it is provided, escaping gradually. These small grooves are formed by steel disks inside the tube, the bullet passing through a hole in the center.

Successful tests of the device were made recently in a New York office. Among many other guns, a United States army Springfield rifle was used. Without the silencer the report from this gun made the window sashes rattle and pained the ear drums of persons in the room. With the silencer attached only a sharp "swisk" was heard.

The value of such a device in warfare cannot be over-estimated. Smokeless powder has made possible long-distance shooting from hidden positions, but at closer range the reports of the rifles have often made secrecy of position impossible. The possibility of discharging rifles without smoke or report divulging the position of the men will prove a great asset to any army.

The military application of this invention has been very limited. Gang gunmen have made some use of it on revolvers and automatic pistols—but its major application has been as a prop in the plots of detective fiction

SULTAN OF TURKEY TO HAVE CUT GLASS STAIRCASE

Abdul Hamid, Sultan of Turkey, still clings to his old ideas of gorgeous Oriental luxury, and has ordered a complete staircase of cut glass for his palace. It will be the most dazzling staircase ever seen outside of the illustrations of a fairy story. It will be 25 ft. wide, and the steps are to be beveled and cut with Turkish inscriptions.

ZEPPELIN'S GREATEST FLIGHT

Count Zeppelin's great airship, the pride of the German people, created a world's record in a flight during the latter part of March by carrying 26 persons. The huge dirigible ascended from Lake Constance bearing Count Zeppelin, 10 aeronautic experts of the German army, and 15 soldiers. Rising as majestically as an eagle, it flew a distance of 150 miles and was in the air 4 hours.

All Germany was aroused to additional enthusiasm by the flight. The comparatively great weight carried convinced the experts that an equal weight of explosives could be carried with the same facility.

In the porch swing, gently swinging on summer evenings, young couples had their courtships, married folks planned the future of their brood, oldsters dreamed of days gone by. Few homes of the period were so humble that swings did not grace their porches from spring to late fall

A WIRELESS BLOCK SIGNAL SYSTEM

A new system of block signaling and train control has followed close upon the heels of wireless telegraphy and is founded on the same basic principle.

RECLINING PORCH SWING

This illustration shows a new idea in porch swings, the feature being in the fact that it is equipped with drop ends for pillow rests. The swing is made of solid oak in all the different finishes. The ordinary porch swing, or swinging seat, as it is called, has solid ends.

Porch Swing with Drop Ends

REPRIMANDING ON THE SLY

A most sensible remark was made by Mr. W. J. Harahan in his paper on "Discipline on Railways," when he said: "When possible to avoid it, men should not be reprimanded within the hearing of other men, as it seems to inflame and wound them, and such reprimand loses a large part of its efficiency." This reminds us, says Railway and Locomotive Engineering, of the ways of a Western general manager who was one of the most popular men in his day and generation. He was familiar with every detail of railroad work and never hesitated to express himself with vigorous fluency when he found anything going in the way he considered wrong. When an individual was at fault, however, or was guilty of any serious blunder, this general manager would pour the vials of his wrath into the delinquent's ear, but always did the reprimanding on what the men called the sly. He would go behind a box car or call the man into a private room or car and roast him to his heart's content, but never a word of reprimand was uttered where others could hear what was said. The consequence was that the worst abused man would depart from the tongue lashing, feeling that he deserved much more than he had received and ready to swear that the general manager was the finest gentleman in Illinois.

Not only does the man not lose self-respect, but the fact that no one else has heard the rebuke, entirely eliminates any exhibition of bravado or resistance to authority. In fact, on one occasion, a boy with a sense of humor, who had been rather severely dealt with quietly and alone by his superior, went out into the roundhouse after he had been "called down" and gave it out that he had been brought in for consultation and his advice on certain matters had been asked for by the boss. His altered behavior in the thing complained of was noticed.

Copyright, Underwood & Underwood, N. Y.

ASCENDED OVER A MILE IN AN AEROPLANE

Walter R. Brookins, although only 21 years of age, has taken a leading place among the aviators of the world. At the Atlantic City meet in July he piloted his biplane, a Wright machine, to a height of 6,175 ft., beating the record of 4,930 ft., established by him at Indianapolis. Brookins has only been actively interested in aviation for about six months. The photograph shows him just before he started the Atlantic City flight.

It's easy to see, in this unusual photograph, why early airmen referred to their planes as "crates." The flimsy supports and controls, joined by ordinary bolts and washers and braced with piano wire, gave an air of fantasy to the feats they performed. In those days a pilot really "flew" an airplane. Today's modern transport, in contrast, is so inherently stable and reliable that it just plows along, hour after hour, with practically no effort on the part of the pilot, if the weather is good. Appropriately enough, a pilot now refers to his airplane as a "ship"

"You can build it yourself" has been the constant advice of Popular Mechanics *to its readers over the years*

Amateur Mechanics

How to Make a Glider

By Carl Bates

A gliding machine is a motorless aeroplane, or flying-machine, propelled by gravity and designed to carry a passenger through the air from a high point to a lower point some distance away. Flying in a glider is simply coasting down hill on the air, and is the most interesting and exciting sport imaginable. The style of glider described in this article is known as the "two-surface" or "double-decked" aeroplane, and is composed of two arched cloth surfaces placed one above the other.

In building a glider the wood material used should be straight-grained spruce, free from knots. First prepare from spruce planks the following strips of wood. Four long beams ¾ in. thick, 1¼ in. wide and 20 ft. long; 12 crosspieces ¾ in. thick, ¾ in. wide and 3 ft. long; 12 uprights ½ in. thick, 1½ in. wide and 4 ft long; 41 strips for the bent ribs 3/16 in. thick, ½ in. wide and 4 ft. long; 2 arm sticks 1 in. thick, 2 in. wide and 3 ft. long; the rudder sticks ¾ in. square and 8 ft long; several strips ½ in. by ¾ in. for building the vertical and horizontal rudders. The frames for the two main surfaces should be constructed first, by bolting the crosspieces to the long beams at the places shown by the dimensions in Fig. 1. If 20-ft. lumber cannot be procured, use 10-ft. lengths and splice them, as shown in Fig. 3. All bolts used should be ⅛ in. in diameter and fitted with washers on both ends. These frames formed by the crosspieces should be braced by diagonal wires as shown. All wiring is done with No. 16 piano wire.

The 41 ribs may be nailed to the main frames on the upper side by using fine flat-headed brads ⅞ in. long. These ribs are spaced 1 ft. apart and extend 1 ft. beyond the rear edges of the main frames, as shown in Fig. 1. After nailing one end of a rib to the front long beam, the rib is arched by springing down the loose end and nailing to the rear beam. The ribs should have a curve as shown in Fig. 2, the amount of curvature being the same

The frames of the main surfaces are now ready to be covered with cloth. Cambric or bleached muslin should be used for the covering, which is tacked to the front edge, stretched tightly over the bent ribs and fastened securely with tacks to the rear ends of the ribs. The cloth should also be glued to the ribs for safety. In the center of the lower plane surface there should be an opening 2 ft. wide and 4 ft. long for the body of the operator. Place the two main surfaces 4 ft. apart and connect with the 12 uprights, placed in the corner of each crosspiece and beam. The uprights are fastened by bolting to the crosspieces, as shown in Fig. 2. The whole structure is made strong and rigid by bracing with diagonal wires, both laterally and longitudinally.

The vertical rudder is to keep the machine headed into the wind and is not movable. This rudder is made of cloth stretched over a light wooden frame, which is nailed to the rudder sticks connecting to the main frame. The horizontal rudder is also made of cloth stretched over a light wooden frame, and arranged to intersect the vertical rudder at its center. This rudder is held in position and strengthened by diagonal wires and guy wires. The horizontal rudder is also immovable, and its function is to prevent the machine from diving, and also to keep it steady in its flight. The rudders are fastened to the glider by the two rudder sticks, and these sticks are held rigid by diagonal wires and also by guy wires leading to the sides of the main frames as shown in Fig. 1. The two arm sticks should be spaced about 13 in. apart and bolted to the long beams in the center of the opening in the lower plane where the operator is to take his position.

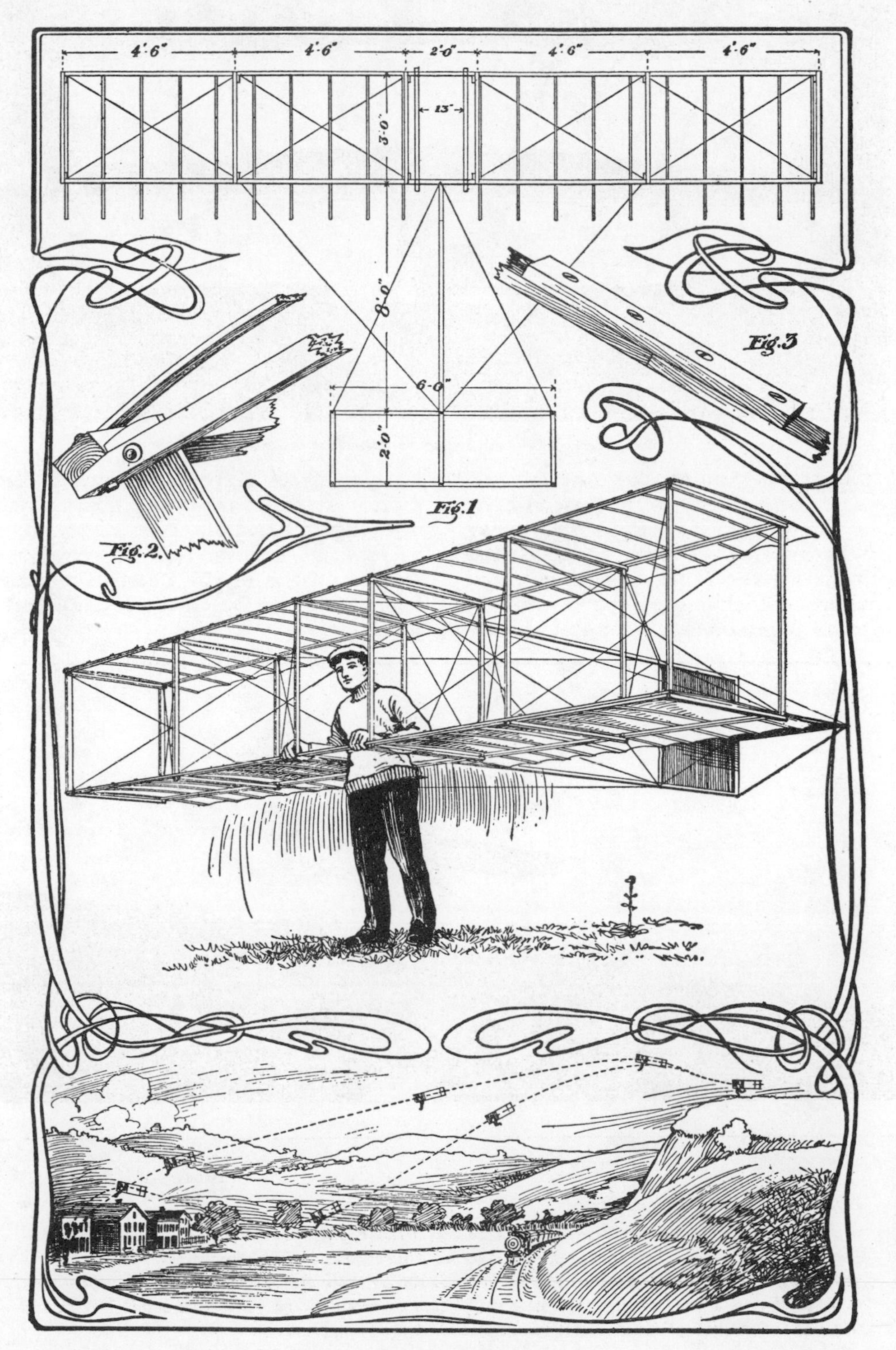

Details of the Glider

With these plans and the instructions, many readers proceeded to build and fly gliders. Control, of a sort, of this rather neat glider was gained solely by the shifting of the weight of the occupant, the only method which worked before the experiments of the Wrights. The development of movable control surfaces which altered the attitude of the airplane by deflecting the air was the great contribution of Wilbur and Orville Wright which finally made flying machines practical

Here are two of the many gliders built following the plans shown on the preceding page which were published a few months previously. On the opposite page is a reader-built gas-powered monoplane, also built from magazine plans

WHAT OUR READERS ARE DOING

Successfully Made According to Our Instructions

The accompanying half-tone engravings are reproductions from two of the many original photographs we receive illustrating articles made from the descriptions given in the Shop Notes and Amateur Mechanics departments of Popular Mechanics. In one of our recent numbers there was given a complete description and dimensioned drawing of a glider. One of the many gliders made from this description is shown in one of the illustrations, and is the work of N. Chadwick, Philadelphia, Pa.

Belmont, California.

Editor Popular Mechanics Magazine:

I thought that you would be interested to know that a glider, patterned after the plans which you published in your magazine, has been made and was very successful. The accompanying photograph is a picture of me as I was leaving the top of a hill. I could not get more than thirty feet above the ground, nor travel more than a hundred yards, because the hill was not steep enough. All of the better hills around here were so covered with brush that it was impossible to try flying from them.

DE RONDE TOMPKINS.

Alberto Santos-Dumont, the idol of this dawn of the air age, gave to the world the plans for his famous light plane, Demoiselle, *refusing to have them patented. The plans were published in* Popular Mechanics, *and large working drawings of the little flying machine were offered in the pages of the magazine. Quite a few readers built and successfully flew copies of the plane*

"Demoiselle" Aeroplane Built in Corinth, Miss.

AEROPLANE BUILT FROM MAGAZINE DESCRIPTION

There is hardly a section of the United States where inventors are not at work building and testing aeroplanes of their own pattern or along the lines of the well known machines. The publication of the plans for the 'Demoiselle" in Popular Mechanics Magazine last summer stimulated the ambition of many enterprising young men who aspire to be airmen. Two of these live in Corinth, Miss. They have made a machine from the description given in the magazine. They followed the directions exactly and as a result obtained a finished product which equipped with a 30-hp. engine, weighs 250 lb., 10 lb. lighter than the Santos-Dumont model that was described. This machine was shown at the St. Louis Aero Exhibition and attracted great attention. A photograph of the Corinth machine which the builders sent to the magazine attests their success.

Pliers Effective Protection Against Hatpins

PLIERS AVERT DANGERS OF LONG HATPINS

A Chicago architect is credited with having first made use of a pair of pliers for this purpose. The protruding point of an exceptionally long hatpin, worn by a young woman standing next to him in an elevated train, not only annoyed him but did him physical harm by scratching his face. Polite requests for the withdrawal of the pin having met with no response, the injured man drew a pair of pliers from his pocket and catching the offending point in their jaws, dexterously bent it upward, thus eliminating all danger.

Women were emerging from the uniformity of the long skirts and starched blouses they had worn around the turn of the century. The new styles were startling enough to draw comment even from the editors of a technical publication

GARTER STILETTO WOMAN'S NEWEST PROTECTOR

Deprived of pockets in which she might carry firearms, and public senti-

The New Garter Stilleto, Snugly Sheathed, but Always Ready for Use

ment imposing on her the use of more subtle weapons than a club or sword stick, which she would find hard to conceal, modern invention has added another weapon to the hatpin for women of fashion. The device is the garter stiletto, a long, sharp, vicious weapon that fits snugly in a sheath attached to the garter. The slender steel blade is so thin and so narrow that it would not attract more attention than a hatpin and could be wielded with more deadly effect, in case of necessity.

MOVING-PICTURE PROFANITY SHOCKS LIP READERS

Moving-picture profanity is the newest discovery that has been made in connection with the many motion-picture theaters throughout the country, many deaf persons who welcomed the gradual spread of the motion picture having discovered that the actors in certain classes of the silent dramas use unprintable language when they are going through with their parts. To the deaf mutes who read the lips with facility, the language used by the people in the pictures was as plain and distinct as the speaking of actors and actresses on the stage is to the average theater audience. These people have been greatly shocked by what they have seen, and in at least two large cities public protest has been made against the continued appearance of such films.

HOPPLES FOR THE HOBBLE-SKIRTED

The hobble skirt is very much inclined to bag at the knees in somewhat the same manner as do trousers, but, whereas the only remedy for the latter is continual pressing, an ingenious European has devised a preventive for the former. This preventive, called a hobble garter, works in exactly the same manner as the more or less well

Horse Harness Idea Adapted to the Hobble-Skirted

known horse hopple. It effectively checks undue length of stride, thereby saving the front of the hobble skirt from being bagged out of shape by the knees.

TROUSERS SKIRT DEVISED FOR OUTDOOR WEAR

The American Interpretation of the French Trousers Skirt

The trousers skirt that has created such a sensation within this country and abroad was designed primarily for out-of-door use. The basic idea, which came from one of the most famous of the Paris dress-making establishments, was to give woman a garment in which she could be comfortable while in the open. It was meant for touring, for walking expeditions, for hunting and other such purposes, and was not at first intended to be used in the drawing room or on the streets for morning or afternoon wear, as the so-called harem skirt has come to be used. American dressmakers have remodeled the garment into more practical form than the original Paris design and have so made it that it can even be equipped with hip pockets, if the fair wearer so desires.

ℭA Chicago amusement-resort promoter has given costly recognition to the limitations of the hobble skirt by rebuilding all the stairways on his grounds, making the steps with a height of six inches instead of one foot, to prevent accidents among the women.

PLACES BURDEN OF HAND BAG ON SHOULDER

Creators of fashions for women in Paris have devised a new adjunct to feminine furnishings which is nothing less than a handbag of large size. The bags are mostly made of gobelin tapestry, are frequently embellished with large tassels and fringes and bear some faint resemblance to the old-fashioned carpet sack. They are so large and top heavy that it is almost out of the question to carry them in the hand, so they are provided with a long, heavy cord of tapestry which is placed around the neck.

ℭSpecial street cars during rush hours for "ladies only" are being considered by the town council of Melfort, Sask.

The harem skirt was a real "shocker," the subject of heated debates in the sewing circles as well as the barbershops. Ostrich plumes were the rage in feminine headgear. The lower photo also reveals that shoulder bags are nothing new

Oldfield's indictment of the racing game was not based on a personal lack of courage. In 1904 he held all of the world's dirt-track speed records, and for three years drove in every major racing event without a single defeat. Later he became the first race driver to attain a speed of 130 miles per hour, a record that stood for some time

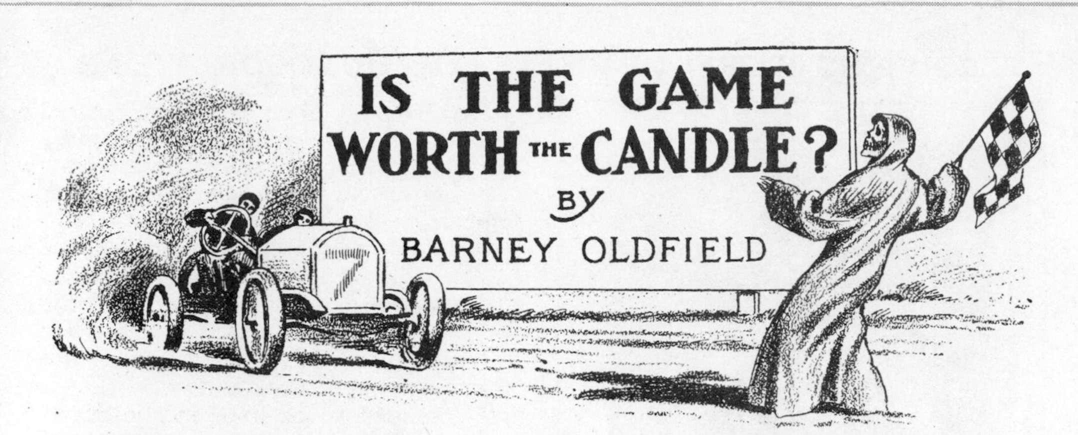

The question which Barney Oldfield answers in this article is one which has been confronting automobile manufacturers for several years. Many of the men engaged in the building of high-class cars have given their answer by refusing to take part in speed contests, not only because they do not consider the transitory glory and slight advertising sufficient reward for the cost of maintaining expensive racing teams, but because they do not consider it worth the cost in human life. Oldfield is probably the most experienced driver of fast cars in the world. He is now out of the game and is merely a spectator. He considers himself lucky to be alive.

Barney Oldfield

IT was in Birmingham, Ala. George DeWitt, who, on the Florida beach, in the flush of his first race after a record, had done 100 miles in 90 minutes, dropped swiftly down past the grandstand into the short turn. It had been a dry summer, and the dust of three parched weeks drove itself across his vision. He checked his throttle, put on his brakes, and then, to the astonishment of everyone, came to a dead stop, while the other racers rushed past him.

"What's the matter?" I asked, as he withdrew from the track, "Smash something?"

George lifted his goggles, blinked his eyes, and gazed back into the seething hurricane of dust and machines.

"Not yet," he answered, with his eyes still fixed on the track; "but that dust doesn't look good to me. There's death in tracks like that, and, take my word, I'd rather live to hear one man talk about my eightieth birthday than to have the whole world cheer me as a dead hero."

I knew he was right at the time, and since then a thousand developments in the racing game have gone to prove him right. The dirt track has been the death, not only of many brave men and good drivers, but, to a certain extent, of automobile racing itself. There are still lunatics who will risk its dangers, but the manufacturers themselves have become weary of its endless death-roll. Good drivers fight shy of it. *The game is not worth the candle.*

It has taken 10 years to prove this, 10 years of driving death, of incessant slaughter, of many broken machines and a few broken records. It has been a decade replete with black headlines and black mourning. Much money has been made by promoters and the sport-governing association; a little has been made by drivers.

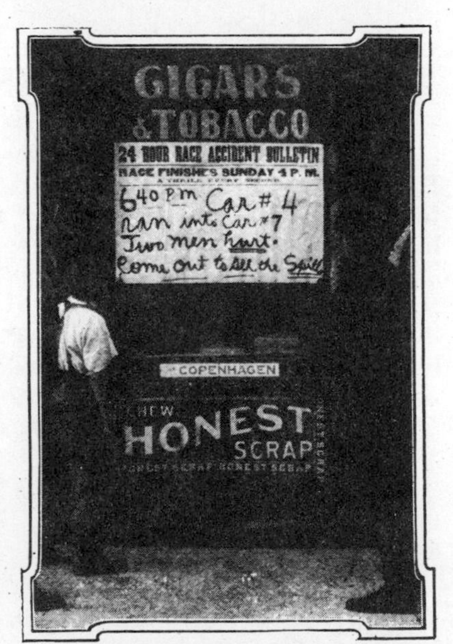

Bulletins Posted During Los Angeles Race. Told of Accidents — not Standing of Contestants

Most Persons Believe Dirt Tracks can be Made Safe by Oiling. This Photograph Shows Barney Oldfield Going into a Turn on the Hawthorne Track, in Chicago, after the Track had been Flooded with Oil and the Surface Put in the Best Condition Possible with a Dirt Track. What Might Happen to a Driver Who was Forced to Follow into Such a Hurricane of Greasy Dirt?

Not Burman vs. DePalma or Aitken vs. Robertson, but the Field vs. Death

The $20,000 Car Which Killed Frank Croker on the Beach at Daytona, Fla.

The Late Lewis Strang Breaking a Dirt-Track Record. Four Cars are in Strang's Wake, but Cannot See or be Seen for the Dust

Oldfield's criticisms led to the adoption of safety measures in racing which sharply reduced the death toll in succeeding years—races were slowed down during rains, after wrecks, etc., while more rigid mechanical inspections were required of cars before they could be qualified

The "Ice Stove"   Professor Bell's Residence

Alexander Graham Bell was 64 years old when he developed this first crude form of air conditioning. Bell continued to experiment in all fields until his death in 1922. He grew to dislike the telephone, his most famous invention, because it interrupted his experiments

"ICE STOVE," PROFESSOR ALEXANDER GRAHAM BELL'S LATEST INVENTION

Prof. Alexander Graham Bell, inventor of the telephone and scientist of world-wide fame, has recently invented and constructed an apparatus for cooling dwelling houses in summer at small cost and with simple operation, which has been used with much success in the inventor's home in Washington, D. C., during the hot spells of the summer.

While other dwellers on aristocratic Connecticut avenue in that city sweltered and wilted under the torrid temperature that, even within doors of the mansions of that wealthy locality, rose daily to 90 deg., Professor Bell sat comfortably at work in his study. On his desk the thermometer, throughout the whole summer, has never registered higher than 61 deg.

While there are numberless appliances for cooling buildings, they are, for the most part, adapted only to large structures and are of a costly and complicated nature, dependent upon involved mechanism and many-syllabled chemicals, requiring an expert to operate. Professor Bell's latest invention avoids all these objections.

He first became interested in the subject during a recent tour of the world, being much impressed in India and other tropical countries with the total absence in the dwelling houses, even of the wealthy classes, of all means of tempering the fierce heat. When he returned to the United States he at once addressed his talents to devising an apparatus that, while avoiding the objections of high cost and complex operation, would yet achieve satisfac-

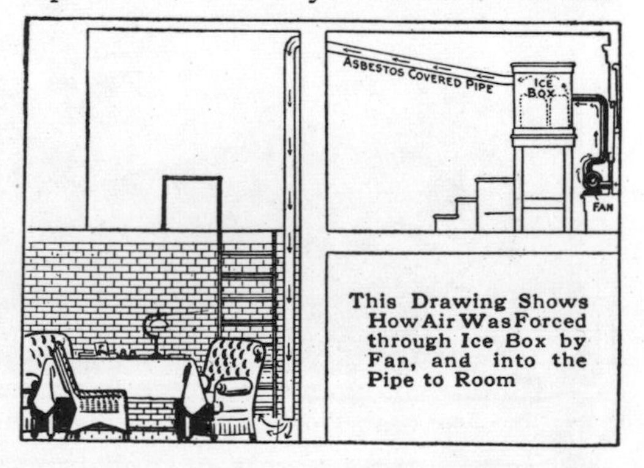

This Drawing Shows How Air Was Forced through Ice Box by Fan, and into the Pipe to Room

Study, Formerly a Swimming Tank, in Professor Bell's Washington Home in Which Thermometer Never Went Above 61 Degrees During the Summer. Cold-Air Pipe, Ending Near Floor, is Shown on Right

tory results in the cooling of private dwellings. With characteristic energy he soon conceived and constructed an appliance which, he thought, would fill the requirements. Nature aided him, for hardly had he installed this latest creation of his genius when a series of blistering hot spells put it to a crucial test.

This is the method of constructing the "ice stove," as it is now installed in Professor Bell's home in Washington:

On the window ledge is set a small fan, about 6 in. in diameter. It is operated by a small electric motor attached by a wire to an electric-light socket. The fan is inclosed in a casing. Under the lower sash of the window is set a board in which is a 2½-in. hole. A short pipe connects this hole with the encased fan, thus supplying pure air from outdoors. Another pipe runs from the fan casing to a large wooden box, which formerly served as a pantry ice box, about 3 ft. high and broad, and about 4 ft. long. In this box are cakes of ice. The lid fits with air-tight snugness. From the opposite side of the box at which the pipe from the fan enters, another pipe leads off to the apartments to be cooled in just the same manner that hot-air pipes lead from a heating furnace. This pipe is heavily encased in asbestos. When this service pipe comes through the wall into the room to be cooled, it runs down to within about 3 in. of the floor, the end being open for the discharge of the cold air.

All that is necessary to cool the room is to turn on the electric current and start the fan. This draws the air in through the window pipe and drives it through the connecting pipe into the ice box. Here the pressure of the air from behind, due to the driving power of the fan, forces it across the ice, thereby cooling it, and thence on into and through the service pipe, whence it is discharged into the room.

While Professor Bell uses electricity as the most convenient method for operating his fan, any other motive power would be equally good.

Bell obtained no patent on his "ice stove," apparently intending it only for his own comfort. Commercial air conditioning developed slowly. In 1914 the Atchison, Topeka and Santa Fe Railroad air conditioned a few dining cars. The first theater was not air conditioned until 1921, and the first office building was so equipped in 1928

1912-1921

THE first decade of *Popular Mechanics* seemed like a Golden Age compared to the 10 years that followed. History had this in store for America: war, depression, violent labor unrest, a period of unparalleled postwar hysteria and a rabidly controversial prohibition law that proved difficult to enforce from the beginning.

Prosperity of a sort and manifest destiny

The decade began quietly enough and with promise. Factories, mines and mills were busy in 1912, and the value of their products was more than double what it had been in 1902. Jobs were fairly easy to get, and real wages about 6 per cent higher.

Woodrow Wilson succeeded William Howard Taft in the White House in 1913, and during his administration the government soon was embarked on a series of adventures in intervention in Mexico, Nicaragua, Haiti and Santo Domingo. The United States finally numbered 48—both New Mexico and Arizona were admitted to the Union in 1912. The Panama Canal was opened in 1914, and the Virgin Islands were purchased from Denmark in 1917.

There were few revolutionary inventions or discoveries during the decade 1912-1921. It was rather a period of smoothing out the wrinkles in the mechanical marvels that had appeared a few years before.

Tin Lizzies and Pierce Arrows

The automobile age was in full swing. By 1912 almost two million cars were in operation in the United States, and 350,000 were made during that year. Model-T Ford No. 500,000 came off the assembly line in 1914, as did the first edition of a popular book, *Best Ford Jokes,* that was to undergo many annual reprintings. America's beloved "tin lizzie" was undersold by the Saxson ($395) and overshadowed by the luxuries of the Pierce Arrow, Cadillac and Buick at the 1914 auto show. The inexpensive models were still open cars, but many boasted "one-man tops" and side curtains against the elements. Although a number had self-starters, electric gear shifts and klaxon horns, serious motoring still required the protection of linen dusters, goggles, veils, wind cuffs and lap robes.

Like the auto, the airplane was undergoing transformation. The basic principles of control established by the Wright brothers remained unchanged, but their awkward biplanes with chain-driven, pusher propellers gave way to a type more familiar to us today. This had the engine and propeller at the front of a fabric-covered fuselage containing a cockpit with windshield to protect the pilot, more or less, from the elements. There were even a few all-metal planes. By 1918 the airplane had become so dependable that air-mail service was established between New York, Philadelphia and Washington, D. C. A year later airmen twice conquered the Atlantic—in May, 1919, by the cautious, hopping flight of the U. S. Navy flying boat NC-4, and again in June with the more daring and nonstop flight of John Alcock and Arthur Brown from Newfoundland to Ireland in 16 hours and 12 minutes.

First flights to Europe

In cities and towns, the nickelodeon had given way to more elaborate theaters which charged higher prices. *The Birth of a Nation* was filmed in 1914 and began to earn an eventual 18 million dollars. Hollywood hit upon the "star system" — and millions shed tears over Mary Pickford, laughed at Charles Chaplin and Mack Sennett's Keystone Cops, obtained vicarious adventure with William S. Hart and felt deeper and darker emotions as they watched sultry, languid Theda Bara, first of the movie "vampires." Regular attendance was encouraged by weekly adventure serials—"Dolly of the Dailies," "Lucille Love" and "The Perils of Pauline" —each episode closing with the heroine in the deadliest of perils.

Newspaper circulation had doubled since 1900, and there were now colored comics — "Buster Brown," "Happy Hooligan," "Bringing Up Father" and "The Katzenjammer Kids." Tin Pan Alley was writing the nation's popular songs, but the classics were enjoying a renaissance on records made by such artists as Enrico Caruso, Amelita Galli-Curci, Frances Alda and Mary Garden. The public was being shocked—for different reasons—by Picasso's colony of cubists and "September Morn." There was a revival of American poetry, led by Edgar Lee Masters, Carl Sandburg, Robert Frost, Vachel Lindsay and Amy Lowell.

Caruso, Picasso and comic strips

Established baseball stars were Grover Cleveland Alexander, Ty Cobb and Walter Johnson, while a portly fellow named George Herman Ruth was beginning his career. The decade saw three great world's heavyweight champions: Jack Johnson (1908-1915), Jess Willard (1915-1919) and Jack Dempsey (1919-1926). The average American was becoming a spectator at sports—when he did play anything himself it was most likely to be golf.

Where women had minced in hobble skirts, they now strode freely in long tunic gowns, slashed modestly at the skirt. Their hats were fantasies in ostrich feathers. Less restrained clothing made for more freedom in dancing, and Vernon and Irene Castle introduced the tango and the hesitation waltz.

War, the political emancipation of women and prohibition marched side by side across the stage of history. The same newspapers that noted the assassination of an Austrian archduke on June 29, 1914, headlined the march of suffragettes on Washington. Meanwhile prohibition spread from state to state, 13 being bone-dry by 1917. Both the 18th and 19th Amendments were declared part of the Constitution in 1919.

But it was World War I that left the deepest scar on the decade and its generation. Americans generally wanted to be neutral, and Wilson's reelection in 1916 was based on the slogan "He kept us out of war." But the sinking of the *Lusitania* and other German acts brought preparedness parades and pressure for war, which Congress declared on April 6, 1917. American reinforcements enabled the Allies to take the offensive and win an armistice by Nov. 11, 1918.

The Lusitania *is sunk*

Peace brought immediate problems. The year 1919 was a turbulent one in labor history. High wartime prices continued, even into the severe economic depression of 1920. The spy hysteria of the war years was followed by red scares and race riots that culminated in the Palmer raids and the revival of the Ku Klux Klan.

By 1921 economic conditions were better. Americans learned they numbered 105 million. The number of persons who lived in cities about equaled those on farms, in contrast to the 3 to 2 ratio in favor of farmers a decade before. Because of advances in medicine, the average American could now expect to reach 51 years of age.

Popular Mechanics *covers are a tradition in themselves. Subjects are nearly always new mechanical devices or technological trends. They are presented in rapid movement, to show their operation or to indicate their power. Machines usually dominate the human element, although figures are almost always present. Here the subject was a motor sleigh of unusual design, exhibited at an early auto show in Berlin*

TEN YEARS' PROGRESS IN THE AUTOMOBILE

From the Motor, London

THE MOTORCAR OF 1902

The motor: Engines with one, two and four cylinders.
Connected by much piping.
Separate cylinder castings.
Small range of flexibility. Efficiency low, owing to a number of causes then unknown.
Camshafts driven by spur gears.
Exposed valves. Noisy valve gear. Valves generally too small, and generally rendered inaccessible by contiguous gear.
Radiator of gilled tubing with exposed gills.
Radiator, in many cases, carried below frame and liable to become mud-coated.

Lubrication: Drip sight-feed lubricators with many pipes; reservoir usually on dash.
Pressure-feed arrangements liable to become choked.

Ignition: Coil and accumulator. Tube ignition considered by many as useful for emergencies.

Carburation: Most uncertain, owing to liability to recondensation. Starting up, very often difficult. Petrol consumption excessive. Efficiency, therefore, low.

Clutch: Leather-faced cone, seldom removable without affecting other units.

Gearbox: Meshing gears. Gear control on a quadrant. Gear-changing on some cars quite an art.

Transmission: Chain drive to rear axle. Chains liable to become choked with dirt and to stretch.

Brakes: External band brakes.

Springing: Not suitable for varying loads or bad roads.

Accommodation: Usually for four people in cramped and uncomfortable positions. Seating high and exposed. Dust-raising and dust-holding bodies.

THE MOTORCAR OF 1912

The motor: Engines with one, two, four, six and eight cylinders.
Cylinders cast in sets of two, three, or four.
Great range of flexibility. Greater efficiency with smaller engines.
Silent chain drive to camshafts.
Inclosed valves, quite silent in operation.
Desaxé crankshafts. Sometimes desaxé camshafts.
Radiator framed honeycomb or gilled tube.
Concealed gas and water and oil pipes.
Complete accessibility.

Lubrication: Pump-circulated lubrication, with single lead to and from small indicator on dash.
Oil-ways cast through crankcase.

Ignition: Magneto general. Supplementary ignition on some cars.

Carburation: Much more reliable and automatically adjusted to engine speeds.
Self-starters (by compressed air, electric current, or foot pressure) gaining favor.

Clutch: Leather-faced and metal-to-metal—easily removable.

Gearbox: Chain-driven gear shafts just introduced. Gears controlled through a gate.

Transmission: Silent bevel and worm drives to rear axles.

Brakes: Internal expanding brakes.

Springing: Well designed for varying conditions.

Accommodation: For five or seven persons in absolute comfort. Seating low and protected. Flush coachwork. Clever double-purpose bodies.

Today's popular-priced cars have high-speed engines of about 100 horsepower. Such things as hydraulic brakes and shock absorbers, independently sprung wheels, crank-operated windows, foam-rubber seats, ash trays, dash lights, upholstered interiors, radios, luggage compartments, low-pressure tires, automatic chokes, windshield wipers, gear shifts, heaters and starters were either unknown or rare luxuries to the passenger of 1912 who was carried in "absolute comfort"

Air bombing had been tried by the Italians at Tripoli in 1907, but the bombs were simply cans of nitroglycerine, as dangerous to the pilot as the enemy. This was the first use of more predictable bombs —equipped with fuses and safety devices

A THEORY BECOMES A FACT

The first actual test of the aeroplane as an offensive weapon and an engine of destruction in warfare occurred a few weeks ago when Italian aviators guided their machines over Turkish troops and Arab camps, dropping bombs with deadly effect and striking terror to the hearts of the Moslem soldiers.

It is possible for people standing at the point shown in this illustration, which is near Dayton, Ohio, to see every one of the eight means of locomotion depicted. The river is the Miami, and running parallel with it are the Miami and Erie Canal, the Dayton & Troy Electric Railway, the Cincinnati & Hamilton Railroad, and the turnpike used by horse-drawn vehicles, automobiles and bicycles. Overhead is a Wright aeroplane.

Given some extraordinary luck, this drawing of a scene near Dayton, Ohio, could actually have been duplicated by a photograph. The new age was treading hard on the heels of the old in 1912. Wagons and horse-drawn canal boats were still a common sight, but by now so were automobiles, airplanes, interurbans and modern trains. A picture of this same spot today would show that the electric interurban cars and canal boats have disappeared and that their functions have been taken over by busses and trucks

The sinking of the Titanic *was the greatest shipping disaster of the period, and a crushing blow to the age's faith in its new marvels. The largest ship of her day—882½ feet long with a gross tonnage of 46,328 tons—the* Titanic *was equipped with all the latest technical devices and was thought to be unsinkable. The tragedy occurred on her maiden voyage, only 500 miles out from Southampton. She sank in two hours, making it impossible for many ships to answer her distress signals. The steamship* Carpathia *rescued 706 people, but twice that many were lost*

HOW THE "TITANIC," THE "LAST WORD IN MARINE ARCHITECTURE," WAS

On the night of April 14th, the "Titanic," steaming at almost full speed through the darkness and
modern devices and mechanical precautions which had led her builders to believe she was unsinkable, went
descriptions furnished by survivors, and by scores of witnesses who testified before the United States

CRUSHED LIKE AN EGG SHELL BY THE SUBMERGED PORTION OF AN ICEBERG

through an ice field of which she had been warned by wireless, struck a berg and, despite the most to the bottom of "Sigsbee Deep," carrying 1,635 souls to death. The above drawing was made from Senate investigating committee at Washington.

Both the United States Senate and the British Admiralty conducted investigations of the disaster. Although the Titanic's *master had been warned of ice ahead, the ship apparently was proceeding at full speed, with an inadequate watch, when she struck the iceberg. No boats were lowered for half an hour, and at first few passengers could be induced to enter them. Later there proved to be not enough lifeboats. After the sinking of the* Titanic, *steamship lanes were located farther south*

Popular Mechanics *invited one thousand world-famous scientists to vote on a ballot nominating 56 scientific and mechanical achievements of the modern world. The 10 highest subjects and the votes given them were as follows:*

wireless telegraphy, 244
telephone, 185
airplane, 167
radium, 165
antiseptics, 140
spectrum analysis, 126
X-ray, 111
Panama Canal, 100
anesthesia, 94
synthetic chemistry, 81

THE SEVEN WONDERS OF THE MODERN WORLD

Result of the International Poll of Scientists

1. Wireless
2. Telephone
3. Aeroplane
4. Radium
5. Antiseptics and Antitoxins
6. Spectrum Analysis
7. X-Ray

THE Seven Wonders of the Modern World!

It were a far easier task for even the learned men who shared in the selection to name seven score than seven. On every hand, by night, by day, we walk and see and breathe amid a multitude of wonders, which are no wonders to us, but only commonplace, because a part of our everyday existence. Today an infant's feeble voice finds its unerring way along a tiny wire across rivers and over plains and mountains to the one home in millions it seeks. To us no wonder, and our young men and women cannot recall the time before the telephone was. They use without a thought, an instrument before which the Seven Wise Men would have prostrated themselves as a thing supernatural.

The Seven Ancient Wonders were selected by the Greeks, and their right to the title was established before Christ was born. During all the intervening years no attempt has been made to definitely revise the "Seven Wonders." Generation after generation has come and gone accepting the decision one from the other. In fact there was no opportunity for a revision. As the years increased civilization ebbed and about all the man-made marvels we have to show for those 2,000 years of human life are a few cathedrals and pictures.

Of the ancient wonders only one was a practical utility—Pharos, the 400-foot lighthouse of Alexandria; one was a hanging garden, not for the people, but built by a queen for her sensual pleasure; two were tombs; one was a temple of beauty devoted to a heathen god; another, the Colossus of Rhodes, was a freakish mass of cast metal, less than half the height of our own Statue of Liberty, and not comparable in dignity; and one was a beautiful statue to typify certain æsthetic ideals. Not a single one created for the uplifting or well-being of the masses.

As brute force, represented in vast armies, was the measure of power, so the Ancients honored the strong arm and the mighty, inert mass. It would seem that the pent-up forces of civilization, held in, thrust back, ruthlessly cut down for 20 centuries, had finally burst forth to fill the 19th century with wonders. And the greatest of these are neither connected oceans, mountains thrust through with tunnels, towering structures each housing the population of a city, floating palaces, land vehicles that outdistance the eagle, nor any of the things which typify the might of muscle. On the contrary each modern wonder is a monument to the might of mind.

As we move out into the 20th century we are pushed on by a tremendous

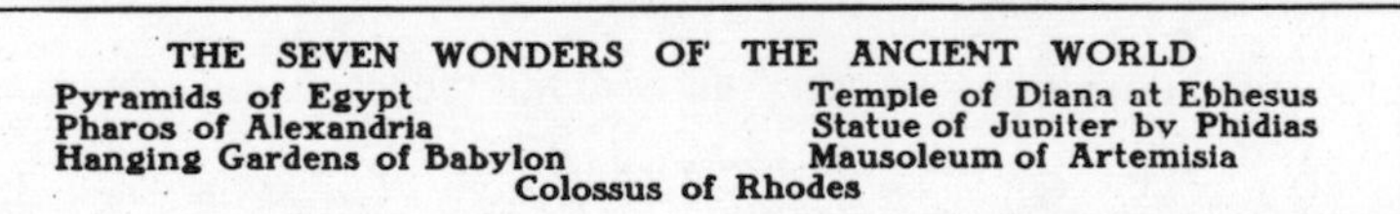
THE SEVEN WONDERS OF THE ANCIENT WORLD

Pyramids of Egypt
Pharos of Alexandria
Hanging Gardens of Babylon
Temple of Diana at Ebhesus
Statue of Jupiter by Phidias
Mausoleum of Artemisia
Colossus of Rhodes

momentum of scientific and mechanical and physiological knowledge of which the Ancients were utterly incapable to even dream.

Shall we contrast the Ancient Wonders and our Modern?

The Panama Canal: An engineering feat so stupendous as to find its equal only in Nature herself—is not thought worthy to be one of the Seven Modern Wonders. And yet Colonel Goethals with his men and machines could erect a mass in a few weeks which would put to insignificance the Great Pyramid, to build which required 100,000 men for 20 years. And when completed it was only a resting place for a few human bones which have long since been desecrated and scattered. The Panama Canal will for all time be of real service to all the peoples of the earth and to republics yet unborn, bringing food in time of famine from lands of plenty to those in want, and by reason of accessibility make alien nations neighbors. Yet this accomplishment with all its mighty possibilities is less a wonder than the story brought by a single ray of light from the smallest star as related by the Spectrum Analysis.

The Hanging Gardens of Babylon—the artificial mountain in a monotonous plain—built by slaves; devoted to the riotous revelry of a wicked court; its beauty known throughout the world: Yet this lofty, hand-made height sinks into smallness beside a single phial of antitoxin as it triumphs over the disease of some poor unfortunate outcast whose pain-racked body the ambulance rescues from the slums.

What is a cold marble statue, however beautiful and stately, to those quivering waves which Marconi snatched from out of space and wove into invisible chords that tether the ships of the seas to ten million firesides!

What even the beauties of the Temple of Diana to the beauties and yet unknown blessings of radium?

The wonder of our Modern Wonders is the thing itself—not the instrument. To the Ancients, a wonder had to be fashioned with the strong arm; its virtues were chiefly those of size and strength. The Modern Wonders find their inspiration in an improvement of human life—every human life—and their conception in minds, not in muscle.

The Seven Wonders! What will they be in the 40th century, when the scientists of those days look back and review the seven wonders which we select today? Unquestionably we can as little forecast or comprehend the Seven Wonders of the Then, as the Ancients, brought to life today, could comprehend the things we know. With all our vaunted conquests we reach out into twenty centuries yet to come with the same feeble comprehension that takes us back to those greatest of all Seven Wonders,—the wonders recorded in the first chapter of Genesis.

H. H. WINDSOR

Essential Parts of First Bell Telephone — 1876

Modern Telephone Instrument

Alexander Graham Bell's First Telephone

Scientists voting in a similar poll today would have to weigh new wonders against those advanced in 1912. Some of the more obvious nominations for such a list would include atomic energy, jet propulsion, television, psychiatry, sound films, radar and antibiotics

A forerunner of the many marriages to be conducted in the sky during the twenties. This ceremony was performed on the ground, for no plane of 1912 could carry a pilot, bride and groom, pastor and two witnesses

Among the many novel and interesting features of the recent Los Angeles aviation meet was a marriage ceremony performed in an aeroplane, and a subsequent honeymcon trip in the sky. The bridegroom was Neal Cochran, and Miss Leona Cowan was the bride. Cliff Turpin was the aerial chauffeur who took the couple on a little jaunt through the clouds immediately after the ceremony.

The one-armed lunch, once to be found in every sizable city of America, is now largely a thing of the past. Solitary patrons of cafeterias now must share cramped table space with complete strangers

This Lunching Chair Has a Special Place for the Coffee Cup or Glass of Milk and Little Wells for Salt and Pepper Cellars

NEW CHAIR FOR ARM-CHAIR LUNCHROOMS

An improvement in arm-chairs used in certain lunchrooms, where the customer serves himself and places his food on the wide arm-ledge provided on each chair, is shown in the accompanying illustration. The improved feature is the additional ledge extension on which to put the coffee or tea cup, or a glass of milk or water, and the little wells for salt and pepper cellars.

¶The New York Park Board has been asked to provide isles of safety for aeroplane landings in New York City as at the present time airmen flying over the city have no place to land. The board may, however, take the view of the Berlin and Paris authorities and secure the enactment of an ordinance forbidding over-city flights.

The fashions of the day, such as the hobble skirt, were sometimes at cross-purposes with the new devices. But the ingenuity of designers was usually equal to such situations

Women Entering New York's First "Hobble-Skirt" Car. The Floor of the Car is But Three Inches above the Pavement

NEW YORK'S "HOBBLE-SKIRT" CAR

A new type of street-railway car, designed by the general manager of the Interborough Surface Railroad in New York City, is shown in operation in the accompanying illustration. It differs from other street-railway cars, in that its floor is only 3 in. above the pavement, so that no steps are needed. There are no end entrances, the doors being located centrally on each side; and the ease with which women can enter and leave this car, no matter how tight skirts they may wear, has resulted in its becoming popularly known as a "hobble-skirt" car.

TO ELIMINATE THE POSTAGE STAMP

A little machine has been invented by a Los Angeles inventor which is intended to eliminate the postage stamp, with the bother of licking the little labels or messing with a damp sponge. It should be of considerable value to the business man who sends out a large mail, and in the case of mail-order firms should effect a saving in time and energy on the part of clerks.

Postage Stamping Machine Which will Not Cheat Government

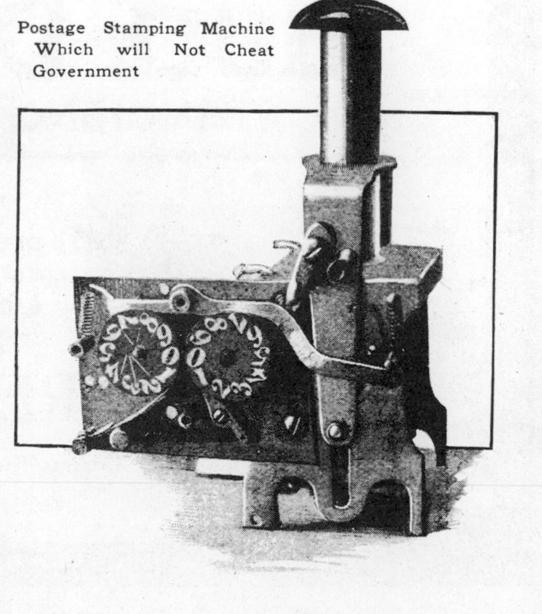

A great amount of attention was given to "eliminating" things. This machine did not eliminate the postage stamp, but one prophecy of the editors was correct: The postage meter of today is a tremendous time-saver for any company handling large mailings

Another lost art, almost as delicate as that of wielding a straight razor, was the rolling of a cigarette. In 1914 only "dudes" smoked tailor-mades; not until after World War I did the practice of "rolling your own" begin to die out generally. A few old-timers revived their skill during the cigarette shortages of World War II

Ingersoll
Dollar Watch

INGERSOLL
YANKEE

Once the Christmas of Kings—
Today the Christmas of Millions

Time was when a watch was the royal gift, crested with jewels and requiring a lifetime of careful labor to complete a single mechanism.

What of all her rich possessions did Queen Bess handle and consult so often as the watch which had been Lord Leicester's Christmas offering?

What today does the prince or princess of the American home make so constant a companion and so trusted a guide as a watch?

What of all things embodies so well the Christmas spirit, happily blending hourly use and beauty and sentiment and mystery?

The old masterpiece valued at so many thousands that all but royalty were excluded from possession, was not worth as much as a time-keeper as the Ingersoll Dollar Watch of today.

A watch is still the royal gift, yet the giving of a watch, because of its great cost, once so rare a privilege, is yours today for little more than the cost of a pocket handkerchief.

So millions of homes on Christmas morning will be happier because of a great American invention which has come to full perfection in the newest models of the Ingersoll Watch.

No boy or girl, no man or woman can fail to find some welcome use for one of the four Ingersoll models.

Americans to this day affectionately call them "dollar watches"—although the cut-rate price for a comparable watch now is around $2.95

Suddenly—it seemed—although the trouble had been brewing since 1871, the Western world was at war. The assassination of an Austrian archduke on June 28, 1914, touched off the conflict and drew in the great powers through alliances. As Germans drove through Belgium, France rushed its forces to protect its eastern frontiers

A hundred years had passed since the last great armed conflict—the Napoleonic Wars. In the opening weeks, the armies advanced in close order, much as they had in the days of Alexander. But very soon the use of the machine gun and other newly invented weapons drove both sides into the trenches

With plumed helmets and armor, these French cavalrymen were better outfitted for Napoleon's dragoons than for this modern battlefield. Cavalry charges survived only the first few weeks of World War I. Armor, however, was revived during World War II— to protect the crews of large bombing planes

GIVING "FIRST AID" ON THE BATTLE FIELD

This Photograph was Taken on the Edge of the Battle Field at St. Quentin, France, While the Fighting Was Still in Progress. Two French Dragoons are Removing the Steel Breastplate from One of Their Officers Who has been Wounded

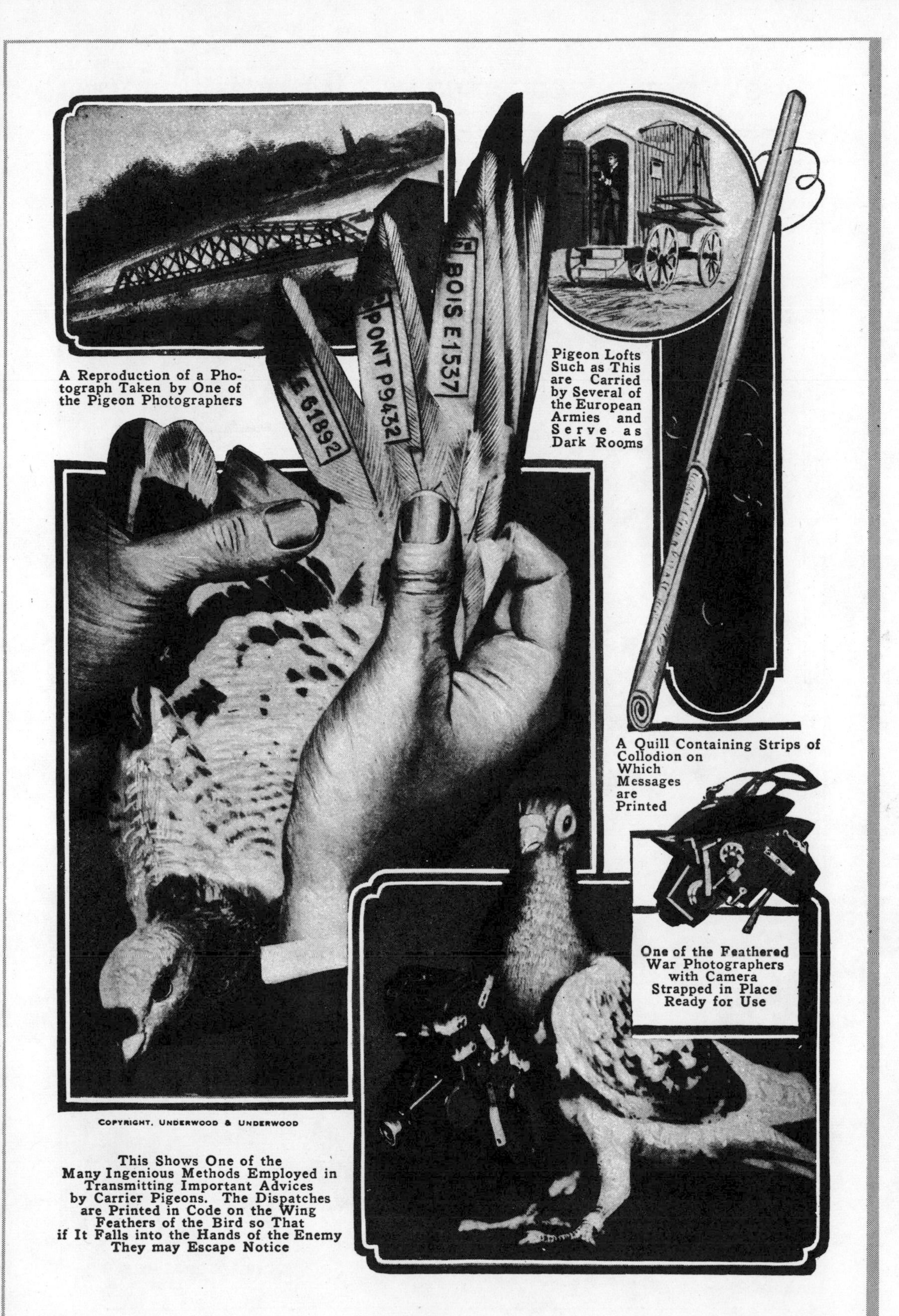

A Reproduction of a Photograph Taken by One of the Pigeon Photographers

Pigeon Lofts Such as This are Carried by Several of the European Armies and Serve as Dark Rooms

A Quill Containing Strips of Collodion on Which Messages are Printed

One of the Feathered War Photographers with Camera Strapped in Place Ready for Use

This Shows One of the Many Ingenious Methods Employed in Transmitting Important Advices by Carrier Pigeons. The Dispatches are Printed in Code on the Wing Feathers of the Bird so That if It Falls into the Hands of the Enemy They may Escape Notice

Pigeons carried vital messages from the front lines and also were used to obtain photographs behind enemy lines during World War I. A carrier pigeon is credited with saving the famous Lost Battalion from a trap in Argonne Forest. The bird, bearing a plea for reinforcements, got through despite a machine-gun bullet in its breast and a shrapnel wound in one leg

The impersonality of modern war was beginning. From this time on, emphasis was to be placed more and more on mass destruction by remote methods rather than on individual conflict between hostile soldiers

HOW MODERN SOLDIERS FIRE AT UNSEEN FOES

COPYRIGHT UNDERWOOD & UNDERWOOD

This Photograph of French Soldiers in Actual Battle Shows How Impersonal Modern Long-Distance Warfare has Become. All the Soldiers Know of the Men They are Shooting At Is the Range and General Direction

COSTLY WAR MACHINES DESTROYED IN BATTLE

Ruins of a German Military Motor Train Set on Fire by Shells in Belgium

What Was Left of a German Machine Gun after a Shell had Struck It in the Battle of Senlis

Wreck of a French Monoplane Riddled by Shells from a Krupp Aeroplane Gun at Namur

PHOTOS COPYRIGHT, INTERNATIONAL NEWS SERVICE

Each new weapon found its counterpart—long-range, high-explosive artillery shells, antitank and antiaircraft guns were developed to meet machine guns, armored cars and planes

From this time on, no civilian was to be wholly safe in wartime. The 10 bombs released on sleeping Antwerp during the siege of September 28 to October 9 opened a new era in warfare. History had known only one previous air attack on a city—in 1849 the Austrians attached bombs with slow fuses to hot-air balloons and let them drift over the city. Most of them exploded harmlessly

WAR IN THE AIR, HERALDED FOR YEARS,

"Heard the heavens filled with shouting, and there rained a ghastly dew

THE great war in the air, long heralded by poets and prophets, has become a reality.

The one strikingly new phase of warfare which makes the present European conflict different from all the wars of all time past is the use of air craft. From the very opening of hostilities the aerial forces of the nations involved have taken part in practically all the operations, scouting, attacking fortresses and even battling against each other. The first spectacular climax came when a German Zeppelin stole past the fortifications of Antwerp in the night and for the first time in history a sleeping city was bombarded from the skies. Here, at last, was the realization of the visions of the seers who had foretold this added horror of war.

Hidden by darkness and with en-

HAS AT LAST BECOME AN ACTUALITY

From the nations' airy navies, grappling in the central blue."
—Tennyson in "Locksley Hall."

gines muffled, the Zeppelin dirigible which made the attack upon Antwerp stole over the city to a point above the palace which the Belgian royal family temporarily occupied. It hovered there, a thousand feet from the ground, an indistinct mass silhouetted against the sky. With a rocketlike fizz a bomb curved downward in a fiery streak. Buildings crumbled, carrying their sleeping occupants down to death or mutilation. The bombardment continued, projectiles exploding within the grounds of the palace and raining upon other public buildings, even striking a hospital. Street after street was filled with debris. Sixty houses were practically destroyed and 900 more were damaged. Machine guns fired shots into the inky darkness without effect. In all, 10 bombs were hurled.

Despite the destruction reported here, the bombs used were very small compared to modern standards. In all, less than 50 tons of bombs were dropped during all of World War I—such a load was often dropped by a single wave of bombers during World War II. During the later days of the war the Germans had developed the Zeppelin to a remarkable degree. In November of 1917, for example, one started from Jamboli, Bulgaria, with 20 tons of medical supplies for the army in German East Africa. When it reached the headwaters of the Nile the commander learned, by radio, that his intended landing place had been captured by the British. He then turned around and flew back to Jamboli, where the airship landed safely, having covered 5500 nonstop miles in four days

As the war raged, America was fiercely neutral until May 7, 1915, when a German submarine sank the Lusitania. *Although she was a British ship, many Americans were aboard, and 115 of them died. The sinking of the* Lusitania *had twofold importance: it marked the turning of American war sympathies to the Allies and pointed up serious defects in transatlantic ships*

The "Lusitania," Built at Glasgow in 1907, Had a Length between Perpendiculars of 762.2 Feet and an Over-All Length of About 787 Feet; the Breadth Amidships Was 88 Feet, the Maximum Draft 37½ Feet, and the Depth from Bulwarks to Keel 60 Feet

World's Greatest Sea Tragedy

By JOHN A. McALEER

[The sinking of the Cunard liner "Lusitania" by a German submarine off Old Kinsale Head, Ireland, on May seventh is unparalleled as a sea tragedy in the history of the world. So many elements enter into the disaster that only time can sift its meaning and its bearing on the standards of civilized peoples. It is neither the place nor the purpose of Popular Mechanics Magazine to enter into this phase of the catastrophe. What the conditions were and how met, the accompanying pictures graphically portray, while the article, written by a nautical expert, conveys a clear idea of just what degree of safety the public may expect in the most modern products of the shipbuilding industry.—Editor.]

BEFORE the sinking of the "Lusitania" it was confidently believed that a ship capable of such speed as that of the ill-fated liner was practically immune from torpedo attack, and that a vessel so thoroughly equipped with water-tight bulkheads, even if hit, could not possibly sink so quickly as to endanger the lives of the passengers. The details of the disaster furnish a startling contrast to this feeling of security. The "Lusitania" was capable of making 25.85 knots, or slightly less than 30 miles an hour. When attacked, the liner was about ten miles off shore opposite Old Head of Kinsale on the south coast of Ireland. It was running at about 20 miles an hour, this reduction in speed having been made to enable the liner to arrive off Liverpool at high tide and thus avoid the necessity for waiting outside the bar at that port. Accounts differ as to whether the ship was hit by one or two torpedoes, but in any event she sank within a period of not more than 20 minutes. The attack came from the starboard side, and with one or more enormous holes torn in the hull below the water line the ship began to sink immediately, listing so quickly to starboard that it was impossible to launch lifeboats from the port side, although boats had been swung from the davits as a precaution against just such an emergency. Some boats were got off from the starboard side, but before they could be filled they were hanging far out from the side of the ship and were practically inaccessible from the decks. Of the 1,906 persons on board 1,134 lost their lives, 115 of these being Americans.

One may well ask how it was that this steamer, representing refinements in construction supposed to make her positively unsinkable, should succumb in 20 minutes, a query which may be further emphasized by the loss of that other palatial specimen of modern arts, the "Titanic." The traveling public have thus had thrust on them two terrible examples of supposedly unsinkable ships going down, in each case with a tremendous loss of life, and may be excused, with considerable margin, if prone to question the efficacy of some of the claims of steamship companies and naval constructors about ships being unsinkable.

If pressed, the naval architect would contend that his calculations did not take into consideration the variable human element, or, rather, assumed that this factor were a perfect one. That is, the architect cannot take into his computations whether or not the doors in the bulkheads are absolutely water-tight when they are called upon for duty, perhaps some years after their installation; nor can he tell whether or not some of the engine force may jam the doors purposely, so that, if suddenly closed from the bridge, they will not, in their descent, crush one of the crew passing, or else make his exit impossible. Any of these things are likely to happen, but the constructor in his figuring cannot take them into consideration. His decison that the boat is nonsinkable means that it will not sink if everything is carried out according to plans, kept in good order, and presupposes, finally, that a bulkhead is what it is intended to be—a water-tight division member—when called upon.

When we come to vessels engaged primarily in the passenger business, all consideration as to the relative importance of safety and profit disappears, and this has been the decision under which most of our large passenger ves-

The sinking brought to a head the difficulties the United States had turned up in attempting to pursue a policy of "freedom of the seas" despite the European war. From the first this freedom was one-sided, for England had driven German ships from the Atlantic in a few weeks. In effect, carrying out a policy of "freedom of the seas" then meant that the United States was carrying on the bulk of its trade with the Allies

Munitions, of course, were not supposed to be shipped. The United States had protested the stopping and searching of American ships by British war vessels. Meanwhile, the German fleet was bottled up, and that nation turned to submarine warfare. At first the U-boats sank only warships, but early in 1914 they began to sink merchant vessels as well. Germany served warning that she would sink any vessel which entered the "war zone," by which she meant the waters around the British Isles, the Mediterranean and Western Europe

Drawing from Illustrated London News, Copyrighted in the United States and Canada

WITH a great section of the hull below the water line splintered by the explosion of the torpedo fired from a German submarine. the "Lusitania" first listed sharply to starboard and then plunged bow first under the sea. An hour or more before the attack was made the officers sighted a submarine, but had left it astern by putting on speed and pursuing a zigzag course. It was apparent later that the liner had run into a submarine ambush. The torpedo that sank the ship and brought about the death of 1,134 persons, many of whom were women and children, was fired without warning. From all accounts, not so much as the periscope of the submarine was seen, the first intimation of danger being the white trail left by the torpedo as it sped straight toward the ship on its errand of destruction. After the torpedo struck, less than 20 minutes were left for escape from the sinking

liner. As the "Lusitania" entered the danger zone where German submarines were thought to be lying in wait, the lifeboats were swung from the davits and made ready for a possible emergency, although there was thought to be little danger that the ship would be attacked or that it would sink in so short a time even if hit. Owing to the sharp list that the ship took within a few minutes after being struck, few of the lifeboats could be launched, and of those that succeeded in getting off, several were wrecked by being dashed against the side of the ship. It is reported that there was little suction as the ship sank. This is explained by the comparative shallowness of the water, the depth being between 300 and 400 feet, and the probability that, with a length of over 700 feet, the bow of the liner found bottom before the stern began to sink.

There is no question but that the Lusitania *was sunk without warning. The Germans took the position that a surfaced submarine was helpless —therefore could not run the risk of rising and conducting a search of merchant vessels. As for the* Lusitania, *the German government justified the sinking on the grounds that she was carrying munitions, arms and other war materials for the Allies*

Diplomatic notes were exchanged over the incident for more than a year. Germany announced that she would sink no more liners without warning, and promised not to molest American ships without cargoes of war contraband. Despite these promises, systematic sinkings continued. In two months during 1917, eight American ships were sunk, with 40 lives lost. The United States broke off diplomatic relations with Germany and began arming merchant ships

sels have been designed. In the case of the "Titanic," it is now well agreed that if the bulkheads had been carried up farther, the adjacent compartments would not have been flooded through overflow. At the time of this accident,

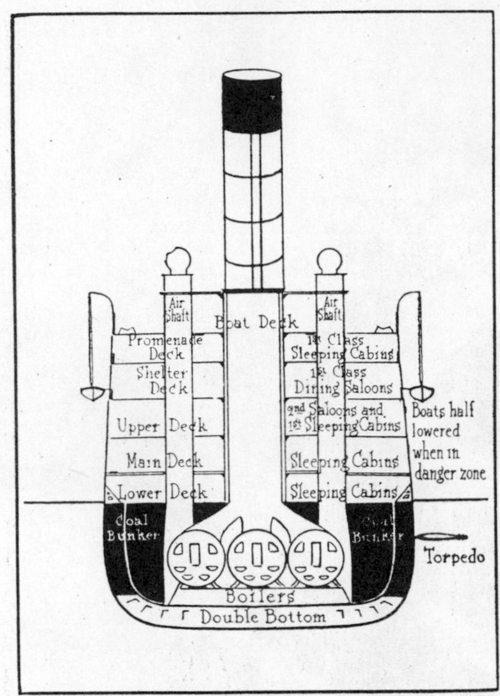

COPYRIGHT, THE SPHERE, LONDON

Transverse Section of the "Lusitania" Showing Where the Fatal Blow was Struck: The Torpedo is Shown at a Depth of About 15 Feet below Surface of Water

it was freely stated that under the same circumstances the "Lusitania" or the "Mauretania" would not have sunk.

The "Lusitania" had 12 transverse bulkheads, some of which were "stepped," that is, not continuous in one plane. The bulkheads in the middle of the ship did not extend above the main deck, but the five forward and five after ones extended one deck higher, that is, to the upper deck. This was to prevent the overflowing which is supposed to have caused the foundering of the "Titanic."

To explain this, let us suppose that a boiler room near the center of the vessel were flooded. The vessel would then sink bodily and probably draw about the same amount of water forward as aft, because the flooded compartment is in the middle of the ship. In other words, she would not trim by the head or stern. But if the boiler room nearest the bow were flooded, the ship would not sink equally at both ends, but would be deeper at the bow, because the flooded section is nearer that end. The water would then rise in the bilged compartment till it was level with the outside sea. Now, unless the bulkheads extended above the water line at which the vessel finally floats as a result of the compartment being flooded, there would be nothing to confine the water and it would overflow into the adjacent compartment and eventually cause the ship to founder.

The longitudinal bunker bulkheads of the "Lusitania" were of great structural assistance and further augmented the water-tight divisions. Their continuity as fore-and-aft structures was maintained by connecting them to the engine-room bulkheads. Between these longitudinal bulkheads and the skin of the vessel were located the coal bunkers, and a small transverse division member, midway between the large transverses, further divided the coal bunkers into halves. The integrity of these longitudinals as to water-tightness was menaced to some extent by the coal passages, but all these openings were well equipped with water-tight doors.

The different fire rooms had access to each other by means of openings out through the bulkheads, but all of these were likewise provided with water-tight doors. All such doors were fitted with the Stone-Lloyd system of hydraulic closing, so that all could be closed from the bridge in a very short time.

Mention has been made of the human equation in handling water-tight doors; that the coal passers and the engine-room crew very naturally object to being locked in, in a time of danger; and that there is a tendency on the part of them to block the doors. In the Stone-Lloyd system these objections are accepted as real, and met. Under

COPYRIGHT, THE SPHERE, LONDON
With the "Lusitania" Listed at a Dangerous Angle and About to Make Its Final Plunge, It Required a Desperate Struggle to Get Any of the Boats Away in Time to Prevent Their being Drawn Down with the Ship or Wrecked against the Side. A Number of the Boats were Upset and the Occupants Drowned

Germany, hoping the United States would continue neutral, nevertheless was depending upon a shipping blockade to starve England out of the war. The U-boat warfare did account for the sinking of 6000 vessels and 13 million tons of cargo. But the United States built faster than the subs could sink, and finished the war with four million tons more ships than at the start. The British managed to replace about half the ships they lost. Despite steel nets, depth bombs and sub chasers, only 203 German submarines were destroyed during the war

it the doors can be opened or closed separately by the operation of a handle placed near the door, or all the doors can be closed in an emergency from the bridge. A loud bell always precedes the closing from the bridge, and if, in spite of this warning, anybody happens to be locked in a compartment, there is the handle near the door for him to operate and open it. After he has escaped, the door closes again.

With all these division members, both bulkheads and decks, it was estimated that the "Lusitania" had 175 water-tight compartments.

Generally when a vessel has a hole punched in her side either from collision or what not, she takes a list toward the injured side. As the water pours in and she sinks deeper, this list increases, and just before the ship founders she may capsize. In fact, in many

The Lusitania *was the last claim of engineers for an "unsinkable" ship. As with the* Titanic, *they had failed to consider all the possible factors and to reckon with human neglect or interference with automatic equipment. It was thought that the* Lusitania, *a triumph of shipbuilding, would be immune even to a torpedo. The* Lusitania *and a sister ship, the* Mauretania, *were the first large liners to use the modern marine turbine engine*

cases when it has been stated of a vessel that "she went down in five minutes after she was struck," if the vessel had had sufficient stability, she probably would have remained afloat much longer. In a great many cases, the immediate cause of the foundering has not been so much that the vessel could not remain afloat with the compartment flooded, as that the bilging of it produced unstable equilibrium. With longitudinal center-line bulkheads, even the flooding of a small compartment may produce a dangerous list, but this will not be objectionable if the vessel has plenty of freeboard, except to make it difficult to launch the boats on the high side. For this reason, middle-line water-tight bulkheads are not adopted in passenger vessels where safety is considered paramount. The longitudinals in the case of the "Lusitania" were kept well into the wings of the vessel so that they gave her practically a double hull for the greater part of the length.

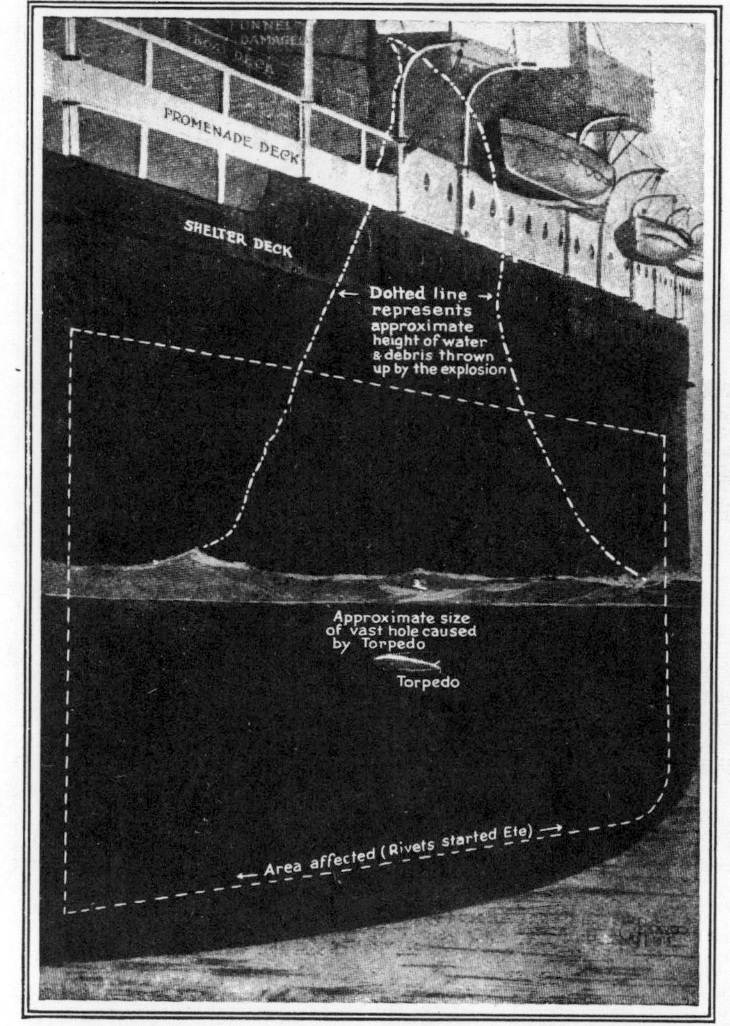

The Explosion of the Torpedo Not Only Tore a Hole in the Hull Well below the Water Line, but Evidently Wrenched Adjacent Parts of the Steel Structure So Severely That the Water-Tight Bulkheads Were Useless

Let us assume that one of the boiler rooms of a vessel such as the "Lusitania" is flooded, due to an injury in the starboard side, for example, that penetrated both the outer shell and the inner bunker bulkhead. The vessel would then take a list to starboard. Let it further be assumed that two compartments are in this condition from an injury inflicted around one of the divisional bulkheads. This will naturally cause a further list to starboard. How far she will list or whether she will remain in stable equilibrium, it is impossible to say without more exact data.

There can be no doubt but that everybody on board the "Lusitania" knew that an attempt would probably be made to destroy her. For that reason it is natural to suppose that they would take all ordinary precautions at least. They would certainly see to it that all water-tight doors were in good working

Thus, largely because of the stands taken on both sides with regard to the Lusitania *sinking, war became inevitable for the United States. More than any other incident that followed, the sinking of this vessel had served to crystallize the sentiment of the American public*

How the Victims of the "Lusitania" Disaster were Taken through the Streets of Queenstown to the Burial Place: The Coffins of All British Subjects were Covered by the Union Flag of the British Empire

order, and Captain Turner has stated that as soon as he picked up the Irish coast, he had the boats got out and all the water-tight doors closed. Therefore, there is every reason to believe that at the time of the torpedoing the conditions on the ship were very near to what the naval constructor would wish them to be to justify his calculations. In other words, a bulkhead was probably a bulkhead.

Still the brusque fact remains that the "Lusitania" went down in 20 minutes, taking with her many persons who perhaps from confidence in her unsinkability—a thing which her very size would inspire—had not even deigned to put on life preservers. She sank, too, despite all this preparation, despite all her details of construction.

Photograph Taken by the Wireless Operator, Showing the Lifeboats Swung from the Davits as the "Lusitania" Entered the Danger Zone. Markings around Edges were Caused by Sea Water After Operator had Jumped from the Stricken Ship

As the Lusitania *investigation went on, another shipping disaster occurred at home. For 11 years the steamship* Eastland *had been one of the most popular excursion boats in Great Lakes service. But to the men who worked her decks and engine room she was a problem—long and narrow like a giant canoe, and just as top-heavy. She listed badly even in smooth water, and an engineer was kept constantly at work on her pumps to hold the vessel on even keel. On July 24, 1915, as 2500 picnickers crowded her decks, the* Eastland *turned turtle at her berth in the Chicago River. At least 1000 were lost in the greatest tragedy in the history of the Great Lakes*

This Shows the General Scene of the Tragedy, One of the Greatest Marine Disasters in History, Which Occurred in the Very Heart of Chicago. Unlimited Life-Saving Facilities Were at Hand in Less than Five Minutes, but for the Most Part They Were Useless. The Victims were Entombed within the Steel-Hulled Death Trap

Both the Buyer and the Seller of a Used Motor Car are Benefited by the Open-Air Mart

USED MOTOR CARS ARE SOLD IN PUBLIC MARKET

In one of the western cities a distinctly new institution, an open-air public market for used motor cars, has made its appearance. The purpose back of the plan is to eliminate the commissions paid to selling agents under the customary method of making such transactions. In this case the owner pays $2.50 a week for the privilege of parking his machine in the mart. It is then continually on display and will be demonstrated to prospective purchasers by attendants without additional cost to the owner. Motorcycles are handled in the same way, although at a lower rate. The purchaser of a car is able to deal with the proprietor of the market, if he desires, or may negotiate directly with the owner. In this way both the owner and the purchaser of a car are benefited.

WALKING MACHINE DESIGNED FOR INDOOR EXERCISE

To make it possible to take long walks even on unpleasant days when the weather does not permit her leaving the hotel, a treadmill walking machine has been constructed for a prima donna who carries out a daily program of exercises in an attempt to ward off obesity. The machine is placed in one of the rooms of her suite where she uses it when an outdoor walk would not be agreeable. Attached to it is a meter which indicates the mileage traveled and enables her to keep account of the distance walked at different times during the day.

This Machine Makes It Possible for a Prominent Opera Singer to Take Long Walks in Her Own Apartment When the Weather Prohibits Outdoor Exercise

While America drifted toward the war, the general public, for the most part firmly convinced we could keep out of it, continued life as usual, noting such innovations as used-car lots and exercise machines. This early lot followed the pattern of the old-time horse auctions—that is, sellers sold directly to the buyers

Spy scares were rampant during World War I. While real incidents of spying and sabotage were few, there were many false alarms—and many wild reports turned in about innocent neighbors

ACCIDENT IN CAR CAUSES PANIC AND PLOT RUMORS

With the nerves of almost everybody more or less on edge because of persistent though generally unfounded rumors concerning anarchists and pro-German fanatics, it was inevitable that panic should follow an accident that occurred recently on a train bound for one of the country's large training stations. Because of some carelessness in packing or handling, a bag carried by one of the passengers burst open and from it several objects, having every appearance of being bombs, rolled down onto the floor. In an instant the car was in an uproar and people were scrambling for safety. As a matter of fact, the objects were bombs, but they did not belong to an evil plotter as was rumored in towns along the line. Instead, they were being rushed to a training camp in response to an order.

Panic Followed the Bursting of a Bomb-Filled Package Carried by a Passenger on a Railway Train and Rumors of Anarchistic Plots were Spread

TRUCK MAKES ANY AUTO A FARM TRACTOR

A new steel truck which permits the use of any automobile for tractor purposes is of special interest because it requires no alteration in the car and leaves the latter available for ordinary driving at any time. The truck has four broad-tired wheels and supports two grooved tracks on which the automobile is driven with the aid of two grooved skids. The only extra parts needed for the car are small sprockets fastened to the flanges of the rear hubs and two castings attached to the rear axle. These need not be removed for ordinary driving. Chains connecting the sprockets with the truck gearing are quickly put in place, after which the car is raised up and rigidly held in position by two jacks provided beneath the rear axle. The truck's steering gear is mounted at one side, the steering wheel being fastened to an arm in front of the driver.

Steel Truck on Which Any Automobile can be Quickly Mounted and Used as a Farm Tractor: The Machine's Speed Is from Three to Five Miles per Hour

SHIP'S COLOR A FACTOR IN ITS SAFETY AT SEA

The submarine campaign has brought to the attention of ship owners with renewed force the importance of painting vessels in a manner which will secure a minimum of visibility. Many a captain has learned to his sorrow that his craft has been a conspicuous mark on the high seas because the lower part of the hull and the funnels were painted black, while between these two extremes was a sharply contrasting strip of white or gray

MOVIES DEPICT WHALING SCENES DRAMATICALLY

One of the most dramatic sets of educational films that have been produced showing various industries of this country is that illustrating the life of American whalers which was exhibited not long ago in Boston. These views take the spectators aboard a vessel, captained by a veteran whaler, which goes out into the stormy Atlantic in search of its prey. At times the big waves roll over the decks of the ship, setting everything awash, and the onlooker feels that the very room in which he is sitting is rocking to and fro. At length a spouting whale is sighted in the distance. A little later the audience witnesses the fight with the whale and his capture. The body is dragged to the vessel and cut into pieces, while during part of the performance a school of sharks, attracted by the prospect of much good food, swim near by

BIG MODEL OF OLD WHALER IS BUILT FOR MUSEUM

At New Bedford, Mass., once the seat of the industry, a museum devoted exclusively to whaling relics has lately been established. Among other things it contains a half-size replica of the "Lagoda," an old whaler accredited with 12 voyages during a 44-year period of service in which it netted the owners about $650,000. The model, which is fully rigged and equipped, was constructed at a cost of $25,000 and occupies most of the floor space in the new museum, a building designed after the old Salem customhouse where Hawthorne was once employed. The lofty spars of the "Lagoda" extend to within a few feet of the high, arched ceiling, stalwartly commemorating the once romantic and flourishing industry of the east coast. The building is 118 ft. in length and 57 ft. wide, while the model ship measures 89 ft. from flying jib to spanker boom.

Left: Fully Rigged and Equipped, This Interesting Big Model of a Once Famous Whaling Vessel is Sheltered in a Museum at New Bedford, Massachusetts. Right: Deck View of the Ship That Commemorates a Once Flourishing and Romantic Industry of New England

In the 19th century whaling was a big industry, employing, during the 1850's, as many as 680 ocean-going ships. Its decline started just before the Civil War and by 1917 it had just about come to an end because of the passing of the whalebone corset and the replacement of whale oil with petroleum products. The young free-lance writer, who received $7.50 from Popular Mechanics *for the piece about the New Bedford whaling museum, was M. Lincoln Schuster, who later became one of the publishers of this book*

Congress declared war on Germany on April 6, 1917. The arrival of American troops overseas was a tremendous boost to the Allies. London gave them a royal welcome, and King George reviewed them from historic Whitehall. The first nickname for the American soldier was "Sammie." This failed to stick but another one—"Yank"—did

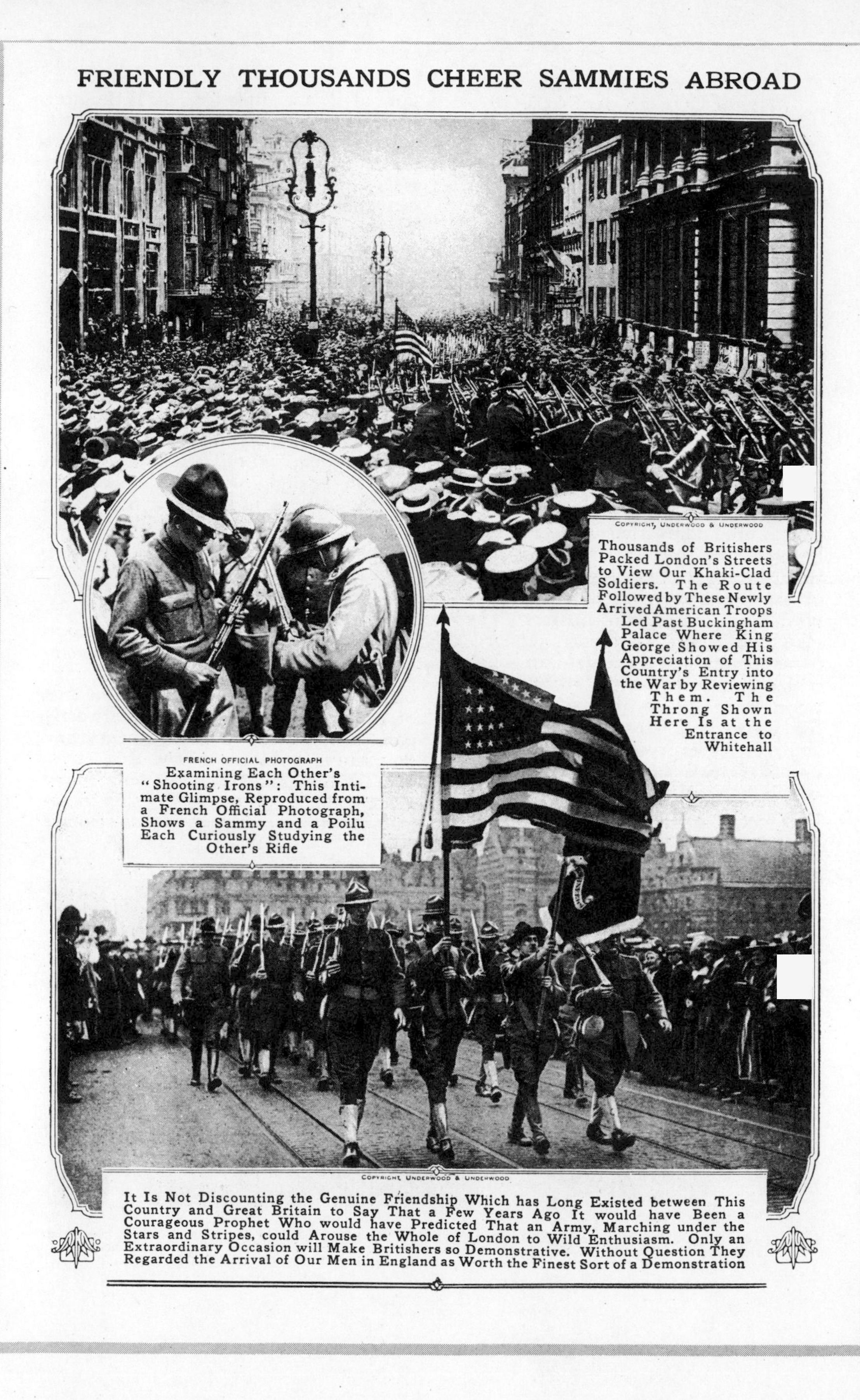

FRIENDLY THOUSANDS CHEER SAMMIES ABROAD

COPYRIGHT, UNDERWOOD & UNDERWOOD

Thousands of Britishers Packed London's Streets to View Our Khaki-Clad Soldiers. The Route Followed by These Newly Arrived American Troops Led Past Buckingham Palace Where King George Showed His Appreciation of This Country's Entry into the War by Reviewing Them. The Throng Shown Here Is at the Entrance to Whitehall

FRENCH OFFICIAL PHOTOGRAPH

Examining Each Other's "Shooting Irons": This Intimate Glimpse, Reproduced from a French Official Photograph, Shows a Sammy and a Poilu Each Curiously Studying the Other's Rifle

COPYRIGHT, UNDERWOOD & UNDERWOOD

It Is Not Discounting the Genuine Friendship Which has Long Existed between This Country and Great Britain to Say That a Few Years Ago It would have Been a Courageous Prophet Who would have Predicted That an Army, Marching under the Stars and Stripes, could Arouse the Whole of London to Wild Enthusiasm. Only an Extraordinary Occasion will Make Britishers so Demonstrative. Without Question They Regarded the Arrival of Our Men in England as Worth the Finest Sort of a Demonstration

SWIFT GERMAN PLANES SWARM OVER LONDON

One of the Small Victims of Germany's Midsummer Aerial Attack upon London: It was Officially Reported That 40 Persons were Killed and 194 Injured. Of the Latter Number, 52 Were Children. Such Pictures Form an Index of Prussianism and Give Warning of the Dangers of Premature Peace

The Flying Huns Approach London in Orderly Formation at a Height of 7,000 Feet. This Is One of the Most Remarkable Aerial Photographs Ever Made. It Shows More Than 30 Bombing and Battle Planes, Most of Them Dual-Motored Gothas, on a Diabolical Mission

Women Ambulance Drivers Racing to Their Posts in Response to a General Alarm Sounded amid the Thundering of Prussian Bombs: The Aeroplanes Appeared over the Metropolitan Area Shortly after 10 O'Clock on Saturday Morning, July 7. About 100 Bombs, Each Weighing 60 Pounds, were Dropped. Distress Calls were Answered by Nervy Women, Such as These, and Red Cross Nurses. Two Outstanding Effects of the Raid were Loud Demands for Reprisals and More Adequate Aerial Defenses. Since, Additional Assaults have been Made

With her Zeppelin fleet destroyed, Germany sent bombers over London in tight formations, with fighter-plane escorts. Civilians were organized for air-raid defense. London was bombed for three years from 1915 to 1918. Some 900 bombs were dropped, killing more than 500 people and injuring a thousand. More than 700 buildings were destroyed or damaged, and total property damage was about $10,000,000

The British developed the tank in secret, and sprang the surprise on the Germans with devastating effect in the Battle of Somme. The tank made possible the "blitzkrieg" tactics used by both sides during World War II

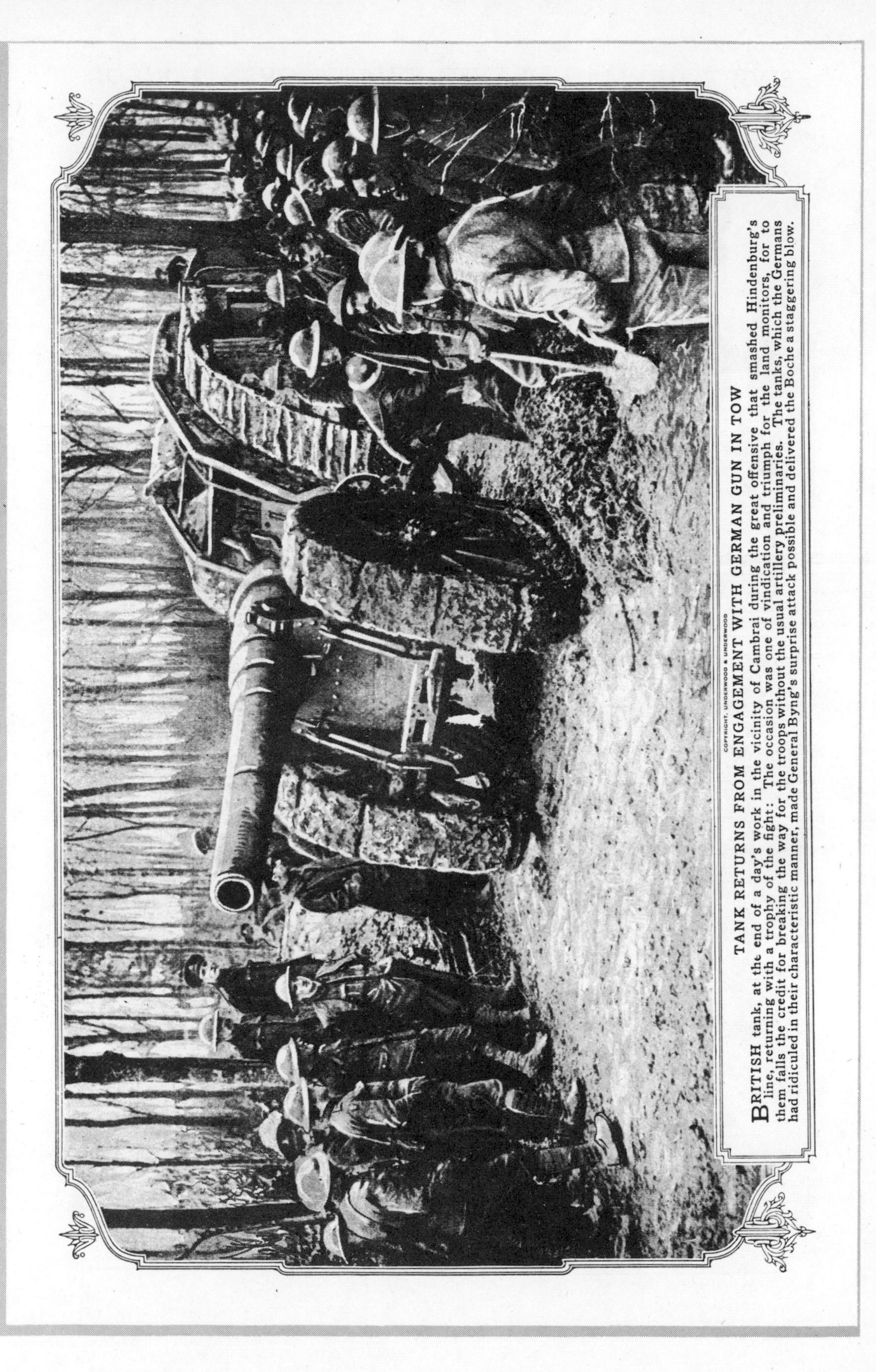

TANK RETURNS FROM ENGAGEMENT WITH GERMAN GUN IN TOW

BRITISH tank, at the end of a day's work in the vicinity of Cambrai during the great offensive that smashed Hindenburg's line, returning with a trophy of the fight: The occasion was one of vindication and triumph for the land monitors, for to them falls the credit for breaking the way for the troops without the usual artillery preliminaries. The tanks, which the Germans had ridiculed in their characteristic manner, made General Byng's surprise attack possible and delivered the Boche a staggering blow.

LONG-DISTANCE GUNS SHELL PARIS

LONG-RANGE guns are bombarding Paris as this is written. Shells hurled from the forest of St. Gobain, 76 miles distant, are bursting in the streets and environs of the French capital. The inconceivable has been accomplished. The Germans have made good their two-year-old boast of a gun capable of laying waste English towns from Calais.

Some fifty-one 9.5-in. shells reached Paris March 23 and 24, the first two days of the bombardment. Almost as many theories of how they might have been hurled there from behind the German lines were offered on the twenty-fifth.

Obviously, for lack of tangible information, discussion of the master weapon at this time resolves itself into rank conjecture. All that is appropriate, therefore, is a digest of the most plausible suggestions advanced on the strength of hastily cabled advices without details.

Thus far (the third day of the siege) two or more guns have been used. This is indicated by the 20-minute intervals between shots and also the plural number used in the official German statement, which reads: "We have bombarded the fortress of Paris with long-distance guns."

As to the character of the gun, we have the analyses of two ordnance authorities who contend that a 76-mile piece would have to hurl a projectile at a muzzle velocity of from 5,000 to 7,000 ft. a second. Here the men part company, one of them contending that such speed would demand a pressure that no gun could withstand. The other, however, continues by estimating that the piece has a barrel about 119 ft. in length and arguing that it necessarily must have been built at the spot from which it is fired. Such a weapon would require a foundation like that of a skyscraper. Its barrel would need heavy, permanent supports.

Another authority advances the theory that subcaliber shells are being used. By this is meant that projectiles of 9.5-in. diameter are held by rings to a false shell of double size, thus permitting the use of a 19 or 20-in. gun. Upon being discharged from the muzzle, the rings release, freeing the real projectile. The advantage of this is increased propulsive force. The base of an 18-in. shell has four times the area of a 9-in. one, and therefore a proportionately greater force is exerted against it as it passes through the barrel. The subcaliber plan reaps the benefit of this by temporarily giving a shell an oversized base against which the expanding gases exert themselves.

A French scientist propounded the theory of tungsten shells. Projectiles made of this element would have the same weight as steel ones of twice as great caliber.

If a shell fired by the new German gun ascends at a 45° angle and follows a normal trajectory, it reaches an altitude of 21 miles or more. Thus a large part of its travel would be through a highly rarefied atmosphere that would offer little resistance. In its whole course it perhaps would not be retarded much more than would a similar missile traveling only half as far at a much lower elevation.

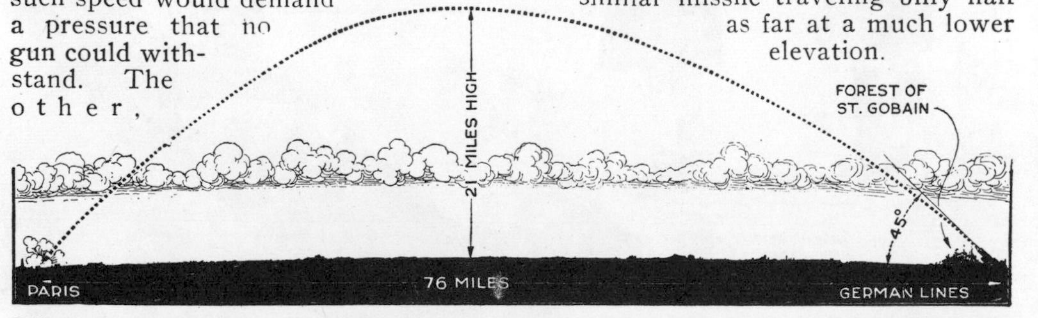

Following a Normal Trajectory, as Shown Above, the Shells Hurled into Paris from the Forest of St. Gobain must have Reached an Altitude of 21 or More Miles and Traveled Much of the Distance through Highly Rarefied Atmosphere. This, Perhaps, Partly Accounts for Their Range

"Big Bertha," as this gun came to be known, momentarily struck terror into the hearts of the Allies but did not prove to be a decisive weapon. The firing began on March 23, 1918, and continued for 180 days. In all, 256 people were killed, the worst day being March 29—Good Friday—when a shell struck the church of St. Gervais and killed or wounded 156 people. In this article, based on the only known facts—that a shell had hit Paris from at least 76 miles away—the editors were amazingly accurate. The actual gun was 110 feet long, weighed 142 tons, had a bore of 8.26 inches and fired a 264-pound shell. The only serious discrepancy with later-learned facts was the height of trajectory of the shell, which proved to be 15 miles instead of 21

Before the end of the war, the U.S. had two million men in France and another million and a half in training at home. During World War II, the U.S. armed forces totaled more than 11 million men

MARCHING YANKEES, OODLES OF THEM, OVERSEAS

COPYRIGHT, INTERNATIONAL FILM SERVICE, INC.

Surviving Heroes of the "Tuscania" Marching between Throngs in the Streets of Southampton. At Every Hand Our Boys were Received with Whole-Hearted Hospitality

COPYRIGHT COM. ON PUB. INF.

Sam's Sons of the 166th Infantry Passing through a French Town on the Way from the Coast to Their Training Camp

COPYRIGHT COM. ON PUB. INF.

American Soldiers Driving Poison Fumes from a Trench with the Aid of Gas Flappers

COPYRIGHT COM. ON PUB. INF.

Life Preservers? Yes, but Made of Bread and Purchased by Sammy at the Outset of a Long Hike

World War I was a chemist's war. Almost a third of American casualties were caused by poison gas. Chlorine gas was first used by the Germans at Ypres, in April 1915, and before the war ended hundreds of chemicals were tried out

OUR FIRST YEAR IN THE WAR

By GEORGE CREEL

Chairman of the Committee on Public Information

World War I gave the world, and Americans, their first real idea of the incredible power of U.S. production. Here George Creel, chairman of the Committee on Public Information, reports on the first year of war. From machine guns to medicine, the production story was dazzling. Manufacturers were understandably doubtful of their ability to mass-produce the French 75, accurate to 2/1000th inch, but this tolerance later became standard machine-shop practice

DURING this first year of war, the army of the United States has been increased from 9,524 officers and 202,510 men to 123,800 officers and 1,528,924 men, and the navy from 83,000 to 350,000 men and officers, so that our armed forces have grown, in twelve months, from less than 300,000 to more than 2,000,000 officers and men.

The work of training, arming and outfitting this force has been colossal. Sixteen huge cantonments were provided for assembling the national army of drafted citizens. On May 7, the order was given to select sites. On June 15, the building began. Ninety days later the first contingents of citizen soldiers were being received in veritable cities that had been erected for them, with hospitals, amusement halls, steam-heated barracks, water supply. sewerage systems, and all the civilized conveniences of community life. Sixteen other camps received the National Guard called into Federal service. Sixteen training camps for officers were prepared for the 70,000 entrants who have passed through them. And the navy built 250 new training stations for its volunteers.

An idea of the amount of work involved in this undertaking can be gained from the fact that the Army Medical Corps, in charge of the health of the men, has been enlarged from 800 officers and an enlisted personnel of 5,000, to a force of 15,000 officers and 100,000 enlisted men. And as an indication of the efficiency with which their work has been handled, consider this: There has not been a death in the camps from typhoid or malaria, the two diseases which, in our Spanish-American war, killed more of our men than were slain in battle.

To outfit the men, the quartermaster's office has had 300 woolen mills working on its contracts. It has ordered 20,000,000 blankets, 6,000,000 overcoats, 20,000,000 pairs of shoes, and so forth, endlessly. Every day 2,500 car loads of food and fuel were delivered to the camps. And there have been no contract scandals, no graft, no shoddy work.

The soldiers have been armed by an Ordnance Bureau that consisted of 97 officers a year ago, and now numbers 5,000 officers and 26,000 men. Since the war began it has provided a million and a half rifles. It has brought the production of rifles to an output of 45,000 a week, which is sufficient to supply three army divisions. It has delivered more than 17,000 machine guns and brought the rate of production from 20,000 guns a year to 225,000 a year. It has purchased a billion rounds of ammunition for the cantonments alone. It has brought to quantity production a light Browning machine gun which weighs little more than an ordinary rifle and outclasses any gun of its kind on the European battlefields. And the heavier Colt-Browning machine, now being manufactured, has made the incredible record of firing "20,000 shots in 48 minutes and 16 seconds without malfunction."

The British and French governments, on their own initiative, undertook to supply our forces in France with heavy ordnance so as to save American ship tonnage for food and munitions. Our Ordnance Bureau has, however, proceeded with contracts for the production of heavy guns here. There has never been any machinery built in this country to work so accurately on so large a scale as is necessary for the production of the recoil mechanism of the famous French 75's. These mechanisms must not be "off" two-thousandths of an inch in a length of more than six feet. The Ordnance Bureau had to persuade manufacturers to undertake this difficult work, and to assist them financially in the building of a 13-acre plant and in the purchase and manufacture of $6,000,000 worth of special tools. That is the explanation of a delay which

Only a tenth of U.S. foreign trade was carried in American ships when the war began. England's 50 million tons was a third of world shipping, but German subs played havoc, sank a million tons in one month in 1917. Faced with the subs again in World War II, the U.S. mass-produced "victory ships" by making the parts separately and welding them together. More than 1800 were built in 1944 alone, and the U.S. emerged with three-fifths of the world's merchant marine

has been attributed by newspaper critics to the desire of the Ordnance Bureau to "improve on" the perfect recoil mechanism of the French 75's. The plant is now completed and it is turning out the recoil mechanisms. A $25,000,000 ordnance base in France is under way. The bureau has had at its disposal an appropriation of $4,756,500,000 which is three times the ordinary annual expenditure of the whole government in peace time.

The growth of the navy has been only less phenomenal than the growth of the army. It has more than quadrupled its personnel and more than tripled the size of its fleet. It has taken over the patrol of the western Atlantic and assisted the allies in patrolling European waters. Since the outbreak of the war, it has been engaged continuously in transporting troops, convoying merchant men, and fighting submarines; and it has lost only two naval vessels to the submarines, the destroyer "Jacob Jones," and the patrol vessel "Alcede." In refutation of the campaign of ridicule directed against Secretary Daniels before the war, he has made a record that has been hailed as "the greatest single achievement" of the United States since the war broke out.

The work of supplying and outfitting our "first line of defense" has been done superbly. Ships have been built, men have been trained, guns have been furnished quietly and efficiently. We have been able to help arm the allied fleets. The navy has built its own factories to supply its needs as cheaply as possible, making even the cloth of its uniforms. Much of its work has necessarily been done in secret, but its performance in European waters speaks more eloquently of the concealed details than does even the enthusiastic report of the naval investigating committee of congress, which found nothing to blame and everything to praise.

The navy's huge program of shipbuilding has made it difficult for the Shipping Board to realize its expected output of tonnage to replace merchant vessels sunk by submarines. At the same time, our foreign commerce has increased from $2,000,000,000 to $9,000,000,000 a year, and our seaboard has been piled with goods waiting transportation abroad. These goods, having filled the terminals, have also congested the railroads for miles back from the coast, and complicated the problems not only of the director-general of railroads but also of the fuel administrator and the food administrator. The congestion of traffic sidetracked so many cars filled with coal that "workless Mondays" had to be decreed, during the winter, in order to free coal for the ships so that the ships might free the railroads. As a result of that order, within twelve days, 450 ships were cleared from our ports with 2,000,000 tons of food, fuel and munitions, the traffic congestion was relieved, and the stoppage in the coal supply was removed. Now, the shortage of ships has backed up our meat supply in the storage warehouses and on the farms, so that the food administration has had to abandon its program of "meatless" days. It is hastening cargoes of meat to Europe and stimulating the purchase of the higher grades of beef by the government, so as to empty the "freezers." And the ship shortage is being relieved by the requisitioning of the Dutch ships and by the addition of new American vessels.

Since the outbreak of war, the Shipping Board has taken over 112 German and Austrian ships of 788,000 deadweight tonnage. It has also taken over 425 steel vessels, privately owned, of nearly three millions dead-weight tons It has let contracts for 720 steel vessels of 5,166,400 dead-weight tons. Of the requisitioned vessels 72 have been completed and put in service, 15 have been reconveyed to their original owners, and 52 have been launched but not completed. And of the contracted vessels two of 17,600 dead-weight tons have been completed and three of 26,400 tons launched but not completed. Of wooden vessels the board has let contracts for 490 ships.

To Reach London German Airmen must Cross a Wall of Bursting Shrapnel. It Is This Barrage Fire That Breaks Up Their Formations, Forces Them to High Elevations, and Allows Few to Penetrate beyond the Environs. At Great Altitudes Bombing Is Ineffective

War in the air was becoming a science—for both sides. The Allies had the Sperry bombsight, and the deadly German Gothas were equipped with the Goerz sight. Both compensated for air speed and altitude. The first "blockbuster," weighing 500 pounds, was in use. It was hung, nose down, from the fuselage, but smaller bombs were already being carried in internal bomb racks. Antiaircraft artillery, set up to form barrages, could reach as high as 20,000 feet. World War I flak was not much of a threat to high-flying planes, however

The face of war had changed forever. Surrounded by new services in a war overwhelmingly complex and technical, the infantry, most ancient of military organizations, had itself become highly specialized

Last of the individualists, World War I aviators decorated their planes from the first with colorful designs, mottoes and insignia. Few equaled the elaborate camouflage of the famed Flying Leopards of the Germans

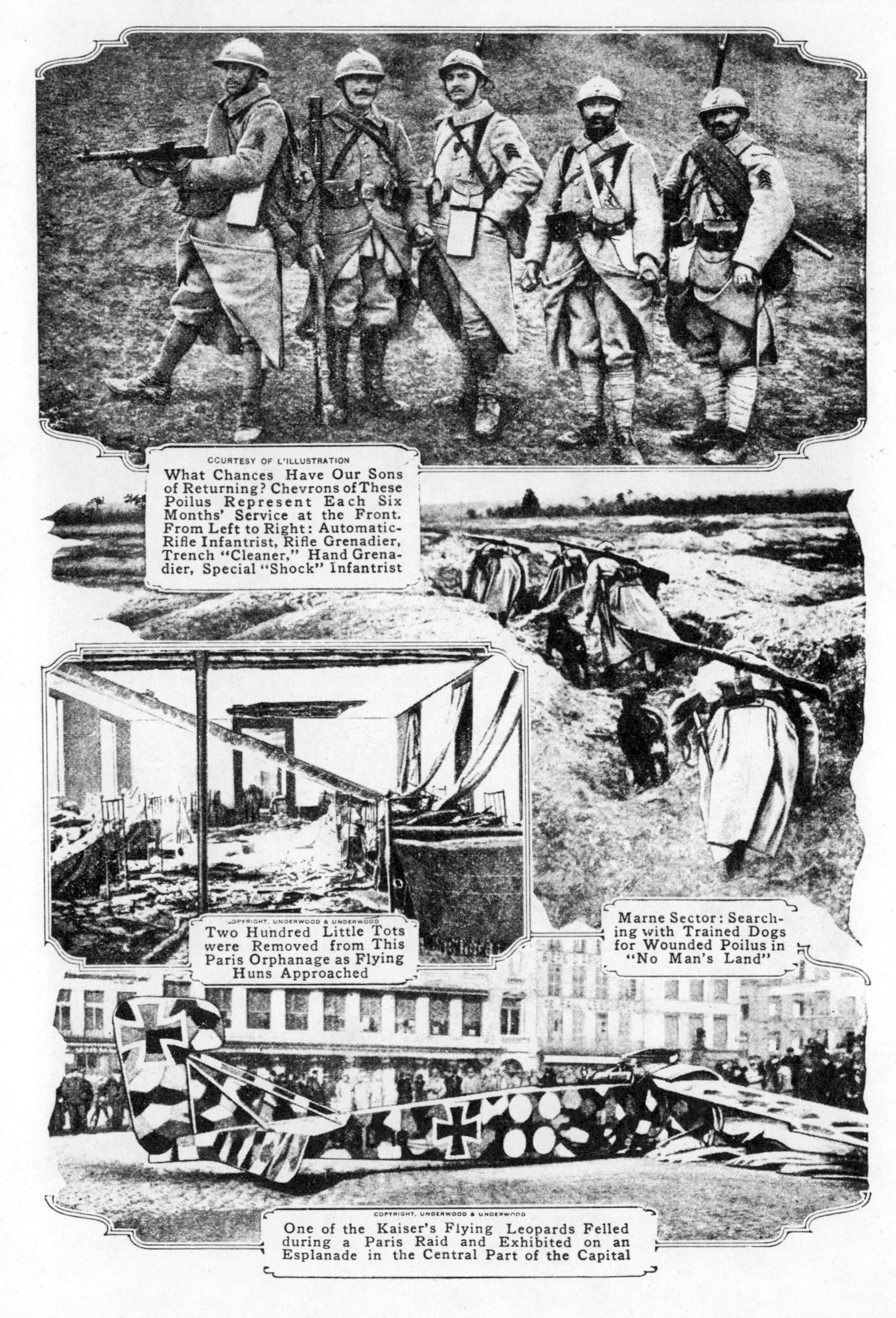

IN FRANCE WHERE WAR IS A STERN REALITY

COURTESY OF L'ILLUSTRATION
What Chances Have Our Sons of Returning? Chevrons of These Poilus Represent Each Six Months' Service at the Front. From Left to Right: Automatic-Rifle Infantrist, Rifle Grenadier, Trench "Cleaner," Hand Grenadier, Special "Shock" Infantrist

COPYRIGHT, UNDERWOOD & UNDERWOOD
Two Hundred Little Tots were Removed from This Paris Orphanage as Flying Huns Approached

Marne Sector: Searching with Trained Dogs for Wounded Poilus in "No Man's Land"

COPYRIGHT, UNDERWOOD & UNDERWOOD
One of the Kaiser's Flying Leopards Felled during a Paris Raid and Exhibited on an Esplanade in the Central Part of the Capital

STRANGE PARACHUTE EQUIPPED WITH PROPELLER AND RUDDER

In This Manner the Inventor would have the Airman Escape from a Burning Plane. The Propeller and Rudder Carry Him to a Desirable Landing Field

One of the strangest parachutes to be patented thus far resembles a Chinese umbrella, with a foot rest, a propeller, and a rudder fixed to the lower end of the "handle." It is the inventor's idea that this propelling and steering arrangement will enable the airman to guide himself to a desirable landing place. In practice he would have the airman remove the folded parachute from a rack beneath the upper wing, step out of the fuselage and upon the platform, finally releasing the parachute. During the descent the airman turns two cranks on the "handle," thus revolving the propeller and giving the parachute horizontal as well as vertical motion. The inventor does not claim to have descended in his invention.

¶Streams formed by melting snow have been used to sluice snowslides from the government railroad tracks between Anchorage and Seward, Alaska. Three slides recently blocked traffic on the road. Two of these buried the track under 50 ft. of snow, while the third was 25 ft. thick.

AUTOMATIC HOG OILER IS ALSO PEN DOOR

One of the newer devices for oiling hogs consists of a metal door that hangs in the hog-pen entrance. It is made in two sections hinged together, the lower of which has perforations in one side and will contain one gallon of disinfecting oil.

OUTFIT FOR WALKING ON WATER

Walking on the water is made possible by the use of a recently patented outfit which is a combination of a balloon and a set of floats. The small gas bag used has a lifting capacity almost sufficient to raise an adult from the ground and it is attached by ropes to a belt worn about the waist of the performer, who also uses a pair of foot boards, each having cylindrical floats fastened to its underside. A hand sup-

An Outfit Consisting of a Small Balloon and a Set of Floats with Which One can Walk on the Surface of the Water with Ease

port, made like the foot boards, is provided with a long handle and is pushed ahead of the walker to aid him in keeping his balance. The wearer of the floats walks with a step resembling that used by a wearer of snowshoes. Beneath the balloon is a canvas-covered ring, with floats attached, which may be used as a life preserver in case the balloon collapses.

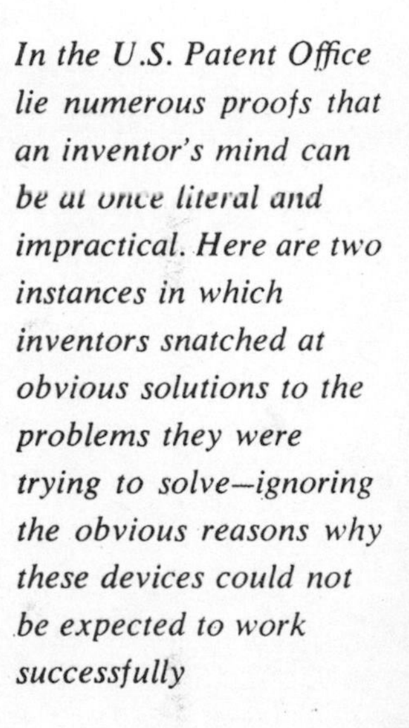

In the U.S. Patent Office lie numerous proofs that an inventor's mind can be at once literal and impractical. Here are two instances in which inventors snatched at obvious solutions to the problems they were trying to solve—ignoring the obvious reasons why these devices could not be expected to work successfully

The Rainbow Division came home—to a welcome fit for conquerors. The parade down Broadway was echoed later on the Main Streets of America—no community was too small to celebrate the peace and its returning heroes

NEW YORK'S MILLIONS GREET VETERAN OVERSEAS

This White, Silken Banner, with Its 1,972 Gold Stars for the Comrades Left Behind, was Carried at the Head of the 27th Division's Homecoming Parade

Diagonally across the Picture Runs the Grand Stand Which Held 75,000 Relatives of the Fighting Men, and Stretched Up Fifth Avenue for Two and a Half Miles. Note That the Crowd has Broken the Police Lines, Forcing the Division to Change from Column of Platoons to Column of Squads

At Night Powerful Searchlights were Flashed on This "Arch of Jewels," from Which Hung Thousands of Colored-Glass Prisms. The Arch Expressed Joy and Thanksgiving

DIVISION IN GREATEST PARADE CITY EVER SAW

Even against This Fifth Avenue Church a Grand Stand was Built for the Spectators Who Applauded the 20,000 Veterans of the Drives That Broke the Hindenburg Line and Started the Germans on Their Last Retreat

The Swaying Balloons with Dangling Pennants Which Tugged at the Ribbons, Anchoring Them to the White Columns of the Victory Arch, Gave an Air of Dreamlike Unreality to the Scene. The Columns were Linked Together with Green Garlands

At 23rd Street, the Division Passed through the "Victory Arch," the Most Elaborate Decoration on the Line of March. Four Captive Balloons Swayed from Pylons on Either Side of the Roadway, and Airplanes Flew Overhead. The Huge Crowd Filled Every Window, and at This Point Was Almost Unmanageable

Clanking tanks left great holes in the city's pavements . . . the gutters were choked with the litter of the celebration . . . plate-glass windows were smashed by the lunging crowds. But nobody cared about such things—peace was wonderful

This first nonstop transatlantic flight was made just 10 years after Blériot startled the world by daring the English Channel. Not so famous as Lindberg's later solo, but equally unheralded, the flight of Alcock and Brown showed that man had at last conquered long-distance flying. Alcock and Brown took off from Newfoundland June 14 and landed in Ireland 16 hours and 12 minutes later, averaging 120 miles an hour for the 1960-mile trip

This Is the Vickers-Vimy Bomber, the First Man-Made Machine to Fly, without a Stop, across the Atlantic Ocean. The Fuselage was Crammed with Gasoline Tanks from the Nose Almost to the Tail, Space being Spared Only for the Small Cockpit in Which Sat Pilot Alcock and Navigator Brown. Either One of the Two Engines could have Driven the Plane at a Good Speed Except at the Start When Heavily Loaded

UNHERALDED NONSTOP FLIGHT SPANS ATLANTIC

By PAUL A. JENKINS

IN writing the story of the "NC-4" one told of months spent in painstaking experiment and preparation, of destroyers and battleships strung across the ocean, and of a "slow but sure" policy which made success almost certain. In dramatic contrast to all this is the tale of the first nonstop transatlantic flight made by Capt. John Alcock and Lieut. Arthur W. Brown on June 14-15, 1919. This is the story of an airplane and two men.

Their Vickers-Vimy biplane was simply a stock model of a type supplied to the British government for night-bombing raids. As such machines go, it was far from large, having a wing span of only 67 ft. But "sweetness" of design and ease of control made the type a favorite with many pilots. Two 350-hp. Rolls-Royce engines were mounted, one on either side of the fuselage, on tubular steel struts. With this power plant the machine was rated at more than 100 miles an hour.

Alcock and Brown are anything but seafaring men. They are both land fliers, rather, but with the broadest experience in that line. Alcock has flown since 1911 often competing with Hawker and Raynham in the early days. During the war he starred in many long-distance bombing raids over Constantinople and other Turkish strongholds, finally falling within the enemy lines to remain a prisoner until the signing of the armistice. On his return to England he signed up with Vickers as a test pilot; and in that capacity successfully pleaded with his firm for permission to try the transatlantic flight. His confidence in himself and his machine were so evident that permission was granted.

Brown, the American, was likewise a prisoner of war for many months, after a career with the British army which dated back to 1914. As an aerial observer he made a name for himself on the western front, until his crash within the German lines. The odd thing about Brown is that he never had any real navigating experience before the "big hop." He had regarded navigation as a mental hobby which he studied with scholarly application. Yet he started from Newfoundland with seemingly absolute confidence in his ability to guide the plane to the center of the Irish coast. And he hit it with almost mathematical precision.

Some weeks of preparation were spent at the improvised aerodrome near St. John's, Newfoundland. Gasoline tanks were squeezed into every available corner of the Vickers-Vimy fuselage. On seeing the skeleton before the application of the canvas covering, some one actually likened the machine to a collection of cans. These tanks held 865 gal. of gasoline, every drop of which was filtered through wire screen and chamois before entering the plane. This, by the way, was a lesson learned from Hawker's disaster in mid-ocean. With other equally elaborate precautions the preliminaries were completed by June 14.

On that afternoon, Alcock and Brown decided to wait no longer. They had seen their huge rival, the Handley Pag , in easy flight above their aerodrome, and knew that haste was imperative. A nasty, choppy gale was blowing; but they decided to risk all. They clambered into their side-by-side seats in the cramped little cockpit. Places were found for the cat, the dog, and the four-pound sack of mail. At 12:13 p. m., New York time, mechanics jerked the chocks from before the wheels. Alcock threw both throttles wide open; the plane gathered speed for the uphill dash across the little field. Burdened almost beyond its capacity, it barely cleared hedges, trees, and houses. But as the engines fought with every bit of their power, they gradually mastered the 40-mile gale; and the biplane turned east with the wind, and streaked for Ireland. The wind, which almost prevented the take-off, now added tremendously to the speed. But the battle had been won at the cost of a broken wireless propeller, striking the Vickers-Vimy dumb for the whole of the lonely trip.

Yet the two men sped on. The wind held at their backs, but the air grew thick with fog. It continued thick. Navigator Brown made only four observations during the entire flight. Past midnight, fog thickened to snow and hail. By six o'clock in the morning both fuselage and wings were covered with ice. Brown was continually forced to climb up in the fuselage to chip ice from indicators and other essential instruments.

So they fought on until within an hour of the Irish coast. Then the weather cleared; and after 16 hours of flying, the two men rejoiced to see the coast line. Tired and happy, they decided to land at once in order to clinch the prize, which might easily be lost were they to sink off the coast of England. Alcock peered down through Brown's window in the fuselage bottom, and picked what seemed to be a good landing field. Gliding down around the wireless tower at Clifden, the weather-beaten machine touched ground, rolled a few yards, and stopped short with a jar. Alcock had completed the world's first nonstop transatlantic flight by landing in a sticky Irish bog.

They didn't care much. They had won approximately $75,000 in prize money by a record-smashing flight of 1,950 land miles in 16 hr. 12 min., about two hours less than the fastest railroad time between New York and Chicago.

They had left two other competitors back in Newfoundland. The giant Handley Page had already made a trial flight. Indeed, it was this very performance which hastened the departure of the victors. The 130-ft. bomber was a very promising competitor, too, with its four Rolls-Royce engines driving it at a speed of 100 miles an hour. The rebuilt Martinsyde was there, also, mechanics hurrying the installation of a new motor.

Other organizations were busy with preparations over in England. The Shortt machine, which fell in the Irish Sea, had been repaired. The Boulton and Paul bomber, and the Alliance entry, were about to start for Newfoundland. The single-motored Fairey seaplane was also a respected contestant because of its variable-camber wings, which permit ascension with a heavy load.

PHOTO BY CENTRAL NEWS PHOTO SERVICE

The Interesting Feature of This Fairey Seaplane, Is the Adjustable Rear, or "Trailing," Edges Hinged to the Wings. By Depressing Them, the Pilot Adds to the Lifting Power of His Plane and Decreases Its Speed; by Alining Them with the Rest of the Wing Section, He Lessens Lift but Increases Speed

The first transatlantic flight had been made a month earlier, but three stops were made—at the Azores, Ponta Delgada and Lisbon. Three navy planes took off from Newfoundland on May 16, and one—the NC-4—finished. It was flown by Commander Albert Cushing Read and a five-man crew. They covered the distance of 4500 miles in 15 days, landing in England May 31. Elaborate preparations had been made for the flight, and a string of destroyers dotted the ocean along the route

This was the first long-distance radio broadcast of entertainment. Up to this time a little circle of amateur radio enthusiasts had nothing to listen to but the coded messages of commercial wireless

WIRELESS MUSIC SENDS JOY IN ALL DIRECTIONS

A phonographic concert was played in Chicago the other day for the pleasure of convalescent soldiers at Fort Sheridan,

COPYRIGHT, UNDERWOOD & UNDERWOOD

Phonograph and Wireless-Telephone Set That Transmitted a Musical Program Hundreds of Miles in All Directions

30 miles away to the north. Without special preparation, a large audience at Rockford, Ill., 80 miles west, managed to enjoy the same entertainment, while more than 100 long-distance eavesdroppers at Detroit, on the east, heard the widely distributed harmony through some 230 miles of space. The success of the transmission over such an unpremeditatedly wide radius marked another step in the delicate art of sending music by wireless. The apparatus used at the government station has a radius of 400 miles, and was designed by officers at the station. As a damped wave of 700-meter length was used, it is probable that many amateur stations also received the music.

WIRELESS CONTROL RETURNED TO PRIVATE OWNERS

All the wireless stations and systems that were taken over by the government in April, 1917, and have remained under military control during the war, were returned to their owners at midnight, February 29, by executive order. The wartime restrictions are now removed.

TAP STREET CIRCUIT TO KEEP AUTO RADIATORS WARM

Keeping the radiator of his parked car from freezing is the least of troubles to the autoist of London, Ont. By paying a flat fee for the season, he obtains a key which unlocks the covers of electric sockets attached to terminal boxes, mounted on posts at frequent intervals along the streets of the city. A small electric heater with a long cord is carried in the car, and connected to the street box by simply inserting a plug. Not only is the car's circulatory system safeguarded, but its interior is kept comfortable during the owner's absence. The electric power used comes from Niagara Falls, more than 100 miles away.

AERIAL HOBO BEATS HIS WAY ON AIRPLANE UNDERCARRIAGE

The airplane hobo was first observed when soldiers at the Fort Bliss airdrome, in Texas, bent their heads back for a farewell glimpse of the "Round-the-Rim" bomber, whose remarkable tour was described in the February number of this magazine. Feet dangling, arms twined about the bracing wires, he was perched on an undercarriage axle of the big plane. A scout plane was ordered into the air at once. Overtaking the bomber, the pursuing pilot revealed the presence of the stowaway, and both planes landed at the first convenient field. The adventuring soldier was transferred, and returned to his station.

When the "Round-the-Rim" Bomber Left the Airdrome at Fort Bliss, Texas, This Soldier Went Along as a Stowaway in the Fashion He is Demonstrating

Behind the Wall of the Innocently Appointed Room Shown at the Left the Federal Agents Found a Prodigious Still. Right: The Still

CLEVERLY CONCEALED STILL FAILS TO FOOL U. S. AGENTS

A still for the manufacture of whisky in a private home, recently discovered by government agents, though hidden behind a cleverly devised screen, was found to be a very good example of mechanical construction. The outfit had a mash-reserve tank of 100-gal. capacity, a still and burner, a condenser, and residue-removal facilities, all neatly fitting within an alcove 5 ft. long, 7 ft. high, and 2 ft. deep. A flaplike curtain hinged at the top to the ceiling and decorated on the outside to resemble walls of the room, hung down across the front of the alcove, concealing the miniature still completely.

CANADIAN WHISKY SHIPPED IN PIG CARCASSES

Canada is no oasis in the American Sahara and illicit liquor trafficking is being developed into a fine art. All manner of

Another Bootlegger's Trick Discovered: A Large Consignment of Liquor Concealed in Pig Carcasses Confiscated by Canadian Officials

clever dodges are resorted to by the whisky runners, possibly one of the most original being the shipment of a large consignment of liquor packed in the carcasses of pigs. The liquor was discovered by officers as the "pork" was being unloaded from the freight cars. Needless to say it was confiscated by the officials.

SMALL BOTTLE CAPPER MADE FOR HOUSEHOLD USE

For household, shop, and laboratory use is now made a little machine that caps a crown-finish bottle of any size. This adjustability is secured by mounting the sealing mechanism slidably on an upright standard. Application of the hand to the lever, clearly seen in the illustration, easily develops at the sealing head a pressure of 750 lb. Prior to the downward stroke of the lever, the cap is held beneath the sealing head by a magnet. A coil spring raises the handle when pressure is removed.

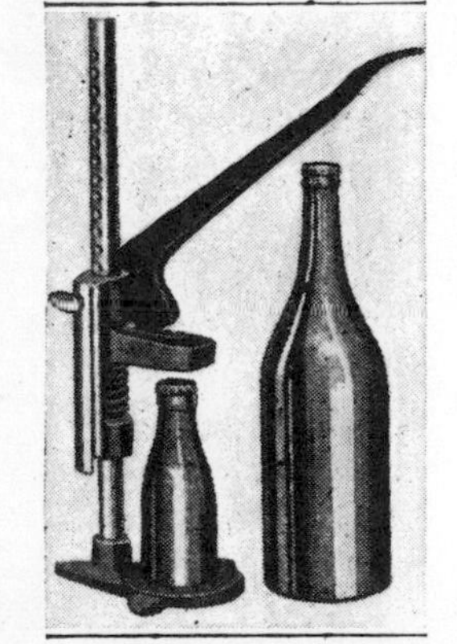

¶Comfortable armchairs are to be placed on British battleships and cruisers for the use of enlisted men when off duty.

As the twenties dawned, a battle of wits with government agents was in full swing. Bootlegging became a full-scale industry with vast underworld empires and secret restaurants and bars which served liquor illegally, giving a new name, "speak-easy," to the language. Many people visited the new "beer flats," made gin in their bathtubs and debated the relative merits of different home-brew recipes

The Epocha *was well named, for it did point the way to the giant air transports to come. Not having the materials or the engine power now available, it was natural for inventors like Italy's famed Caproni brothers to multiply what they did have—hence the nine wings and eight motors. The result, to modern eyes, strangely resembles a Mississippi river steamer of a hundred years ago. A few weeks after this picture was taken, and before the huge seaplane could be given a test flight, it mysteriously burned at its dock. An intensive investigation by the Italian government failed to reveal the cause of the blaze*

The "Epocha," Built by the Caproni Brothers, Famous Italian Aerial Engineers, Is at Once a Daring Achievement and an Even More Daring Prophecy of Greater Wonders to Come. The Nine Great Planes, with an Area of Over 7,000 Square Feet, Support the Full 25-Ton Weight of the Magnificent Aerial Argosy and Its Cargo, with Something to Spare. Eight 12-Cylinder Engines, Working and Resting in Groups, Develop a Maximum of 3,200 Horsepower Which may be Instantly Called Upon to Drive the Great Craft at a Speed of 90 Miles an Hour. The 66-Foot Hull Accommodates 100 Passengers

The Breakfast Nook

BY H. C. CROCKER

IN almost every kitchen there is sufficient space for the construction of a "pullman," or built-in, breakfast nook. It may be made by any man possessing a little mechanical ability, at a cost of only a few dollars for lumber, and will save the housewife innumerable steps between dining room and kitchen.

The seats and table may be built with only the simplest outlines, as in the left-hand illustration, or may be decorated with curves, carvings, or cut-out designs, the latter form of treatment being shown in the right-hand view.

The space required for such a nook is about 5 by 8 ft. The backs of the seats should be about 8 ft. apart, and the length of the table should be about 5 ft., when built for use by four persons. Either cypress or fir should be used for the pieces, the latter being preferable when the finish is to be white paint or enamel.

The seat ends should be made first; if four ends are employed, the first one made will serve as a pattern for the remaining three. Only two seat ends may be used, if desired, instead of four, the inner ends being recessed into the wall, or supported on plain feet, as may be found necessary. The mortises for the seat tenons should be cut so that the seat will slant slightly toward the rear, and the armrests may be made at any height desired, although 3 or 4 in. above the seat will usually be all that is necessary. The inner seat ends are securely fastened to the wall, and the outer ones to the floor, by heavy screws driven at an angle from the inner side of the base. The seat itself is fastened to the ends by screws.

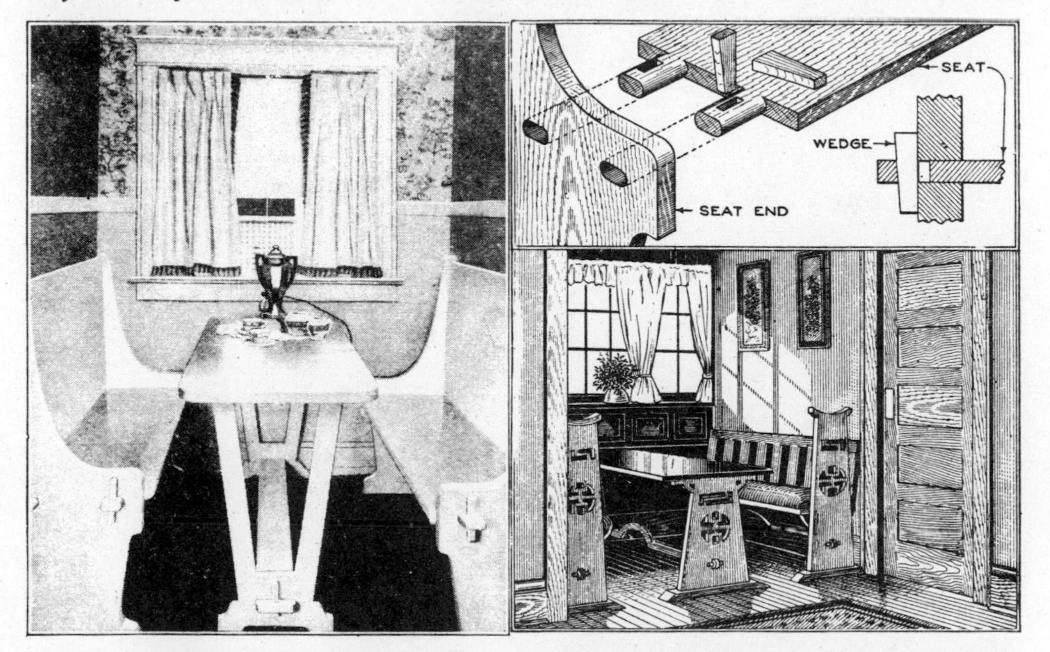

An Easily Constructed Breakfast Nook That Saves the Housewife Innumerable Unnecessary Steps in the Course of a Few Months: Two Designs are Shown, with Details of the Method of Fastening Seats and Footboards

The breakfast nook became an American tradition, and thousands were building their own in spare corners of their kitchens. Saving space and kitchen labor, they later became incorporated in architect's plans for new homes and apartments

THEY have been given many names—those years of the flapper and the hip flask, of Florida's boom and the bursting of Wall Street's bubble, of marathon walks and flagpole sitters, of mah-jongg, crossword puzzles and the cultivation of nonchalance by reaching for a Murad. The period has been called "The Jazz Age," "The Fabulous Twenties" and "The Roaring Twenties"—and those who came of age in this time have been identified as "The Lost Generation." So individual was the flavor of those years that Americans frequently have turned back to this decade for re-examination.

1922-1931

Prohibition, prosperity and a brokenhearted president

World War I and the brief but sharp depression that followed it left Americans in a bitter mood. Congress rejected United States' membership in the League of Nations, and Woodrow Wilson failed to rally public opinion to his cause. U.S. citizens took as little interest in domestic issues as they did in international matters—a series of irregularities during Harding's administration, climaxed by the Teapot Dome oil scandal, attracted relatively little attention. The eyes of most Americans were on their fortunes in a period of unprecedented prosperity that began with Harding, continued with Coolidge and ended with Hoover.

Business was on the march during most of this decade. The national income rose from 66 billion dollars at the beginning of the twenties to about 82 billion in 1928. Industry as a whole doubled the value of its products between 1921 and 1929. It was a period of mergers and the formation of holding companies. Chain stores had captured one-fifth of the nation's retail trade by 1929.

The automobile industry became a giant during this decade, consuming vast amounts of steel, copper, plate glass, rubber and fabrics. Auto manufacturing alone employed more than four million workers. The Model-T Ford—that wonderfully simple mechanism that millions were able to repair with a hairpin or a piece of binder twine—gave way to the Model A in 1927.

A new industry—radio—was born. At first it was a parts industry—people made their own sets by winding a round cereal box with wire; adding loop and sliding tuners and a "cat's whisker" to scratch a crystal, and hooking the whole up to batteries and earphones. Then the vacuum tube made possible more powerful and more complicated sets, and manufactured radios took the field. Sales of radio sets and accessories increased from 60 million dollars in 1922 to more than 842 million in 1929, when one family in every three owned a radio.

There was a real-estate boom, and new suburbs sprang up around every major American city. Miami Beach, Palm Beach and Tampa became the Meccas of vacationists as the population of Florida increased 50 per cent during the twenties. California's Chamber of Commerce got into the act, and the population of that state increased 2,250,000.

The end of silent movies

Hollywood became a center of Arabian Night fantasies. To feed the 20,000 motion-picture theaters in the country, 500 feature films were turned out every year. Producers spent an average of $100,000 a picture; *Ben Hur* alone cost $6,000,000. Movie-star salaries began their rise; steel-eyed, two-gun man William S. Hart received $900,000 for his two best years at the box office. Clara Bow, the "It Girl" . . . hot-eyed Rudolph Valentino . . . zany Harold Lloyd . . . chandelier-swinging Douglas Fairbanks . . . John Gilbert and Wallace Reid . . . Gloria Swanson and Constance Talmadge . . . these were the heroes and heroines of the last days of silent films. Many of the old stars became victims of technological unemployment after 1928 with the appearance of Al Jolson in *The Jazz Singer,* the first talking picture to be shown to nation-wide audiences. Within a year silent films were gone.

Sports became big business. Football coaches earned more than college presidents, and stadiums outdoing those of the Romans were built by the earnings of the "Four Horsemen" of Notre Dame, Princeton's "Team of Destiny" and the "Praying Colonels" of Centre College. Million-dollar gates were earned at the "Battle of the Century" between heavyweight champion Jack Dempsey and Georges Carpentier in 1921 and when Dempsey lost his title to Gene Tunney in 1927. Babe Ruth dominated baseball throughout the period, knocking out his record 60 home runs in 1927. No one could be found to beat Bill Tilden at tennis, Bobby Jones at golf or Man o' War on the race track.

Once a prize fight—now a boxing contest

When not a spectator at sports, the American of the twenties could choose many other divertissements. Simon and Schuster, a new publishing firm, introduced what they called "the eighth lively art," and two editions of the *Cross Word Puzzle Book* became best sellers. Mah-jongg, a rediscovered game of ancient China, was another fad. Shipwreck Kelly perched for 23 days on a flagpole—and a wave of flagpole sitters followed. C. C. Pyle staged a cross-country walking marathon—the "Bunion Derby."

Not all of America was smug. Sinclair Lewis, Theodore Dreiser, F. Scott Fitzgerald, John Dos Passos, Henry L. Mencken and George Jean Nathan were among the many writers who found fault with the American scene. Eugene O'Neill and Maxwell Anderson were among the rising playwrights who were closely examining values of the period.

Outside such circles, however, the trivial became important. Short skirts became shorter; cosmetics grew into a big industry. The flaunting of prohibition laws became widespread, and the free-lance bootlegger was drawn into warring syndicates that operated beer flats and roadhouses, and supplied them from gang-operated breweries and distilleries. The divorce rate rose to one out of every six marriages. Judge Ben B. Lindsey of Denver touched off a debate by proposing "companionate marriage." Current topics were the "monkey trial" in Dayton, Tenn., the Hall-Mills murder case, Lindbergh's lone Atlantic flight, Byrd's flight to the South Pole, Gertrude Ederle's English Channel swim. Popular dances were the Charleston and the Black Bottom; songs of the day included "Barney Google" and "Yes, We Have No Bananas."

The crash that shocked the world

Widespread prosperity was reflected in a runaway stock market. General Electric shot from 128 to 396, A. T. & T. from 179 to 335, Radio Corporation from 94 to 505. Those who played the market included not only the wealthy, but their bootblacks, barbers and chauffeurs. There had been indications of industrial depression, and even warnings from a few economic prophets. But most of America was deeply shocked when the crash came in 1929. Stock prices plunged downward under waves of selling, thousands of margin operators were wiped out and hundreds of these committed suicide. Prices and wages followed the market down, and so did industrial production. In three years the national income fell from $82 billion to $40 billion. Unemployment increased steadily—by 1932 there were between 12 and 14 million jobless. Farm prices were at the lowest levels in 50 years, while bread lines set up in the cities grew blocks long. The nation that began this decade in a gay but bitter mood ended it in confusion, puzzlement and a general hopelessness.

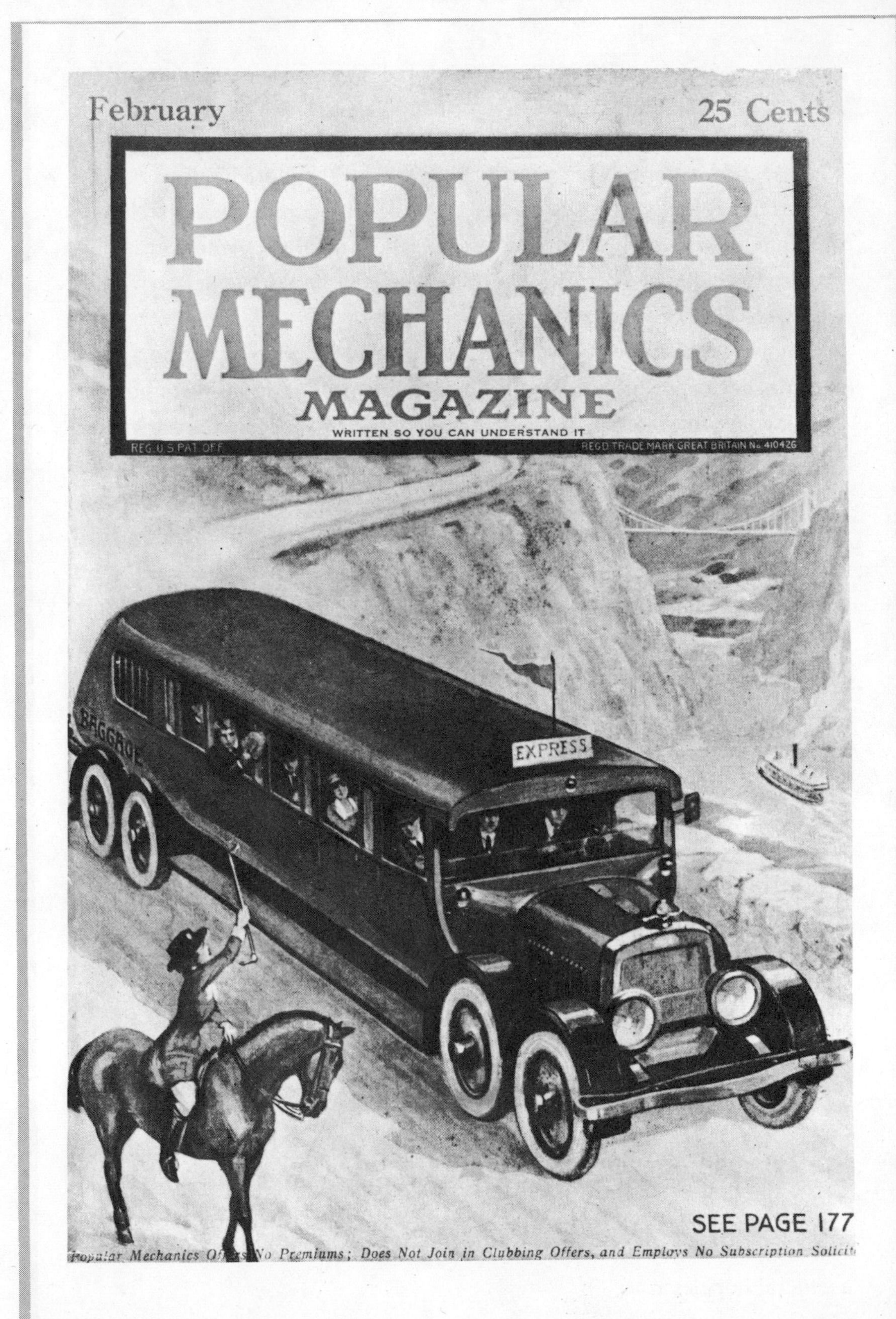

The cover story hailed a new development in transportation—the long-distance motor bus. America's highways now were safe enough and sturdy enough to maintain regular-schedule bus lines. The coach shown here was one of the first eight-wheeled models. Despite its size, the capacity was limited to 20 passengers

DISHWASHING IS PLEASURE WITH PORTABLE MACHINE

No more frowns or sighs will accompany the task of washing the dishes,

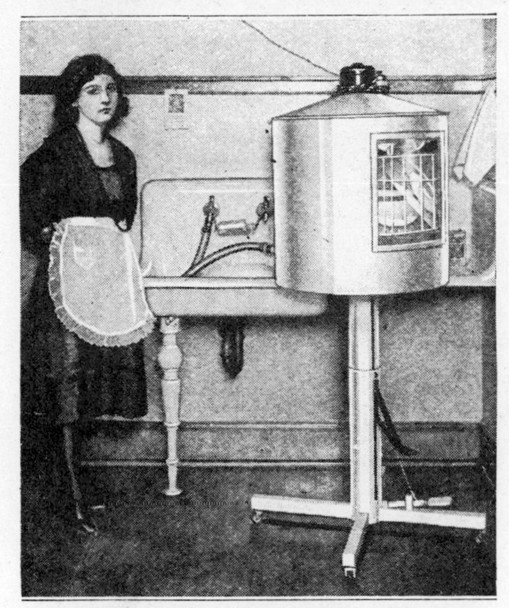

The Portable Dishwasher in Operation, Showing the Dishes Inside and the Connection to the Water Faucet: The Pedal for Raising or Lowering, and the Casters, are Seen at the Bottom

if a new portable dishwasher is used. The machine can be raised or lowered by a pedal, and is mounted on casters, so that it can be loaded at the table and then wheeled to the sink, where the water is run in. Five minutes of washing cleans the dishes, after which the dirty water is drained and hot water run in again, which rinses the dishes and cleans the washer at the same time. A small electric motor is used to circulate the water.

"NICKEL-FIRST" TURNSTILES FOR SUBWAY ENTRANCES

Turnstile admittance gates, with attendants watching them, are a common sight, but the spectacle of a gate of this kind operating automatically is a new feature. When a person wishes to pass through the gate, a nickel must first be dropped into a slot on the turnstile, and this coin allows one prospective passenger to enter. Passengers arriving at their destinations can use the gate as an exit, as it turns freely in the reverse direction. One of the subway systems of New York City is conducting experiments with this automatic gate.

DIVORCE RING LATEST FAD FOR GRASS WIDOWS

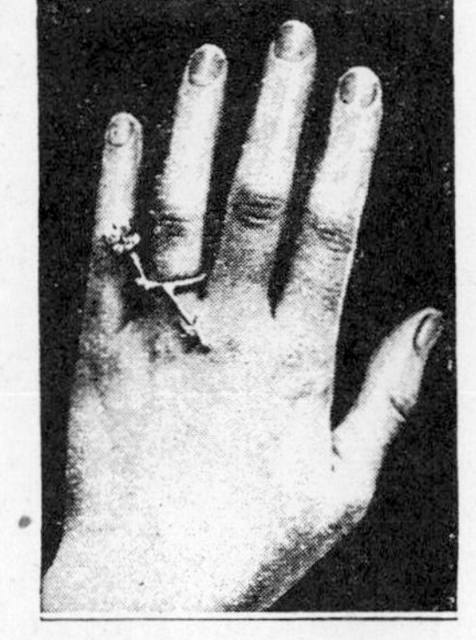

A novelty ring for grass widows is now on the market. It is worn on the same finger as the wedding ring, the design being a broken Cupid's arrow. For those who have the habit, space is provided for jewels, each jewel to signify one divorce.

ELECTRIC PRESSURE COOKER REPLACES STOVE COOKING

An electric pressure cooker has now been placed on the market. Like other pressure cookers, it is a metal container

in which food is cooked under steam pressure, but it has an electric element imbedded in the bottom to supply heat. Current can be obtained from an ordinary 110-volt circuit by means of a plug and cord. A three-heat plug is provided. Pressure is brought up to 20 lb. on "high" and cooking continued on "medium" or "low" The operating cost is three cents an hour on high, two cents on medium and one cent on low. The cooker comes in 10 and 12-qt. sizes, with insets to permit the cooking of several articles at one time.

¶Ghostly materializations of a Danish medium aroused such widespread interest that scientists of Stockholm, Sweden, decided to verify the performances. During a seance, when a "soul" was projected outside of a body, a photograph showed that the filmy emanation was nothing but a piece of chiffon.

After the war, a flood of new inventions burst the bounds of material and labor shortages. The pressure cooker caught on almost immediately, while the dishwashing machine had to await further refinements before it captured the mass market

World War I veterans had no swords to beat into plowshares, but they upheld a Yankee tradition for souvenir hunting. They brought back countless rifles, pistols, trench knives, hand grenades, artillery shells and other lethal reminders of the war. A favorite souvenir was the infantryman's steel helmet

UTILIZING NEW STEEL TRENCH HELMETS

Fruit Dish, Poultry Nest, and Umbrella Stand Made from Helmets

The three ideas illustrated in the large drawing, the fruit dish, poultry nest, and umbrella stand, were submitted by J. V. Romig, of Allentown, Pa.

The fruit dish is supported on feet, about 1½ in. long, turned from brass rod. These feet are inserted into holes drilled through the helmet, and riveted, the finished article being decorated in any desired manner, and then lacquered.

Parasites that infest wooden nest boxes refuse to have anything to do with metal nests. Consequently, by mounting trench helmets in the manner shown, the general condition of the flock will be improved. The steel nests are indestructible, and, having no corners or crevices, easily cleaned.

A trench helmet will make an admirable drip bowl for an umbrella stand. The frame is made from ½-in. pipe and fittings, of polished brass, nickeled brass, copper, or painted iron. Holes are drilled in the rim of the helmet to slip over the pipe standards, where it is held in place with cotter pins. The small hole in the center of the crown may be plugged, so that, by removing the plug, water from the dripping umbrellas can be drained off without removing the helmet.

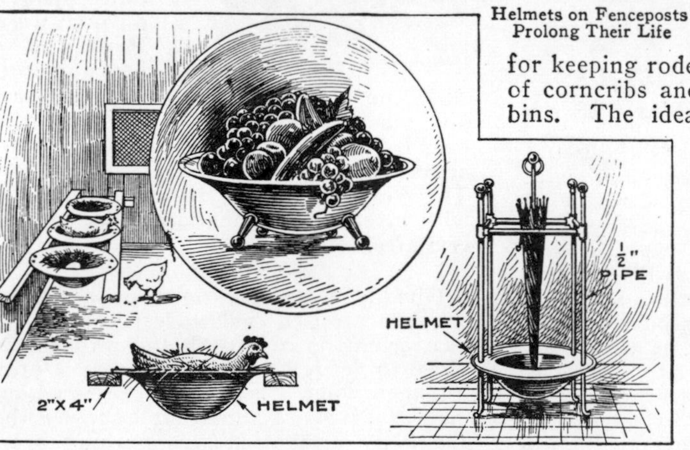

At the Left, the Helmets are Shown in Use as Sanitary Nests; in the Center, as an Attractive Fruit Dish; and at the Right, as a Drip Bowl for an Umbrella Stand

Helmets on Fenceposts Prolong Their Life

Rats Kept Out of Corncrib by Helmets Nailed on the Posts

Helmets Keep Rats Out of Corncrib

Truman R. Hart, of Ashtabula, Ohio, who won the third prize of the contest with his idea of utilizing helmets for bird baths, also contributed another plan that makes use of them for keeping rodents and other vermin out of corncribs and similar elevated storage bins. The idea involves nothing more complicated than capping each of the supporting posts with a trench helmet that has been drilled with two or three holes so that spikes can be driven through the plate into the post.

Fenceposts Preserved by Helmets

From saving the lives of soldiers on the battlefield, the trench helmets have been adapted by R. C. Leibe, of Chase

City, Va., to prolonging the life and usefulness of fenceposts on the farm. The drawing shows how each post is surmounted by a helmet that is held in place with a long spike. Naturally, this protection prevents water, that would cause the post to check and split within a comparatively short number of seasons, from coming into contact with the exposed end.

Trench Helmet as Charcoal Brazier

A rather original idea in which a trench helmet is used as a charcoal brazier in the kitchen stove during the heat of summer, is the contribution of Roland B. Cutler, of Springfield, Vt. The crown of the helmet is perforated with ¼-in. holes to permit circulation of air through the burning charcoal that is placed inside. In use, the helmet is set into one of the openings of the kitchen stove, and a grid from an oil or gas stove, resting upon a plate fastened to the rim, completes the arrangement.

This Brazier will be Found Very Effective during the Summer

A Helmet Drinking Fountain

From New Hartford, N. Y., Floyd A. Krenzer submitted his idea for making a sanitary drinking fountain, using the trench helmet as a receptacle for catching the waste water. The water-supply pipe, with a suitable nozzle at its upper end, comes through the center of the crown, while the overflow is carried off by a waste pipe that is arranged a little to one side of the center. The fountain is mounted on a pedestal, that can be made to correspond with its surroundings; in some instances, it might be found preferable to mount it on wall brackets.

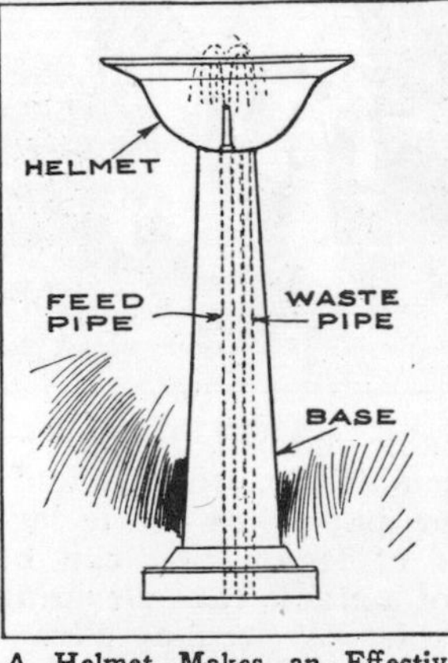

A Helmet Makes an Effective Drinking Fountain

Helmet for Stovepipe Cap

To prevent rain from blowing down a stovepipe chimney and causing it to rust to pieces rapidly, Anthony Jacobucci, Philadelphia, Pa., suggests that the army trench helmet be used as stovepipe caps in the manner shown in the drawing. A strip of flat, stiff iron is riveted around the stovepipe as a reinforcement for helmet-supporting braces, which are riveted to it and the helmet. Not only does a cap of this kind prevent entrance of rain, but, as the helmet is somewhat larger in diameter than the stovepipe, there is slight possibility of a down draft blowing the smoke out into the room below.

A Helmet Cap on the Stovepipe Prevents Rust and Down Draft

A Neat Sewing Stand

Arthur Gulbranson, of Chicago, Ill., has fashioned from a trench helmet a very substantial addition to the sewing equipment of the feminine portion of his family. As the photograph shows, feet, of ⅛ by 1-in. annealed brass strips, are riveted or soldered to the crown of the helmet. A combined spool rack and scissors holder, of the same material, is soldered in place, ⅜ by ⅞-in. brass pins being soldered to the crossbar to hold the spools. This crossbar has small projecting ears passed through slots in the sidepieces, soldered in place, then scraped bright. A clip and socket for the scissors are also soldered to one of the sidepieces, and a small brass pin, soldered to the top of the rack, makes a convenient holder for a thimble. The helmet and fittings were rubbed to a high polish with fine emery cloth and then lacquered, completing a very useful and substantial piece of work.

A Substantial and Attractive Helmet Sewing Stand

Popular Mechanics *sponsored a contest among its veteran readers for the best ways in which to utilize their trench helmets in peace. Some explosive souvenirs also were brought home, exhibited briefly, and then stored away in attics, closets and basements. In later years some were discovered and detonated, sometimes with tragic results*

Postwar prosperity brought millions of new dwellers into the city, and America's greatest building boom in history was on. Cramped for space, builders met the problem with a new type of furniture. Inadoor beds, kitchens that folded out of the wall and convertible couches began to appear. This combination bed and table was an early effort to solve the space problem

ISLAND WIRELESS STATION NORWAY'S WEATHER OUTPOST

On the little arctic island known as Jan Mayen Land, about 71° north latitude, there is a wireless station which serves as a weather outpost for the coast of Norway, 500 to 600 miles to the east and southeast. The island is only 34 miles long and 9 miles wide, its mean temperature is about 4° below freezing, and its weather is exceedingly stormy. Only once, until recently, and then only for a year, has anyone ever remained on it. Because it lies in the direct path of violent storms, which often strike the coast of Norway suddenly and with great damage to shipping, the idea occurred to Norwegian meteorologists to establish a radio station there. An appropriation of $10,000 was secured and the difficult task of establishing the station accomplished last summer. Since then regular reports, and warnings of storms, have been sent from the Jan Mayen. Once a violent storm blew down the masts and the reports were interrupted, but in a few weeks they had been replaced and the reports were resumed.

TABLE AND BED ARE COMBINED IN "EFFICIENCY" FURNITURE

Every inch counts in the modern "efficiency apartments," and an aid in the saving of valuable space has appeared in the production of a new combined table and bed. In appearance, the table resembles the ordinary four-legged library type, but inside of the legs are a second set of legs which can be raised by means of a crank, thus elevating the top of the table. A peculiar advantage of this innovation lies in the fact that the table need not be cleared off before the top is elevated, as the mechanism simply causes the whole to rise. With the top raised out of the way, the exposed mattress is then unfolded.

Right: Combined Table and Bed Shown as Ordinary Library Table. Left: Elevating the Table Top Preparatory to Making Up the Bed

Below: Combined Table and Bed with Mattress Unfolded and Bed Made Up. The Articles on Top of the Table are Seen Undisturbed

ROLLER CURTAIN IS MOUNTED ON BOOTBLACK STAND

Feminine customers showed so much embarrassment while having their shoes shined, that a sympathetic New York

Bootblack Stand with Roller Curtain, Enabling Women Customers to Protect Themselves against Annoyance from Passers-By

bootblack mounted a roller curtain on his stand. Now the wearer of the most abbreviated skirt can pull down the curtain to suit herself, and sit unconcernedly in the elevated chair for a "shine" without being annoyed by the interested glances of the rude passers-by.

QUARTER-IN-SLOT MACHINES FOR RADIO SERVICE

Evidence of the popular trend of radio is the announcement of a manufacturer of wireless apparatus, of contracts for 25,000 receiving sets to operate on the deposit of a quarter. Most of the outfits are for hotels and hospitals.

LIFE-SAVING BELT ADOPTED BY BOLD BOOTLEGGERS

Recent raids by prohibition authorities in Milwaukee, Wis., have furnished another proof that the ways of the bootlegger are devious. In one of these raids, the chief prize consisted of a life-saving belt, the interior of which was designed to hold liquor, instead of the old-fashioned cork compositions. In use, the belt was hung by straps from the shoulders, resting just under the armpits, so that by pressure of the arms the vender could force the liquid through a faucet.

ANCIENT CHINESE GAME NOW FAD IN AMERICA

An ancient Chinese game dating back to the time of Confucius but only recently introduced here after the translation of its rules into English, seems to be becoming the fad of the hour in America. The game has been likened to a "glorified game of rhummy" and is played with ivory tiles, with picturesque trimmings in the form of dragons, the four winds, flowers, birds, and other characters. Many leading stores are exhibiting the game sets in their display windows amid Oriental decorations. Some sets are selling for about $15; others are higher-priced.

The Tiles and Other Parts of the Game in the Illustration All Have Picturesque Names. When Not in Use, the Set is Placed in a Box, as Shown Above

New wealth and leisure allowed people to try their inventiveness on amusement devices, and fads began by the thousands. The U.S. reached to the far and exotic corners of the world for novelties. Most popular Chinese importation was mah-jongg, the first great game rage of the decade

The "bungalette" was the ancestor of today's motel. By 1922, almost 12 million automobiles were registered in the United States, as compared to the 8000 of 1900, and the motorist was roaming far and wide

A Street in the "Bungalette" Village Which will Accommodate 500 Motorists When Completed: At the Extreme End of the Street, on the Right, can be Seen a Store Which was Erected Expressly for the Convenience of the Villagers. When Finished, This Street will be Paved with Crushed Stone

"BUNGALETTE" CAMP FOR MOTOR TOURISTS

By JOHN ANSON FORD

HERE is the latest idea in camps for motorists. An Oakland, Calif., concern is spending no less than $80,000 in erecting "bungalettes" on an eight-acre tract, to be let to motoring tourists by the night or for any longer period "up to fifteen years" (as the management jokingly announces), which is the length of the lease on the land. These simple residences are designed to take the place of tents, and while their furnishings are meager compared with regular houses, they offer considerably more in the way of conveniences than is commonly offered by an ordinary tent. These bungalettes are of two types some with one room and some with two rooms. They are built entirely of wood. and are equipped with sinks, running water, electric lights, two-burner gas plates, etc. They rent for $20 to $35 per month, and at corresponding rates for shorter periods. A third type of structure is designated as a "shelter house," and consists of a shed, about 9 ft. square, open on two sides, furnished with a combination table and benches for four persons, and a two-burner gas plate. These shelter houses rent for 75 cents per day or $4.50 per week.

The Building on the Left Is One of the Sanitary Toilet Houses of the Village, While the One on the Right Is a Laundry. Both Structures Possess Modern Plumbing

Another View of the Village Street, Showing Some of the Houses Which Contain Electric Lights, Running Water, and Two-Burner Gas Plates

Above: Radio Garter, Showing the Receiver, Crystal, and Snap Chains. Left: Illustrating How the Radio Garter is Worn and the Manner of Using It

RADIO GARTER LATEST FAD FOR WIRELESS FANS

Feminine wireless fans will be interested in the introduction of a tiny radio set which is made in the shape of, and is worn as, a garter. Wire is coiled around a piece of cardboard, which is covered with silk, and attached to this are two ordinary eyeglass snap chains, one fastened to the foot and furnishing the ground, while the other is affixed to a coil of wire in the hat and forms the aerial. A small bottle containing the necessary crystal, or rectifier, and a receiver complete the apparatus, which has undergone tests and proved practical.

SPECIAL PHONOGRAPH SENDS CONCERTS BY RADIO

The fact that it is not always possible to employ expert musical talent for broadcasting wireless-telephone concerts has led to the development of a special phonograph for transmitting music. The tone chamber is larger than that of the ordinary phonograph and is supported on three posts which rest on a sound box.

FOUR SETS OF HEADPHONES ON RADIO APPARATUS

Four sets of headphones, or receivers, can be attached to a new article of radio equipment which has recently made its appearance. The appliance is placed on a table, or stand, and an ordinary receiver held tightly on top of it by means of an elastic band. Rubber extension tubes are then affixed to its base, and an assembled quartet can "listen in" to the broadcasting.

Radio Apparatus Placed in Center of Table So That Four Persons can Listen to the Broadcasting

RADIO SET AND PHONOGRAPH MOUNTED IN ONE CABINET

A one-control radio-receiving set with a super-amplifier that accomplishes with three tubes what has previously required five, has been mounted in a console phonograph cabinet and is connected to the horn of the phonograph. The outside aerial and ground are dispensed with by the use of a special loop antenna, contained in the instrument, which eliminates a large amount of static disturbance. The one control makes the tuning very simple. It has a dial that is graduated in definite wave lengths so that all that is necessary is to turn to the wave length on which any particular broadcasting station is operating. In the cabinet are storage batteries.

Radio-Receiving Set Mounted in a Console Phonograph Cabinet: No Outside Aerial and Ground are Needed. With Only One Control, It Is Very Easy to Tune In

The age was a cornucopia of long-dreamed-of marvels: the automobile, the airplane, and now the radio. In 1922 the nation owned some 60,000 radio sets. While neighbors gathered admiringly to listen in on the first earphones on the block, the younger member of the family was already building a private transmission set, which he kept under his bed to send messages into the night to unseen friends who were to become part of a vast network of radio amateurs, or hams

The passing of the fire horse was a real blow to fire-company enthusiasts and to the coach dogs which many companies maintained as mascots

Numerous inventors were working on the problem of talking pictures at this time. Recorded here are De Forest's solution, the principles of which are in general use today, and a rather impractical approach to the matter

The Horse-Drawn Fire Engine Making Its Last Appearance in a Parade to Signalize the Complete Motorization of the Detroit Fire Department: With Bell Ringing and Whistle Blowing, the Apparatus Drawn by the Magnificent Team Led the Procession. The Team at the Right Also Took Part in the Procession

FIRE HORSES MAKE LAST RUN AS FEATURE OF PARADE

Making their last spectacular run, teams of fire horses dashed down one of the main thoroughfares of Detroit, recently, before thousands of spectators who had gathered to witness a parade of the city's fire-fighting equipment. Complete motorization of the Fire Department is responsible for the passing of the faithful animals. They have been turned over to the park commissioner for use on light hauling work.

VOICES REGISTERED ON FILM FOR SPEAKING MOVIES

Registering voices simultaneously with the action of a motion-picture film is an invention recently announced by Lee De Forest, pioneer in the wireless research field. The voice, according to the inventor is registered on the narrow margin of the film by light action, the margin thus bearing a veritable picture of the vocal effort. Through the medium of a special attachment on the projection machines, the spoken words are reproduced in synchronism with the motion picture.

"TALKING PICTURES" MADE WITH AID OF RADIO

"Talking pictures" have been demonstrated as a practical possibility by Chicago men, who adopted the synchronization of radio and the motion-picture machine as the basis for their experiments. An ordinary picture is first enacted, then duplicates of this film are made and distributed to numerous theaters. The actors and actresses now repair to a radio-broadcasting station, where the original picture is thrown on a screen before them. As the story unfolds on the screen, the assembled cast again speak their parts, simultaneously with the action of the film. The projection machine in the station controls the starting and the operating speed of the machines in the theaters, so that, as the voices are broadcast, the different audiences are entertained with a synchronous blending of both action and sound, all of which makes the picture seem almost lifelike.

NEW TELEPHONE CABLE LAID ACROSS IRISH CHANNEL

A new cable, 25⅓ miles long, has been laid from Port Mora, Scotland, to Port Patrick, Donaghadee, Ireland, which will greatly improve telephonic communication between those two countries. If the new cable is found to be satisfactory, trunk circuits will be provided between Glasgow and Belfast by joining up the land lines. The new cable contains four copper wires, insulated by balata, which provide two so-called "physical" circuits. A third circuit will be obtained by the system known as superposing.

COMMERCIAL FLYING SERVICE STARTS IN CALIFORNIA

A passenger air route has been established between Los Angeles and San Francisco, Calif., and two regular trips will be made each day. Flying time between the two cities will be five hours, with a stop at some central point for luncheon and rest. The single-trip fare is $50, and the distance approximately 400 miles.

Above: Five of the Airplanes That Made the Flight When the Service was Inaugurated. Below: A Close-Up of One of the Planes That Carries Four Passengers and Pilot

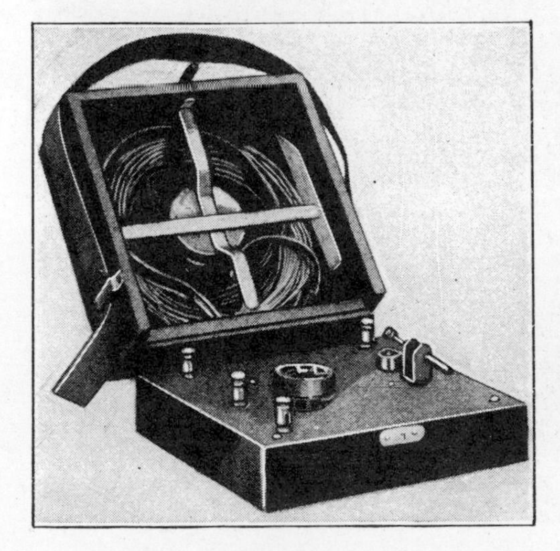

USE OF PHONOGRAPH TO MAKE MOVING PICTURES AUDIBLE

The use of the phonograph in connection with moving pictures to make the actor's speech audible has been tried for some time, but never with very satisfactory results. A demonstration was recently given in England of a newly invented apparatus which electrically synchronizes the lip movements of the actors on the screen with the sounds emitted by the phonograph. That part of the problem was solved perfectly, but there still remained the characteristic defects of the phonograph, such as the scraping of the needle, and occasional harshness or indistinctness of the voice. These defects were enhanced by the amplifier horns, which were indispensable in spreading the sound over a large auditorium. If these shortcomings can be remedied, and clearness of enunciation, together with tonal volume, can be obtained, the perfect synchronization of the new apparatus should make audible moving pictures a practical success.

PORTABLE RADIO EQUIPMENT SET UP IN FEW MINUTES

Portable radio sets for boy scouts, campers, motorists, yachtsmen, or vacationists in general, and which are contained in a 6 by 6 by 3-inch box, weighing 3½ pounds, are now available. The outfit consists of a crystal-detector set having a range of 25 to 30 miles, which can be tuned to wave lengths of 100 to 600 meters; 90 feet of antenna wire; two insulators; 10 feet of ground wire; one ground spike, and a headpiece, all of which may be set up, ready for receiving, in 15 minutes.

¶Recently a musical program, played on a phonograph at the Canadian wireless station at High River, Alta., was heard by a station on Maui Island 100 miles from Honolulu, or about 2,800 miles.

Regular air passenger runs from Key West, Fla., to Havana had already been in operation for two years. Now a great number of small commercial lines appeared, making short hops throughout the country. The first regularly scheduled commercial airplane service had been established between London and Paris in 1919

Still in the earphone stage, and trailing a long and indispensable aerial, the radio was excitedly installed in every possible sort of receiving place. The set on this railroad represented a step in transition, having both earphones and a loud-speaker. The first program broadcast from a moving train was made on the Baltimore and Ohio Railroad in 1932

RADIO EQUIPMENT INSTALLED ON RAILROAD TRAINS

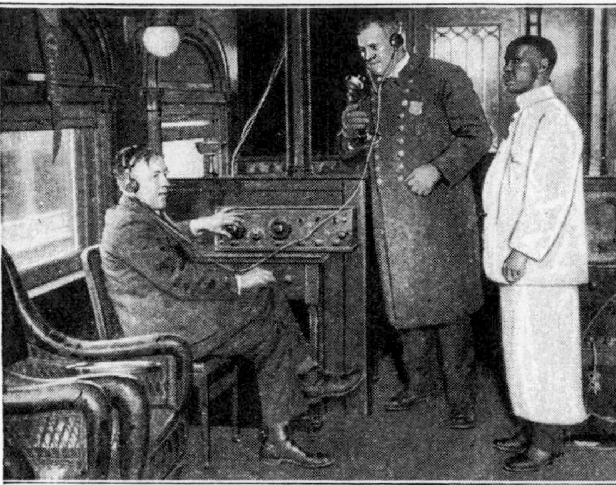

Radiophone Equipment Installed in a Buffet Car on the Lackawanna Railroad being Tested Prior to Its Regular Use on the Trains

Radiophone equipment has been installed on trains of two railroads in this country, namely, the Lackawanna, and the Chicago, Milwaukee, and St. Paul. Both these companies have converted buffet cars into virtual receiving stations, wherein the passengers can don headpieces and listen to the various broadcasting. Or, if the headpieces are not desirable, the occupants may be entertained by means of a loud-speaking horn, which is also connected in the circuit. The coaches are surmounted by special aerials running the length of the cars, and are of different construction, the Lackawanna using six wires, and the other road two, with the entire set being grounded through the axles to the rails. Although activities along this line have hitherto been more or less of an experimental nature, it is thought that the success achieved by these companies will induce other railways to provide similar amusement for the traveling public; also, that the next logical step will be to install transmitting apparatus on these trains for the further convenience of the passengers, who will then be enabled to send messages while en route.

Specially Constructed Aerial for the Radiophone Equipment on the Lackawanna Railroad Buffet Car being Connected on Top of the Train before Making an Experimental Trip with the Apparatus

Radiophone Installation on the Chicago, Milwaukee, and St. Paul Railroad

Aerial of Radiophone Equipment on Top of the Chicago, Milwaukee, and St. Paul Railroad's Buffet Car, Showing How Two Wires are Carried on Two-Foot Posts, the Full Length of the Car

---

¶Wattle wood and the spent bark from the wattle-extract mills, are to be used in the manufacture of wrapping paper, according to the announced plans of a company in Natal, South Africa.

The mechanical age reached down to the young—the ones who would keep it going when they grew up. On days when the ball game was rained out, and the clubhouse was flooded, boys found fascinating hours with their Meccano and Erector sets, their Lincoln Logs and model kites

This was the first known commercial use of radio communication to a mobile station. A year earlier, St. Louis police had begun one-way radio messages to patrol cars. Today two-way radio telephone systems are in operation by every metropolitan police force and by many long-distance truck and bus systems

INDUSTRIAL FILMS WILL BE CENSORED BY EXPERTS

With the great increase in the number of subjects being shown on the screen, that are prepared and taken in a wide range of industries, there comes the need of making certain that all scenes are technically correct in every detail. Especially is this true of the more scientific subjects, where the moving-picture camera is to record processes of manufacture or scenes taken in conjunction with research problems, the results of which are to be shown before a great many critical observers. A board of censorship has been set up by the Bureau of Mines, in conjunction with the Department of Commerce. It consists of three members, one representing the Bureau of Mines, and one from the Department of Commerce, while the third member is a representative of the industrial activity with which the picture deals. This board will do much to eliminate errors and correct technical details often overlooked.

FIRST COMMERCIAL VEHICLES USING RADIO EQUIPMENT

Equipping its delivery trucks with wireless outfits, so as to keep constantly in touch with the drivers, is the original method employed by a Philadelphia company. Since the installation of the apparatus, the travel of the machines over the routes has been greatly facilitated.

Delivery Truck Showing the Aerial for the Wireless Messages Which Enable the Manager of the Company to Keep in Constant Touch with the Drivers: Note the Receivers on the Man's Ears

TENNIS ON "POGO STICKS" LATEST FAD IN SPORTS

For a brief season, the pogo stick had adults as well as youngsters bounding along the sidewalks. A typically nutty enthusiasm of the period, these devices also were called "kangaroo sticks"

Playing Tennis on "Pogo Sticks": The Manipulation of a Racket in a Tennis Game, or the Handling of a Pogo Stick, Is Enough for Most People Separately; Their Combination Fascinates Experts

Tennis on "pogo sticks," which is rapidly becoming a fad on the Pacific coast, was first suggested by a Los Angeles sportsman. The "pogo stick" is a slender upright pole, with steps on opposite sides for the feet and a handle at the top. The base operates against a heavy spring contained in the stick. Balancing on the stick, one starts to hop, and the spring accelerates the bouncing so that each hop takes one two or three feet into the air. It requires considerable skill to handle the stick and, when the maneuvers of tennis are attempted, falls are almost unavoidable. Needless to say, the game furnishes plenty of amusement for those that are watching it.

CLEVER AIRMAN TRACES HUGE WRITINGS IN SKY

View Showing Extended Exhaust Pipe of Airplane Used in Sky Writing

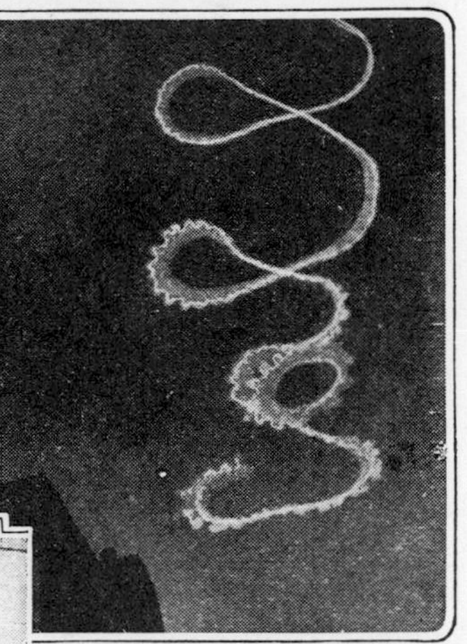

COPYRIGHT, JACK SUSSMAN
Start of Sky Writer's Message Suggesting Call of a Given Phone Number

Close-Up Showing Captain Turner Seated in the Cockpit of the Airplane Which He Piloted in His Recent Sky-Writing Stunts over New York City

Undoubtedly the tallest and broadest letters and figures ever written, were those formed in the sky over New York City in a recent series of stunt flights by Capt. Cyril Turner, of the British Royal Air Force. This clever flier has astonished and delighted thousands of people by doing queer things, like scrawling his telephone number and short messages in the sky. The exhaust pipe, extended to the tail of the ship, serves as his pen, and a chemical introduced into the exhaust as the "ink."

The Wedding Party as It Appeared to Those Who had Gathered in the Exposition Hall: The Booth Was Soundproof and Connected with a Broadcasting Station

THOUSANDS SEE AND HEAR RADIO WEDDING

What is believed to be the first performance of its kind occurred in Pittsburgh recently when a wedding ceremony was performed in a large glass booth, visible to thousands attending an electrical exposition, while radio apparatus broadcast the words spoken to those at the show and countless others listening in. The booth, specially constructed for the occasion, was soundproof and connected by telephone to a station at East Pittsburgh, where the sending apparatus was located. Loud-speaker receivers in the exposition hall carried the words to those who had gathered there.

Two developments typical of the age—the birth of a new advertising technique and the blending of marriage vows with a new technology. The first telephone wedding and the first wedding in an airplane had been held years before, and the future (1951) held in store the first wedding on television

BY COURTESY OF THE GENERAL ELECTRIC CO.
Big Airplane Carrier as It will Look When Completed: The Electrically Operated Power Plant, Which Is Large Enough to Serve a Modern City of 700,000 People, will Drive the Ship through the Water at a Speed of Nearly 40 Miles an Hour

The carriers were the Lexington *and* Saratoga. *Converted from two battle cruisers, they were completed in 1927 and were the fastest ships in the U.S. fleet for many years. They carried from 80 to 100 planes and about 2000 men*

TWO BIG AIRPLANE CARRIERS BUILDING FOR U. S. NAVY

Two ships, said to be the longest naval vessels in the world, are now under construction for the U. S. Navy, and while the arrangements below decks are not being announced, it is understood that airplanes in great numbers will be cared for in each ship. There will be provisions for hoisting the planes to the flying deck, which will be unbroken except for the funnel inclosure set at one side of the hull. The ships will be completely equipped for sending and receiving radio messages. Each ship will be electrically driven and will have a power plant of 180,000 horsepower, which would be sufficient to serve a city of 700,000 people, and which will propel the more than 33,000 tons through the water at a speed of nearly 40 miles an hour. The ships will have a length of 850 feet, a beam of 105 feet, and four propellers, each driven by two 22,500-horsepower motors.

The automatic gyro-pilot, developed by that genius of the gyroscope, Elmer Sperry, solved the problem seamen call the "snake in the wake" —or the lurching of a ship from a straight course because of wave and current action

AUTOMATIC STEERING GEAR USED ON U. S. SHIP

The first American passenger ship to be equipped with automatic steering gear, recently completed a successful return voyage to the West Indies, under the guidance of this apparatus, which does away with the necessity of a quartermaster continually at the steering wheel. The instrument consists of a gyroscopic compass arranged to open and close an electric circuit controlling the stopping and starting of the rudder-operating mechanism. The instrument is capable of being set for response to different amounts of deviation from course, one case being noted where the departure from the true course was set as close as one-sixth of a degree.

Gyroscopic Compass, Which Automatically Makes Electrical Connections and Forms the Controlling Element of the Steering Gear for Ships

Thrills Made to Order in the Movies at the Risk of Life and Limb

Stars of the Silver Screen Often Called Upon to Face Death as Result of Demand for More Realism in Pictures

HANGING by the heels on a 6-inch ledge with the street cavern yawning 12 stories below is no trick at all—in the movies.

Missing a foothold on the edge of a tall brick precipice and being caught by the hands of a clock 10 floors above the earth, however, contains almost as many thrills for the actor as it does for the spectators.

For these are the days of realism in pictures, the result of a ceaseless demand on the part of a public long accustomed to seeing speeding automobiles plunge over steep cliffs, death-defying leaps into a raging surf, and airplane crashes, for more thrills.

While only a few years ago most of the "stunt" pictures were the result of trick photography, double exposure, and splicing of the film in the cutting rooms, today the highest-priced stars of filmdom are often called upon to risk their lives.

In other cases "doubles" are employed to take the place of the star for the more hazardous undertakings. Dressed and made up to resemble the actor, they brave death in leaps from speeding trains to airplanes, jump over cliffs, and ride motorcycles into locomotives with no chance of winning either fame or glory for themselves. They are the unsung heroes of the movies.

Many risks, however, are taken by the stars. In one instance, during the filming of a western melodrama, the heroine was called upon to plunge into an icy mountain torrent and float downstream toward a cataract. Camera men and the director trailed along in a boat behind so that a close-up of her face in the water could be obtained.

It had been found by experiment that the current would carry floating objects to a sand bar just above the falls, and a watcher was stationed there to pull her from the water as she swept past. But, instead, the current swept her to the other side of the stream and she would have been dashed over the falls to certain death had not her secretary managed to grab a bit of her dress and draw her to the shore. One of the strongest bits of realism ever shown on a screen probably, was the expression of hopeless horror on the face of the victim as she realized her danger. This was caught by the camera in the boat.

Considerable hazard often is eliminated by the use of wires that protect the actor against falls. These cannot be seen when the picture is shown on the screen. In the comedies, also, many other tricks are employed. One is a rest at the back of an automobile that holds the actor out parallel to the road and makes him appear to be stretched out like a ribbon.

To do this two pictures are taken and spliced together. In the first, he chases after the automobile and catches the rear seat with his hands, throwing his feet into the air. Then the automobile goes back, the actor takes his place on the rack and it covers the same course. Later the films are cut and joined at the point where he first leaped into the air.

In making a picture of a man climbing the side of a building and doing apparently perilous stunts many floors above the street, a real building was selected and a circus performer employed to double for the actor in the "long shots." Then a fake building was built on top of the real one. The "set" was built in far enough so that the roof would break any fall and also would provide a platform for the camera. By "shooting" at a proper angle, however, the drop to the street looked straight down.

Silent-movie patrons demanded lots of action, and the producers gave it to them. A new profession—that of the movie stunt man—was born. They leaped from burning buildings and runaway locomotives, ran motorcycles off the ends of docks into the bay, hung from airplanes and fought so often on the crumbly edges of cliffs that movies of this type came to be known as "cliff hangers"

The scene is from Safety Last, *an early Harold Lloyd thriller. A million spines tingled as Lloyd slipped around the flagpole, clung by fingertips to a ledge and finally hung on the hands of the clock, which then began to bend ominously. Shots of the street 12 stories below heightened the audience participation in danger—but a safety net and a replica of the building cornice set well back on the roof gave the actor ample protection*

MAKING DARING STUNT PICTURE FOR THE MOVIES

How It Looked to the Camera's Eye More than Twelve Stories above the Street, and How It Appeared from the Top of the Skyscraper Where the Scene was "Shot"

Popular Mechanics Magazine

REGISTERED IN U. S. PATENT OFFICE

WRITTEN SO YOU CAN UNDERSTAND IT

Vol. 40 OCTOBER, 1923 No. 4

View of Fifth Avenue in New York, Taken in 1923

Horses Increasing in Numbers Despite Automobiles

WITH more than 13,000,000 automobiles now in use throughout the country, a recent census has shown that the horse, instead of becoming a museum curiosity, has increased greatly in numbers.

Better horses, and more of them, it is reported, are being bred now than at any time during the past quarter of a century, a gain in numbers of 2,750,000 being shown in the 25 years since motorized vehicles began to appear.

While more horses than ever before are being used on farms, they are gradually disappearing from city streets, many municipalities having laws forbidding their use on certain thoroughfares and in congested districts, in order to expedite the flow of traffic.

With the change, new problems in city planning have arisen. As the speed of transportation increases, square street corners are being changed to long, sweeping curves. It has been found by experience that the short turns slow up, while the long ones hasten, traffic. Fronts of buildings also have been cut away, the sidewalks being placed under the overhanging second stories to permit the widening of the streets.

Another problem has been the growing number of accidents. Approximately 14,000 persons were killed by motor cars last year, it is estimated. Based on figures, furnished by surveys of 60 cities with populations numbering 25,000 and over, during the past eight years, the following table has been prepared:

Year	Deaths per 10,000 Cars	Total Deaths
1915	24.0	5,800
1916	20.8	7,300
1917	18.2	9,000
1918	15.5	9,300
1919	13.0	9,700
1920	12.0	11,000
1921	11.9	12,500
1922	11.6	14,000

To meet these conditions, double-decked streets have been proposed in New York and Chicago. Subways and great underground parking spaces also are seen as a means to relieve the crowding. One-way streets already are in use in many cities with good results.

During recent years the annual motor-vehicle death toll has increased to more than 40,000 persons. But the ratio of deaths to the number of automobiles in operation has steadily decreased since 1923

On August 21, 1923, air-mail planes left Los Angeles and New York, heading toward a rendezvous in Cheyenne, Wyo. After dusk they were guided by an 885-mile string of lights—5000-candlepower beams every three miles, 5,000,000-candlepower lights at emergency landing fields 25 miles apart and giant beacons of 500,000,000 candlepower at eight main stops over the route. The flights, covering 2680 miles in 26 hours, proved that night-mail flying was feasible. Regular service began the following year

From the Explorers, Goldseekers, Stagecoach, and Pony Express, to the Night Air Mail Flying Down a Pathway of Light to Great Landing Fields

Native Tells of Great Quake

From Popular Mechanics Magazine's Japanese Correspondent,
N. SAKATA OF TOKYO

[Popular Mechanics Magazine believes it need offer no apology for presenting an account of the Japanese earthquake at this late date, when it is the experience of a native eye-witness, N. Sakata, this magazine's special correspondent in Tokyo. The tale is a moving one and written from the native point of view. In the stress of his emotions, Mr. Sakata seems to have suddenly developed a fluency in English, which former contributions lacked to some extent. His "copy" has been edited in order that his pitiful adventures may be more readily grasped by the reader.—Editor's Note.]

THE morning of September first was stormy. A strong wind was blowing, and I could scarcely hold an umbrella. It was raining heavily, but when I reached my office it began to clear up, and the dark sky changed to a cheerful blue.

At 11:58 o'clock I heard a strange sound from the earth through the building wall, but since it was so slight, and, because I afterwards learned that other men did not notice it, I paid little attention. Soon afterwards, the building began to shake very softly. Inasmuch as we Japanese are familiar with small earthquakes, I paid little attention to it and felt that it would soon pass, but, alas! it grew into an uncomfortable shock.

I heard the crying of women and the sounds of the cracking of the adjacent building walls. We had in our room a large case for filing papers which measured about 10 feet high and 20 feet wide. This now began to sway from left to right, and back. Finally, it fell over forward. The bookcase crashed to the floor and my writing cabinet fell over. The huge body of the office building was still shaking, giving off an indescribable sound.

The movement of the first shock still continued, and I cannot tell you how dreadful it was to me. The walls had not cracked in my room, but I could hear them from all sides. I supposed, of course, that my room would finally crush in, and in my mind I said farewell to all my brothers, my mother, and my sister. I crawled under the heavy desk, hoping that I might thus be saved.

After the first tremendous shock, I resolved to go to the Imperial Palace Square, which is a very wide field and near our building. As I rushed out the front door, I noticed that the huge buildings all about me were broken. A man,

Eyewitness accounts of tragedy are chiefly impersonal ones. Here is an unusual report of the worst earthquake in the history of the world, told from the heart by one still soul-shaken by the danger to his loved ones. N. Sakata still is a valued correspondent of Popular Mechanics

On Sept. 1, 1923, the earth rumbled and yawned in great cracks, and Tokyo and Yokohama were both almost completely destroyed. A hundred thousand people were killed, and uncounted thousands were injured. The quake was followed by fire that made a 100-square-mile area a burning rubble for more than a week

terribly hurt, was sitting on the ground by the building. I ran on to the square.

Many fires now arose throughout the city. Black smoke and red flames were cast over the sky. I could not see the natural color of the sky anywhere because of the dense smoke. Hunger and thirst came next.

Indeed, the first night of the earthquake, September first, was a very dreadful one. I still find it difficult to believe that it is all true. In every direction one might look, the city was a mass of flames. The Imperial Palace Square was the middle of a great furnace. Crimson flames and billowing clouds of smoke covered the city.

We could find no light or gas in the square, for these had been extinguished at the producing station because of the danger of fire. There was, however, no need of man-made illumination, for the holocaust provided as brilliant a light at night as the sun did in the daytime. The temperature of the air being raised, we were forced to breathe quickly, the heavy air almost stifling us. I could not sleep, for I was nearly frantic thinking about my mother and sister whom I had left at home.

Hunger attacked us. Tokyo is very cold in September, and although the flames gave off great heat, the midnight air chilled us.

I tried to get out of the crowds. There were more than 100,000 gathered in this small square, so it was very difficult to get away. Indeed, I could not get a bit of space to stand up. It took me 30 minutes of crawling and stumbling to move 200 feet, but finally I emerged.

After a very long time, and by devious routes, I reached my home. Alas! I found my house burned to ashes, and I could not find any members of my household. I searched and searched

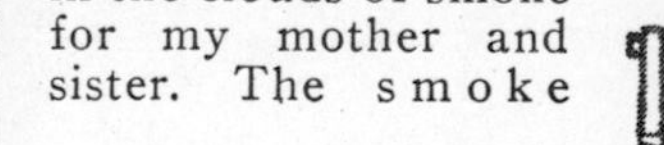

in the clouds of smoke for my mother and sister. The smoke

filled my eyes and I could not see. I tried to find even a bit of my mother's burned body, but I could not. After hours of vain search, my eyesight nearly gone from smoke, I had to stop, and I could only hope that my mother might have escaped to safety somewhere. I could not think of any place she might be. All the homes of my relatives were destroyed. "Oh, where could she be!" I asked myself, and cried and cried. I thought that I might not be able to find them anywhere any more in this world. All my courage had disappeared.

It was in this state that, as I was walking along the river which is near my house, I saw a woman dimly through the smoke—just an outline. The phantom shape seemed to resemble my mother. I approached and asked her who she was, and then, I could not believe it was real! I thought it must be a dream, but it was not. It was my mother! It was my mother! She and I embraced each other again and again, thanking God, and again I cried and cried for joy.

Coming home from my office I saw hundreds of dead bodies of men and women. I had had nothing to eat for more than three days, and the odd odor of the hot wind often caused me to fall down fainting. But my mother and sister were safe, so my courage had returned to me. Everywhere, I saw thousands of people running to escape from the city to the suburbs. I had taken my mother and sister to the suburbs, and was trying to get into the city. I understood fully that I might be wounded or killed by fire and falling buildings, but we nevertheless kept on our way.

Occasionally I was asked who I was by a policeman. They urged me to stay out of the city, and at times even attempted to prevent me, for by this time the government had declared the city under martial law, and soldiers stood on the road with their guns loaded and swords bared. If we insisted, then it would

The Tokyo tragedy brought Frank Lloyd Wright belated recognition as a practical as well as a creative architect. Wright had designed the famed Imperial Hotel in Tokyo to withstand earthquakes, and it was the only large building that did survive

When the city was rebuilt many steel-frame structures were erected in place of the former wooden ones, and a number of streets were widened into broad highways to reduce the danger from any recurrence of the catastrophe

mean we would be shot or cut down. Sometimes we were attacked by flames and smoke. Frequently, to protect ourselves against such terrors, we were forced to dash into the water and get ourselves wet from head to foot. It was very dangerous work. The fire continued eight days.

We Japanese have one thing in mind to tell you; that is, our great thanks for the wonderful help you gave us. If you will, please, print on your pages that the Japanese people are thanking the American people, and will never forget your kindness at this time.

I am now at Shibaura, which is the shipping center on Tokyo Bay. I can see many ships flying the American flag on the calm sea. It is an inspiring sight, and I thank God for it.

U. Sakato

ELECTRIC "VALET" FOR PRESSING TROUSERS IN HOME

For pressing trousers quickly and conveniently, an electrical device is being

Copyright, Underwood & Underwood

Device Operated by Electricity to Press Trousers Quickly and Conveniently in the Home

marketed that attaches to the ordinary light socket. There are two sections, the lower one, which is heated and over which the trousers are laid, and the upper, which is attached to the former by clamps. In pressing, one has only to fasten the two sections together and turn on the electricity. Within a few minutes, the garment is reshaped and ready to wear.

SHIPS PASS ABOVE LOFTY HILLS IN JOURNEY OVER SEAS

By means of a new method of surveying the floors of oceans, it has been possible to chart some of the deepest waters. These maps show that transocean steamer paths pass over mountain chains, valleys, and plateaus that lie hidden beneath the seas. From the eastern shores of the United States, ships sail above continental slopes, extending far out like a great shelf, beyond which is a vast rolling plain, unbroken until it rises and forms a great ridge of mountains south of Iceland, virtually dividing the waters.

SHEETS OF METAL TO REPLACE PLASTER AND WALL PAPER

Thin metal sheets are being used instead of plaster and wall paper in France. Among the advantages claimed for the plates are that they cost less, and can be put on cheaper than the old materials. The air in a house thus equipped is said to be easily maintained at an even temperture, as the walls are almost air-tight. The sheets, which are sold in standard sizes, are mounted on laths. They are stamped with decorative designs which can be painted in any colors desired. A dwelling lined in this way is also reported to be proof against many insect pests.

HOLDER FOR SERVING SPOONS KEEPS HANDLES FROM FOOD

To prevent spoons from slipping into food in a serving dish, a metal holder, to be attached to the rim of the vessel, has been placed on the market in Europe. It is

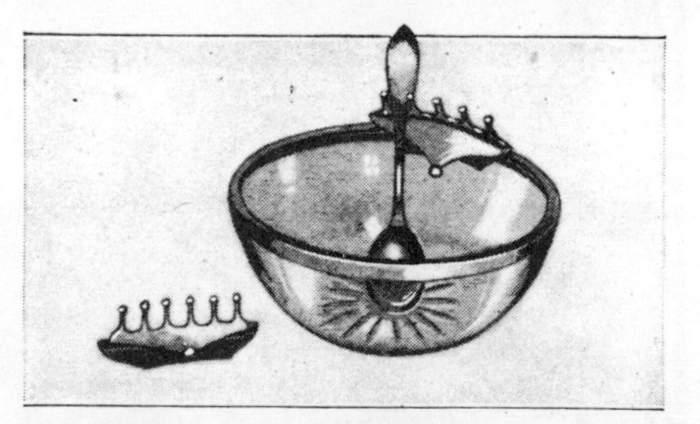

Metal Holder Placed on Edge of Serving Dish to Keep Spoons from Slipping into Food

specially designed to keep the handle of a ladle well above the edge of a container for sauces, gravy, and other liquid foods.

Luther Burbank, the "Plant Wizard," Is Still Poor After Making Others Wealthy

Luther Burbank

By H. H. DUNN

MOST men making millions for themselves carry other men into fortunes with them. But it is doubtful if there is more than one man in the world who, from his own creations, in one of the least explored fields of human endeavor, has piled up millions for other men and, at the same time, little more than a livelihood for himself.

To have done this willingly, to have sought the satisfaction of the sower, rather than the remuneration of the reaper; to have seen the ripened grain from his cultivation piled in the granaries of others, and yet to be contented with the knowledge that by his work the world has been made largely better as a place in which to live, is the story of this man's life, which this year passed the third quarter of a century. He is Luther Burbank, often called the "weed wizard," but who would be renamed the "plant philanthropist," were his lifework better known.

Probably from the time Burbank sold his first plant development, the potato which bears his name, for $150, through all the fifty years of his activities along these lines, he has actually given away more in dollars and cents than any other man who ever lived. Yet he is today comparatively a poor man, while all around him, from the wheat fields of the Saskatchewan to the cotton plantations of Louisiana, and from the apple orchards of New Hampshire to the plum groves of California, hundreds of thousands of dollars of increase in the value of more than 2,000 products of the soil are pouring every year because of his efforts.

It is estimated that his addition of two grains to an ear of standard wheat has added more than $5,000,000 to the annual wheat crop of the world. He reduced the size of the pit in a plum, and from two valleys in the West last year there went out more than half a million dollars' worth of these plums, larger in meat, finer in flavor, better equipped to resist shipment and change of climate. The artists of France wanted a flaxseed which would furnish a pure white oil for their paints. Burbank produced it, and increased the oil content by 20 per cent. The Japanese producers asked him for a mulberry tree which would furnish better and more food to the leaf for their silkworms. He evolved such a tree, with leaves three times the size of those of the then-known mulberry, and, just for good measure, brought it to development in two years, instead of the seven to ten years the best of the old-time mulberries required.

Ever since men have had feathered chickens, and jewelers have made delicate chronometers, sunflowers have been grown to produce seeds for the fowls and oil for the instruments. But all sunflowers—until Burbank showed them the error of their ways—grew on tall stalks and turned their faces to the sun, devoting most of their energy to getting up into their places in the sun, and the small remainder to producing seeds. The plant philanthropist took several sunflowers on his botanical knee and taught them first, to grow close to the ground; second, to devote their strength to seed production; and, third, to turn their faces away from the sun, so that the wild birds should not be able to gather the seeds. Now, these same sunflowers are down where the

Burbank's genius lay in a deep knowledge of botany and an infinite patience. Working to improve a species, he often grew a hundred thousand plants before one was approved as the parent of a new breed

Despite his contributions to horticulture, Burbank had no formal scientific education. Born in Lancaster, Mass., in 1849, he worked for a time as a factory hand in near-by Worcester, then became a truck gardener for the town market

chickens can harvest them; they produce blossoms nearly two feet in diameter, and each seed is three times as large and contains twice as much oil as did the seeds of those first sunflowers which Mr. Burbank took as pupils in his California School for Plants.

A man, who is still living near Santa Rosa, some forty years ago wanted 25,000 prune trees, in time for the next year's setting-out. Burbank took 30,000 almond seeds, planted them under wet burlap, grew almond trees more than a foot high, budded them to prunes, and delivered the tremendous order, when everyone else said the job could not be done. Those trees are growing and bearing today. A firm of American vegetable packers sought a small, sweet-flavored field pea, like the French petit pois, which would ripen uniformly over a large acreage. Burbank took a gallon of seeds of the large American field pea, and six years' time brought forth a small pea, of which more than 6,000,000 cans were packed and sold last year.

When black walnut began to disappear as a commercial wood, the plant philanthropist developed a black walnut which grows, in ten to twenty years, to the same height and diameter as the wild black walnut does in forty to fifty years. The wood is as dark in color and as fine and close in grain as its wild prototype. Just for fun, among several thousand other plant experiments, Burbank guided the lives of several chives—you have met the chive, like an onion, only smaller and without the onionesque perfume — until they bore fragrant flowers like freesias, and became, in addition to edible vegetables, sweet-scented flowering plants for borders. He noticed that Nature, when she made the petunias, overlooked blue as a color, so he introduced blue to the petunia family, and, just to give it a prominent place, made the blue petunia four or five inches in diameter across the blossom.

Those who have been trained to eat artichokes usually consider themselves slighted if they get less than one of the buds to an order. Burbank has produced an artichoke, however, which is large enough for the ordinary family, since the blossom is 14 inches in diameter when the bud has opened. An ever-blooming sweet pea, a perennial poppy, a sweet-scented verbena, a primrose nearly five inches in diameter, and a brilliant-red California poppy, not to mention the well-known Shasta daisy, are among the results of his excursions into the flower garden.

With him into the realms of weeds and grasses and fruits and flowers, the noted naturalist has carried a sense of humor. Aside from taking the thorn off the blackberry, he put more pop in popcorn, so that now it puffs out to three times the size of the ordinary "popper," while there are more kernels to the ear than in the ordinary kind. He is undecided whether the joke was on the potato or the tomato when he crossed the two and presented the world with a plant which grows potatoes above ground, and another which grows tomatoes on the vine and potatoes on the root. It should be said that both are freaks, and not commercially valuable. Thinking that most chestnuts are too old before they begin to show results, he developed a chestnut tree which attains its growth in two and one-half years,

Noted Naturalist Heading Ground-Breaking Procession at the Commencement of Work on the Burbank Memorial Park in California, Where a Collection of His Creations Are Kept

Luther Burbank and Paderewski, the Pianist, His Friend; and, Above, the Noted Naturalist and His Dog. A Model of Proposed Memorial Statue Is Shown at the Left

Burbank moved to California in 1875 and started a small nursery near San Francisco. This he sold in 1893 and established an experimental farm at Sebastopol. He lived in near-by Santa Rosa, where he died two years after this article was published

Copyright, Lester Rounds

Pontoons Attached, the Gleaming "Chicago" Noses Northward over Puget Sound after Hopping Off from the Sand Point Flying Field at Seattle on April 6

Round World in Eight Days Next?

History-Making Journey Is Declared to Have Proved the Practicability of Air Transportation between Continents

The answer to the question in the headline was to be "Yes." The next successful flight around the world was made by Wiley Post and Harold Gatty in 1931. They took just eight days, 15 hours and 51 minutes to circle the globe

WITH the triumph of the American army fliers' effort to circumnavigate the world, greater developments in the realm of aviation are predicted for the next few years than in all of the twenty years that have passed since the Wright brothers first began, clumsily but miraculously, to skim over the Atlantic coast.

Sixteen-hour airplane service between New York and San Francisco and round-the-world passenger service in 170 hours, including a sixty-five-hour air route between Gotham and Pekin, China, are some of the developments which may be expected, according to Brig. Gen. William Mitchell.

In circling the globe, covering a distance of approximately 24,000 miles in less than six months, the army fliers are declared to have proved the practicability of air transportation between continents with the present type of craft, to have stimulated the adoption of planes for the needs of commerce and to have brought to the United States the great honor of being the first to accomplish this feat.

The flight of these modern Magellans was started March 17 from Clover field, Santa Monica, Calif., the squadron being made up as follows: "Seattle," flag plane, with Maj. Fred L. Martin as pilot and Sergt. Alva Harvey as mechanician; "Chicago," Lieut. Lowell H. Smith and Leslie P. Arnold; "Boston," Lieut. Leigh Wade and Lieut. H. M. Ogden; "New Orleans," Lieut. Eric Nelson and Lieut. John Harding, Jr.

Upon the arrival at the nation's capital, September 9, the flight had covered 22,874 miles and the airplanes had been in the air 320 hours and nineteen minutes, during which time they had consumed approximately 19,200 gallons of gasoline and 4,800 quarts of oil.

Trail of the Air Magellans, and Fliers Lieut. Harding, Gen. Mason Patrick, Who Welcomed Their Return, Squadron Commander Lieut. Smith, and Lieuts. Wade, Ogden, Arnold and Nelson

The flight mapped here was made under almost incredible difficulties. There was frequent motor trouble, and the fliers were caught by ice gales off Alaska, torrential rains over the China Sea and a desert sandstorm. In Asia, curious natives almost wrecked the planes. Over Turkey they ran into a swarm of hundreds of storks. In Burma a native rowed a sampan into one plane, breaking off a lower wing. Of the four planes that started, only two—the Seattle *and the* New Orleans*—completed the trip. The others were wrecked, one in Alaska and one in the Atlantic near the Faroe Islands, but none of the crews was hurt. The whole trip took 175 days*

Radio made as much of an impact on American life as the gramaphone had done previously and that television was to in the future. In 1924 3 million sets were purchased, compared with 400,000 two years before. Most of the new radios were equipped with loud-speakers, but many earphones still were in use

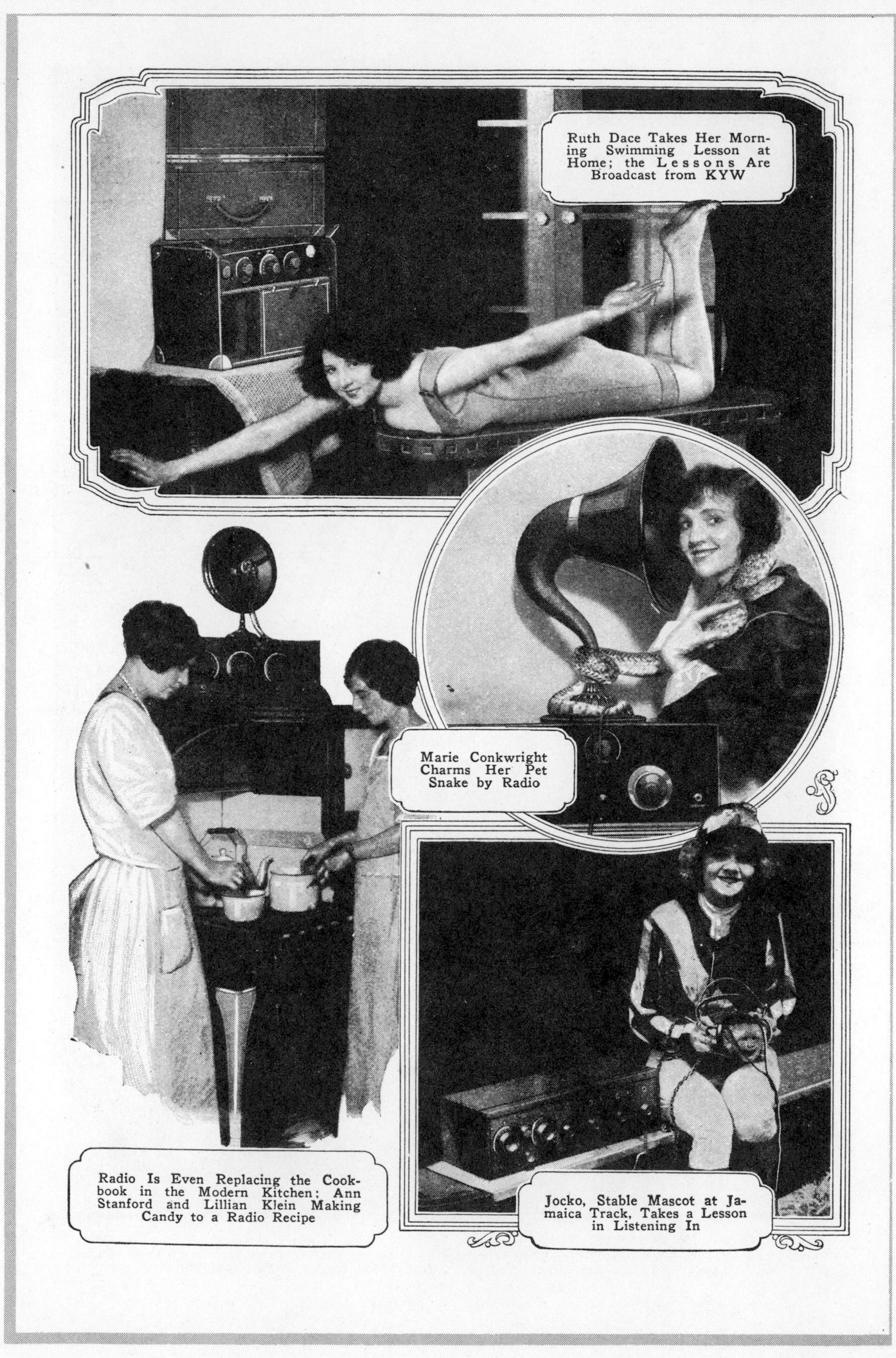

Ruth Dace Takes Her Morning Swimming Lesson at Home; the Lessons Are Broadcast from KYW

Marie Conkwright Charms Her Pet Snake by Radio

Radio Is Even Replacing the Cookbook in the Modern Kitchen; Ann Stanford and Lillian Klein Making Candy to a Radio Recipe

Jocko, Stable Mascot at Jamaica Track, Takes a Lesson in Listening In

Madge Bellamy, Well-Known Screen Star, Whiles Away the Tedium of a Wait on Location in Nevada

Estelle Taylor Has Found the Radiator of Her Automobile an Effective Aerial

Broadcasting a Baseball Game Play by Play

Radio was quick to broadcast sports events. The first football game had been broadcast in 1920, and the following year the Dempsey-Carpentier fight and the World Series between the New York Giants and Yankees were broadcast. All-day programs began in 1925, starting at daybreak with setting-up exercises and ending at midnight with dance music. The first network, NBC, began in 1926

How to Build the Popular Mechanics' Superheterodyne Eight

By F. L. Brittin

The beginning of a two-part article detailing one of the most popular of hundreds of build-it-yourself radio sets which Popular Mechanics *was to offer its readers. The superheterodyne circuit was a great forward step in radio, making possible marked increases in sensitivity and volume. Note the seven controls (not including the on-off switch) in the illustration*

REPRESENTING the closest approach to perfection yet attained, the superheterodyne circuit well deserves its widespread popularity. It is the general opinion of radio experts that any further advancement will not come until some discovery is made that will upset all our present methods of radio communication.

The superheterodyne receiver described in this article embodies all the most advanced ideas pertaining to this circuit. Nothing has been overlooked that would add to the efficiency of the instrument. Every piece of apparatus used in its construction has been carefully selected and thoroughly tested by the author; the completed instrument seemingly leaves little to be desired in selectivity, range and clearness of tone. All body - capacity effects have been eliminated by simple shielding, and the instrument is easily tuned, even by a novice, after a few minutes of instruction. The receiver can be built at a fraction of the cost of similar manufactured instruments, and has many refinements not yet included in the superheterodyne receivers on the market.

Any radio fan can build this instrument as only a few simple tools are required. If the reader follows the directions closely he will encounter very few difficulties. All parts are standard, and easily obtained from any dealer in radio supplies. There are many good instrument kits on the market for the construction of superheterodyne receivers, but the instruments in such kits are intended for operation in a circuit especially designed by the manufacturer. Such kits should not be purchased with a view to using the instruments in the circuit described here. as any departure from those specified herein will result in loss of the perfect balance that is absolutely necessary in this type of receiver.

Matching Cunning with Strategy Coast Guard, in Speedy Patrol Boats, Pickets Liquor Schooners and Fends Off Bootleggers

By AUSTIN C. LESCARBOURA

The effort to enforce prohibition was assuming the proportions of a war. Rumrunners invaded every spot along the Canadian and Mexican borders and every strip of coast. The Government was successful in keeping the smuggling within limits, but enough liquor was made inside the country by both underworld and private citizens to more than offset the excellent work of the Coast Guard, border patrols, state troopers and other enforcement agents

SOMEWHERE off Block Island, a few miles from the Rhode Island shore, the winter night has settled down on a December gale, scudding snow and a welter of tumbling waves. As the early twilight deepens it blots out a frowsy, unkempt old schooner, resurrected from some graveyard of once good ships, and now riding out the blow at anchor just safely outside the twelve-mile limit where the jurisdiction of the United States ends.

Round and round the old ship, deep-loaded with a hundred thousand dollars' worth of contraband liquor, scuttles a trim little seventy-five-foot patrol boat, keeping a lonely sentry duty. The big-graybacks, rolling in before the storm, slide under the little speeder's hull, lift her high in the air, and drop her, nose first, down the next trough, rolling her at the same time from side to side so that our landsman's legs, even after three days at sea, are hard put to it to keep a footing.

But in the tiny cabin it is warm and cozy and thick with tobacco smoke. Surely, the visitor thinks, no bootleggers from shore will be venturing out on a night like this in search of a cargo of contraband. And then an eager-faced young coast guardsman bursts into the cabin, salutes, and announces a rum runner sighted off the port bow. The skipper slides into an oilskin coat and we dash on deck, where only the soft red and green of the running lights and a dim glow over the compass relieve the gloom. The youthful officer, not long out of the coast-guard academy at New London, shouts an order. A powerful searchlight snaps into action and picks up the rum runner's boat. Squat, paintless and time-worn, she looks, under the searchlight, like any ancient and peaceful old fishing boat, plodding along about its business. But as the searchlight beam centers on that stolid-looking boat there is a staccato roar and she starts away from that spot somewhere off Block Island like a thoroughbred racer. Concealed beneath her peaceful-looking deck are two or three ex-airplane engines, each with twelve good cylinders and tuned like a high-priced watch.

The patrol boat goes into high and starts in pursuit, but is no match for the speeder ahead. But up forward two young coast-guard sailors have slipped the tarpaulin lashings off a businesslike one-pounder, and at a shouted order, slide a shell into the breach, snap the block shut, and pull the lanyard.

We watch for the splash of the shot, but there is none.

By agreement with Great Britain, the U.S. agreed not to molest any boat outside a 12-mile limit, or an hour's sail from land. On one occasion, government men took advantage of the wording of the agreement to speed a high-powered sea sled past the 12-mile limit within the hour and nabbed a large steamer with a cargo of contraband. Storms often forced liquor boats inside the limit and into the hands of waiting Coast Guardsmen

Loading a Three-Inch Gun on One of the Big Coast-Guard Boats; These Furnish Pointed Warnings to Rum Runners to Stop

"Blank," the skipper briefly explains. "Just a warning."

Up ahead, the rum runner ignores the warning, and, with her superior speed, is rapidly drawing out of range, while the beam of the searchlight grows fainter and fainter where it reflects back from the boat.

Another shell, and this time there is a fountain of water shooting skyward just ahead of the rum boat. A third shell, and a splash well astern. Superior speed, and the pitching of the patrol boat through the waves, have won a victory for the bootleggers, at least for the present.

The captain hurries back to the radio shack and gives an order, and then we adjourn to the warm cabin to continue our interrupted conversation.

A half hour later and the radio operator comes in, grinning broadly.

"The destroyer got that one," he reports.

Rum running, even on stormy nights in winter gales, is not so easy. If the picket boats don't catch you, the destroyer often will.

The wholesale revival of the age-old custom of smuggling has been met by Uncle Sam with wholesale preparations to prevent it. Every mile of coast where the rum boats flourished has been charted and divided up and patroled. Out at sea, where the liquor-loaded ships from abroad drop anchor with their cargoes, lie the picket boats, one for each liquor ship. In each district, commanding the activities of the picket boats, checking arrivals and departures on rum row, and lending a hand to run down the bootleggers' speed boats that come out from shore, is a converted war-time destroyer, capable of making thirty-five to forty knots, carrying a heavy armament of long-range guns, and a crew of 120 men.

Inshore, among the bays and coves from which the runners come, is the third line of defense, speedy little thirty-five-foot craft capable of holding their own with even the best of the bootlegging boats. And along the shore itself are the seaworthy little Seabright dories manned by coastguard crews, armed and ready to resist the actual landing of liquor, if it gets past the other defenses.

The defenses are so effective that, since they were inaugurated, the rum row off Long Island and the New Jersey coast, from which the bulk of the liquor landed near New York comes, has dwindled from as high as 101 ships at one time, to an average of not more than four or five. Steamers have disappeared entirely from the trade, both because they represented too great an investment to risk seizure, and because, with picket boats constantly near, it takes weeks or months to unload a cargo, too long to tie up a valuable ship and feed its large crew.

Instead, such rum boats as persist in the trade are usually old schooners, reconditioned for the business. If they are lost or captured the loss is not great, and the carrying capacity of even an old schooner of average size is sufficient to pack anywhere from $50,000 to $100,000 worth of whisky, at rum-row prices.

The United States has always had a certain amount of smuggling, but, before prohibition, it was confined largely to bringing in diamonds and other precious stones, to escape the duty; to bringing cigars from Havana, to importing contraband drugs, and to smuggling in Chinese and Hindus, who had been barred from the country for many years.

Some of the Disguises and Deceptions, Practiced Long Ago by Rum Smugglers in England, Which Are Now Being Revived by Crafty Boatmen to Cheat the Coast-Guard Patrol

Rumrunning was an extremely hazardous occupation at best. A dark night in a howling ocean gale is not the best time to put out to sea in a small motorboat, but the worse the night the better from the rumrunners' point of view. Many of the boats were frail craft and easily overpowered by Atlantic storms. Many went down when quite safe from the government men. Patrol boats were built for seaworthiness rather than speed. They did not try to outrun the fast smuggling craft, but radioed ahead to another patrol or to a converted destroyer assigned to each coastal district

The twenties were also the "Golden Age" of sports. Boxing, baseball, football, tennis, golf and swimming each contributed one supreme and magic name around which legends were built. No one symbolized so well the temper and tempo of the time as the tigerish, explosive Dempsey. His two defeats at the hands of Tunney stunned millions of fans. The first they explained by his long inactivity of three years. The second was complicated by the "long count," and many fans still haven't conceded his defeat

WHEN *they*

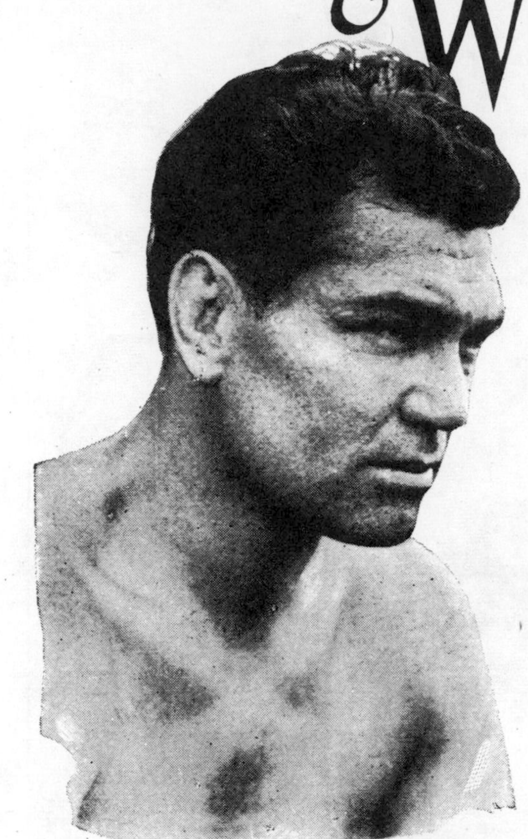

Jack Dempsey, Unshaven and Scowling, as He Appears When He Enters the Ring for a Fight

By TEX RICKARD
(As told to A. A. Albelli)

NO one but Jack Dempsey himself will ever know what it cost to try to do what no other world's heavy-weight champion has ever done—regain a lost crown.

Usually a champion or a near-champion gets knocked out and fades fast into oblivion. There is nothing under the sun which can entice him back to the ring. He's through. But, you know, Dempsey was not knocked out when he lost his championship. If Tunney had put him away in Philadelphia, I do not think he would have ever made his way back to the front lines this year. The mental hazard would have been against him. A knock-out is bound to spell the end of a champion. That is what it has done in every case heretofore. Somehow, the dethroned champion of the past has never risen out of the depths of defeat. It hangs over him like an everlasting doom. It takes a mighty fighting man to brave the hardships and hazards that lie in the way of a come-back.

If it does not seem too presumptuous on my part, I might venture to say that I know Jack Dempsey better than any other man. I have studied him for years. I know him as a man and I know him as a fighter. Of course, I do not mean to draw conclusions from the Tunney match. So I shall leave Tunney out of the discussion. It is Dempsey, the phenomenon of the prize ring, who interests me.

Dempsey Giving the Dummy a Stiff Battle in a Workout before a Fight

Bud Taylor Using Both Left and Right on Tony Canzoneri Just before the End of Their Battle, in Which Taylor Won the Bantam-Weight Crown; Several Championships Are Now Vacant

Every world's heavy-weight champion has tried to come back after losing his crown. Great fighters of modern times, like Jim Corbett, Bob Fitzsimmons and Jack Johnson, tried to get back to the top. But they failed. There was something saddening in their failures. They were beaten by Father Time. In the ring game the onrushing years mean the downrushing ability of the fighter.

.Circumstances for a come-back were different during the early part of the century. When Jim Corbett came back to recapture what Bob Fitzsimmons snatched from him in that memorable fight in Carson City, Nev., in 1897, he did not have to step across a third gladiator to reach his old crown. Nor did Fitzsimmons later have to cross gloves with any other than the mighty Jim Jeffries. And then, after Jeffries retired, he did not have to make his way across pugilistic battlefields. He had been in retirement for five years when he tried to climb back. The title was still his when he fought Jack Johnson, in 1910. But the idleness of Jeffries told. Here, also, time took its toll.

And when Johnson met Jess Willard in the sun-scorched ring in Havana, time and indolence were again fatal factors. Johnson's skill and stamina had waned. Johnson could not come back. Willard stretched him out there and put a finis to the career of a great fighter. Idleness and time proved a nemesis for Willard too. He never had any great desire to fight after he won the crown in 1915. Eventually, defying time and tradition, he tried to come back and defend his title against the youthful and almost nondescript Dempsey at Toledo. That was in 1919. You remember how Willard was put away in the third round. Another failure.

That knock-out doomed Willard. Once, years later, he tried to leap back into the spotlight when he fought Luis Firpo. You remember how Firpo knocked him out in the eighth round.

Georges Carpentier was another great heavy-weight who never recovered his bearings after having been knocked out. Dempsey flung him into limbo after that "Battle of the Century," at Boyle's Thirty Acres, in 1921.

Dempsey's friend and promoter, Tex Rickard, avoided the long-count controversy raging in the sports world, but made it clear he did not think it the decisive factor. The efficiency of science had reached into boxing too. New training methods and fighting styles, which Dempsey himself had helped innovate, required added speed in the heavyweight as well as brawn. At 33, Dempsey was no longer young enough for a fighter of Tunney's quality

Men of 40 and even 50 sometimes fought in bare-knuckle days. In the years before Dempsey, the slower style still allowed men to last longer. Fitzsimmons won the title at 36; Sullivan, Johnson and Willard were all past 35 when they lost it. Many fans who had thrilled to Dempsey's apparent slam-bang style had not realized how much skill, calculation and rhythm were in it. The new, faster fights made heavyweights "old" at 30, some of them earlier. New York refused to allow the Firpo-Willard fight to be held in the state because of Willard's age

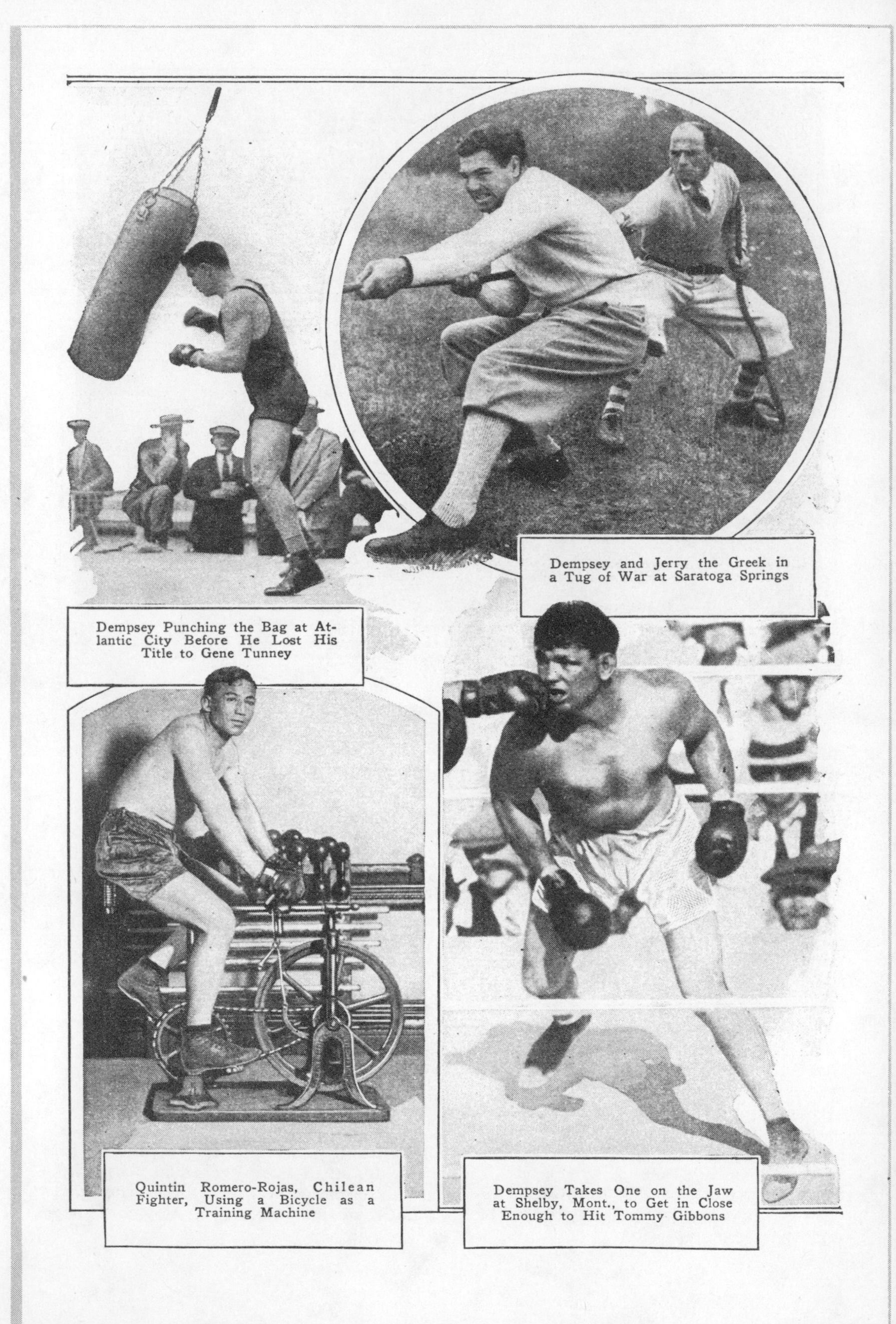

Dempsey and Jerry the Greek in a Tug of War at Saratoga Springs

Dempsey Punching the Bag at Atlantic City Before He Lost His Title to Gene Tunney

Quintin Romero-Rojas, Chilean Fighter, Using a Bicycle as a Training Machine

Dempsey Takes One on the Jaw at Shelby, Mont., to Get in Close Enough to Hit Tommy Gibbons

Paris Flight Shows Need for SPEED INDICATOR

CAPTAIN Charles Lindbergh's epochal non-stop flight from New York to Paris emphasized the need, in the opinion of aviation engineers, of one more instrument to make such long journeys across the ocean safe and sure. That is, some device for measuring the speed of an airplane across the surface of the earth, without the necessity of taking complicated sights at sun or stars, which are often impossible because of fog and storms.

Lindbergh reached Paris, 3,600 miles from his starting point, in thirty-three hours and thirty minutes, with nothing but an earth-inductor compass and an air-speed indicator to guide him. Fortunately, for his success, the latter not only indicated his speed through the air, but showed fairly well his actual ground speed, for he had a tail wind most of the way. Had he met head winds, however, which would have slowed down his plane and burned up his precious store of gasoline, he would have had no way of knowing the fact so long as he was flying over the ocean.

It is to offset that one great lack in flying instruments that aerial navigators are cudgeling their brains. At three-quarter throttle, the speed at which Lindbergh operated his engine throughout the flight, the Ryan monoplane "Spirit of St. Louis" has a speed of 100 miles an hour in still air. With a tail wind that is increased in proportion to the wind's strength, and with a head wind, it is correspondingly decreased.

Inasmuch as Lindbergh averaged about 113 miles an hour for the entire distance, he apparently had a tail wind most, if not all, of the time. So long as the air-speed indicator, which shows the plane's speed through the air, registered better than 100 miles an hour, the pilot had nothing to worry about, for the excess mileage over 100 could only be due to a wind behind him. But if the indicator had dropped to 100 he would not have known whether he was flying in still air or against a head wind, for the head wind, plus the plane's speed, would have continued to register as 100 regardless of the strength of the wind. The latter might have attained a velocity of forty miles an hour and cut the ground speed of the plane to sixty miles, and still the indicator would have shown 100, while the plane could never have reached its destination with the gas it carried. With nothing below, even in daylight, to check his ground speed by, the flyer would have sailed on, ignorant of his danger, whereas with a ground-speed indicator he could have sought safety by turning back.

Centuries of navigation have never produced anything better than the sextant and stellar or solar observations to check the position of a craft at sea. Patent logs, to be trailed through the water, are fairly

No barnstormer in the old tradition, young Lindbergh was flying mail from St. Louis to Chicago when he became intrigued by Raymond B. Orteig's $25,000 prize for a nonstop New York-to-Paris flight. His plane was purchased by citizens of St. Louis, and Lindbergh set the stage for his transatlantic flight by blazing a new transcontinental record from San Diego to Curtiss Field, L. I., in 21 hours and 20 minutes. Ten days later he had pointed the nose of the Spirit of St. Louis *toward Paris*

Lindbergh's flight, while not the first crossing of the Atlantic, was important in that it demonstrated the superiority of the monoplane and the radial air-cooled engine. The fact that it was a solo flight captured the public imagination, and the "Lone Eagle" was given an unprecedented reception and parade down Broadway upon his return to the U.S. As predicted in this article, modern navigation uses radio. A bearing is taken on two widely separated ground stations, and the exact position of the plane at any moment is calculated by triangulation. Radar techniques are also used today

reliable, but far from being exact enough even for a surface ship to depend on.

Flying through the air over the ocean, even the trailing log is impossible. If the problem is ever solved, it may possibly come through some new discovery in radio whereby practical instruments may be developed to indicate the distance from a broadcasting station by measuring the amount of power with which the signal reaches the plane.

The Lindbergh flight brought home more forcibly than anything that has happened in aviation the high degree of perfection which planes and aerial motors have attained. That a single motor could operate, without stopping, for more than thirty-three hours, that it could do 6,100 miles without overhaul, and still be ready to continue, proved a revelation to many who have not closely followed the improvements made in flying. Lindbergh's average speed from New York to Paris was 113 miles an hour. A few days later, at Indianapolis, ten of the finest racing creations in the automobile world were worn out in the first half of a 500-mile race while trying to meet the 109-mile-an-hour pace set by the leader.

The air-cooled motor, which Byrd used in his flight over the north pole and which Chamberlin and Acosta used in setting a new world's duration record, has proved ideal for flying. It eliminates the weight of the radiator and its water supply, and also all the manifold possibilities of broken water connections and clogged tubes, or a fractured radiator pipe. Every tube, pipe and joint on a plane is a liability, since the failure of any one of them is usually sufficient to force a flyer down.

A Hop of 1,600 Miles to St. Louis, a Skip of 900 Miles to New York, and a Jump of 3,600 Miles to Paris Carried Lindbergh a Third of the Way around the World in Fifty-Five Hours and a Quarter; at Right Is the Pilot Examining His Motor and, Below, His Instrument Board

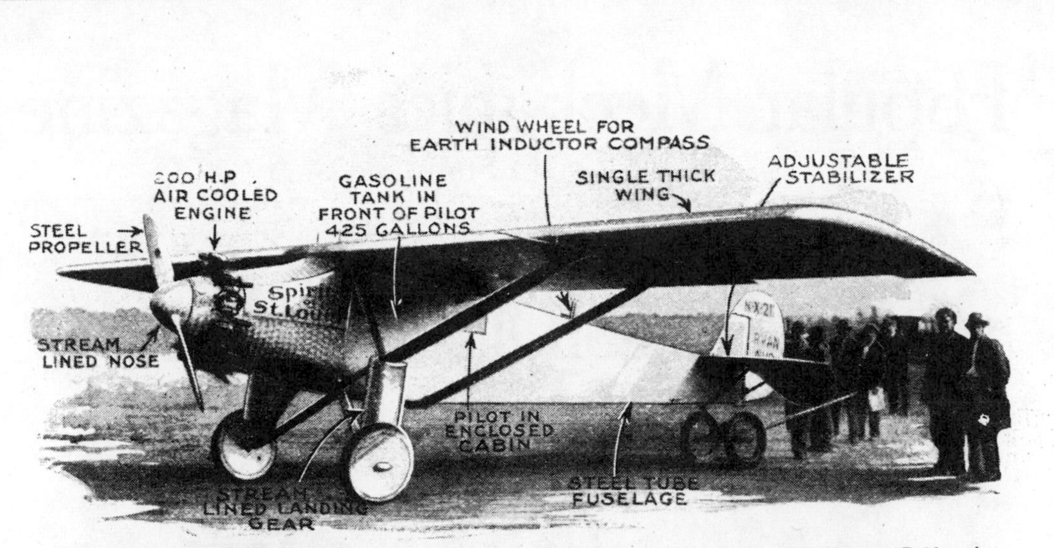

The "Spirit of St. Louis" in New York, and Some of the Principal Features of the First Airplane to Bridge the Gap between Two Great Cities on Opposite Sides of the Atlantic in One Flight

In staking his life on his earth-inductor compass, instead of carrying the excess weight of a companion to act as navigator, Lindbergh likewise was not taking such extreme chances as many might think. Loss of flying speed due to a head wind would have upset all the calculations on which his navigation was based, but, with the exception of that one possibility, his method of flying was fairly safe.

The earth-inductor compass is not a compass at all, in the usual meaning of the term, since it does not employ a floating needle to be attracted toward the magnetic north. He carried a magnetic compass, too, but they are far from being reliable in the air, since the presence of the mass of metal in the engine and the electrical effect of the ignition system make them difficult to correct. The earth inductor is nothing but a small electric generator, driven by a tiny air fan, a "dummy" compass dial by which the electrical field of the generator can be varied, and a galvanometer, which looks like the familiar "charge" and "discharge" ammeter on the automobile instrument board. The generator is placed far back in the tail of the plane, to remove it from the electrical influence of the ignition system. Its vertical shaft projects up through the body of the plane and carries a little two-bladed wind propeller, as the photographs of the "Spirit of St. Louis" show.

In flight, the aviator charts his true course, and then turns the dummy compass pointer to the route chosen, upsetting the magnetic field of the generator in its relation to the earth. Then he swings his ship until the galvanometer hand rests on the top center of the dial, and is then on his chosen course. Any variation to left or right will cause a corresponding deflection of the needle, just as the ammeter hand on the automobile swings to one side for charge and the other for discharge.

To fly across the Atlantic, Lindbergh plotted his course in advance, basing it on the great circle, which is the shortest distance between two points on the earth's surface. Actually he did not fly a circle, but rather a series of short legs of 100 miles or so each. As plotted, his course required him to fly one hour in a fixed direction, then reset his compass for another hour, and so on. Since all the courses, or one-hour legs, had been calculated in advance, the changes were simple to make.

The feasibility of transatlantic flying was further strengthened only two weeks after Lindbergh's flight when Clarence Chamberlin and Charles A. Levine flew almost to Berlin in their Bellanca monoplane. They remained in the air for forty-two hours, finally running out of gasoline and descending within 110 miles of Berlin, at Eisleben. That was at 5:00 a. m., Berlin time, after nearly two days and nights in the air, yet they immediately regassed and took off again, but, becoming lost, finally descended seven hours later, still 70 miles from the German capital.

"Lindy," the son of a noted Minnesota congressman, was born in Detroit on Feb. 4, 1902, and raised in Little Falls, Minn. After attending the University of Wisconsin, he enrolled in a flying school at Lincoln, Neb., enlisted as a cadet at Kelly Field, Tex., and was commissioned in the spring of 1925. When he made his famous flight he was a captain in the Air Corps Reserves. Upon his return from Paris he was commissioned a colonel

Inventors had been on the trail of television for many years. These programs by General Electric, sent out three times a week, were the first regular broadcasts. A few months before, England's John Baird had sent a still picture from London to Hartsdale, N.Y. Charles F. Jenkins, inventor of the first movie projector that produced life-size images, transmitted the first moving images by television on June 13, 1925. As high government officials stood by to watch, he flashed a view of the turning blades of a toy windmill from Bellvue to Washington, D.C. Baird sent a moving image the same year. Both Jenkins and Baird used vacuum-tube amplifiers and photoelectric cells

Popular Mechanics Magazine

REGISTERED IN U. S. PATENT OFFICE

WRITTEN SO YOU CAN UNDERSTAND IT

Vol. 49 APRIL, 1928 No. 4

Television for the Home

Behind a Little Three-Inch-Square Aperture, the Moving Picture from the Radio Studio Appears, While the Watcher, with a Push Button in His Hand, Keeps the Picture Synchronized

GROUPS of people sitting in various homes at Schenectady, N. Y., a few weeks ago, saw the performers in a distant broadcasting studio flit across a tiny screen, and from the loud speaker of a radio set heard them talk.

Television, a laboratory plaything that has interested scientists for several years, had arrived.

A large, square cabinet, built somewhat like the bigger talking-machine models, is the first home receiver for radio-transmitted images. The dials of a receiver protrude from its middle, and above them, at the eye level of the seated spectator, appears a three-inch-square window, behind which is the screen on which the images are formed.

The one great problem that has perplexed television experimenters for years —how to synchronize the transmitter and the receiver—was solved by simply ignoring it. Instead of all the elaborate, and very expensive, equipment necessary to keep the whirling disk of pinholes that paints the image on the receiver screen in absolute step with the corresponding mechanism that transmits the original

The Motor-Driven Pinhole Disk, the Neon Lamp That Reproduces the Image and the Picture Receiver

image, the television receiver for home use has a simple rheostat control on the end of an extension cord that permits the spectator to do the synchronizing himself. If the receiving motor runs a trifle fast or a bit too slow, the picture will begin to get out of focus—to slip off the screen. The effect is much like that at the movie theater, when the "frames" of the moving film and the shutter do not work in unison and you see the bottom half of one frame and the top half of another on the screen. The operator makes a simple adjustment to the projector, and the picture is restored to position; and in the same way a slowing down or speeding up of the television-receiver motor brings the picture back into place.

"It is as simple," explains Dr. E. F. W. Alexanderson, of the General Electric laboratories, who developed the machine, "as learning to drive an automobile."

David Saranoff, vice president and general manager of the Radio Corporation of America, predicts that within five years television will be an art and an indust y in this country.

Here is how the first practical demonstration in the home worked:

In the studio the performer stands before an ordinary arc light. Between him and the light is a large disk, revolving eighteen times a second, and in the disk are forty-eight holes, arranged in a spiral, so that, in each revolution, successive beams of light are swept across each part of the performer's face. A photo-electric cell is directed toward the performer, and as each light beam is reflected back from his face, it affects the cell, which converts the light into electrical energy.

From there on, the transmission system differs in no important respect from the usual broadcasting outfit. The tiny current wave from the photo cell is magnified and amplified into a powerful signal, which is then dispatched into the air through the antenna on a wavelength of 37.8 meters. The antenna is a new type, the wires arranged in a checkerboard square, each wire being half a wavelength long and so coupled that they are always in phase, eliminating the necessity of antenna tuning. The WGY transmitter, on its usual wavelength of 379.5 meters, was used for the accompanying voice transmission.

In the home there are two receivers,

The necessity of scanning mechanically was all that held television back. Paul Nipkow of Germany originated this method around 1885. He used two disks, one for scanning, one for receiving, as did the later inventors. Nipkow also worked out one of the basic principles still used in television: when light is reflected from an object and strikes a light-sensitive cell, it sets up an electric current of corresponding intensity

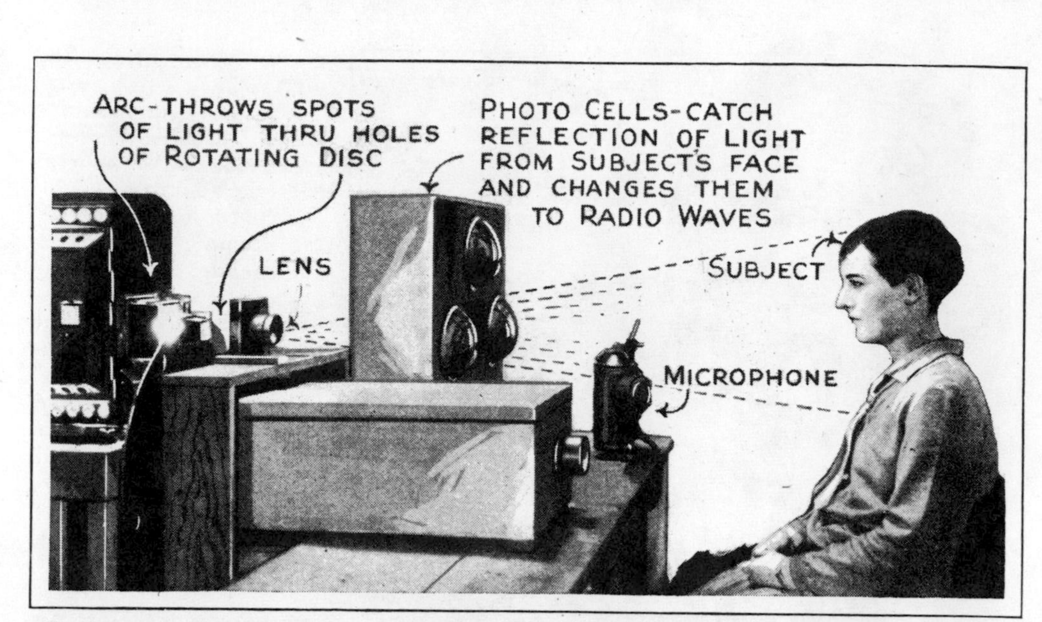

The Transmitter for Radio Pictures Is a Battery of Sensitive Photo-Electric Cells That Transfer the Reflected Light into Electric Current to Be Broadcast through the Air

Not until 1930 was a live program sent as far as 6 miles. The cathode-ray gun, which made electronic scanning possible, was considered a laboratory device at this time. In addition to disks, these early inventors experimented with both mirrors and lenses, even attempted color television

one to pick up the voice, on one wavelength, and deliver it, amplified in volume, to the loud speaker. The other, operating on a different wavelength, receives and amplifies the electrical signals produced by the image. Instead of being connected to a loud speaker, the output of this receiver goes to a small "cold light," a neon-gas-filled bulb, which is so sensitive that it can be turned on and off a million times a second, if necessary, with no lingering afterglow, and which has the peculiar property of producing its glow on one side of a targetlike electrode only.

In front of the neon globe, a duplicate of the pinhole disk at the broadcasting station is revolving eighteen times a second, kept in step by the control in the spectator's hands. As its forty-eight apertures sweep in turn across in front of the light, they pass the pulsating light beams, now rising in brilliancy for a high light, and then fading off for a shadow. The disk is twenty-four inches in diameter, and the forty-eight holes each thirty-five millimeters across. The distance between the outer and inner holes of the spiral is calculated to make an image only an inch and a half square, but between the disk and the spectator's window is a magnifying lens that doubles the picture each way, bringing it up to three inches square.

The rate of revolution of the disk—eighteen times per second—produces a corresponding number of images, or two more per second than are seen when movie film is operated at standard speed.

The Moore neon lamp, invented by D. McFarland Moore, an engineer of the Edison lamp works of the General Electric company, gives the picture a distinct pink cast, one of the characteristics of neon which is seen in the new type of signs now in use.

In the demonstration at Schenectady, performers in the studio talked, moved about, lit and smoked cigarets, exhibited their bobs and permanent waves, and performed other stunts. As all the apparatus as yet built has such small receiving screens, no attempt has been made to transmit an entire studio scene, an orchestra playing, or even a full-length portrait of a moving person.

One of the interesting things about the television demonstration is that, when the broadcasting of images becomes a regular feature, anyone will be able to build receivers, for none of the principal features will be covered by basic patents. The revolving disk, the neon lamp and the photoelectric cell are all old inventions. There are patents, of course, on the improved features of late models, but the basic ideas involved all date back before the days when radio pictures were thought of.

Women Are Manifesting an Enthusiastic Interest in Aviation, as Is Evidenced by Their Use Daily of Air-Travel Facilities, and the Fact That They Have Gone In for Not Only Transatlantic Flights but for Endurance and Altitude Records as Well; Above Is Shown Mrs. Louis Thadden, a California Woman, Who Stayed in the Air over the Oakland Airport for More Than Twenty-Two Hours to Establish an Endurance Record for Her Sex, While at the Left Is Pictured Miss Marvel Crosson, Another California Girl Pilot, Who Took a Cabin Monoplane to an Altitude of 24,000 Feet in an Effort to Set a Record for Height for Other Women Flyers to Emulate

Altitude Flyers Must Carry Their Air Supply Along; Right, Lieut. Apollo Soucek with the Apparatus He Used in His Recent Record Flight

Women took to the air early. Blanche Scott, a pupil of Glenn Curtiss, soloed at Fort Wayne, Ind., in 1910, reaching an altitude of 12 feet. A few years later, Harriet Quimby repeated Blériot's channel flight. In 1927, Phoebe Omlie became the first woman pilot to be licensed under the Air Commerce Act. Maryse Hilz of France still holds the world altitude record for women —46,948 feet—set in 1936

Amelia Earhart had already crossed the Atlantic with Wilmer Stutz and Louis Gordon in 1927. On May 20-21, 1932, she made the first nonstop, solo flight across the Atlantic by a woman. Her time, from Newfoundland to Ireland, was just under 15 hours

In 1903 the overtaking of a passenger train by an airplane was in the "artist's conception" stage (see page 25). Here, in almost the same composition, the picture is a reality. In 1903 the locomotive would have won easily. Now the situation was reversed. The world speed record for land planes at this time was 250 miles an hour, for seaplanes 300 miles per hour, and no locomotive could begin to keep up

Combined Rail-Air Service Now Transports You from Coast to Coast in Less Than Forty-Eight Hours; Twentieth Century Limited Salutes a Fokker Passenger Plane

Above, the "Robin" Which Stayed in the Air for Over 420 Hours at St. Louis, and, Below, One of the Refueling Contacts That Made the Endurance Flight Possible; during Refueling, a Speed of Seventy Miles an Hour was Maintained at 3,000-Foot Altitude

Endurance records were made and broken rapidly in the great upsurge of interest in aviation. A year after this issue appeared, John and Kenneth Hunter stayed up 553 hours and 41 minutes. Later, as long-range planes approached, then passed, the speed of sound, such air endurance ceased to be important. In 1949, an Army Air Force crew under Captain James Gallagher flew a B-50 superfortress, Lucky Lady II, *around the world nonstop in 94 hours and one minute*

The Air Commerce Act of 1926 did a great deal to stimulate commercial aviation. It established air lanes and air-traffic rules; government supervision of airports; registration, inspection and licensing of planes and pilots; and made provision for regular weather information. In 1929 Pan American World Airways began the first passenger service to Europe and service was also established between San Francisco and the Philippines. The following year through air service was begun between Los Angeles and New York, making it possible to fly from the Philippines to Europe, via the U.S.

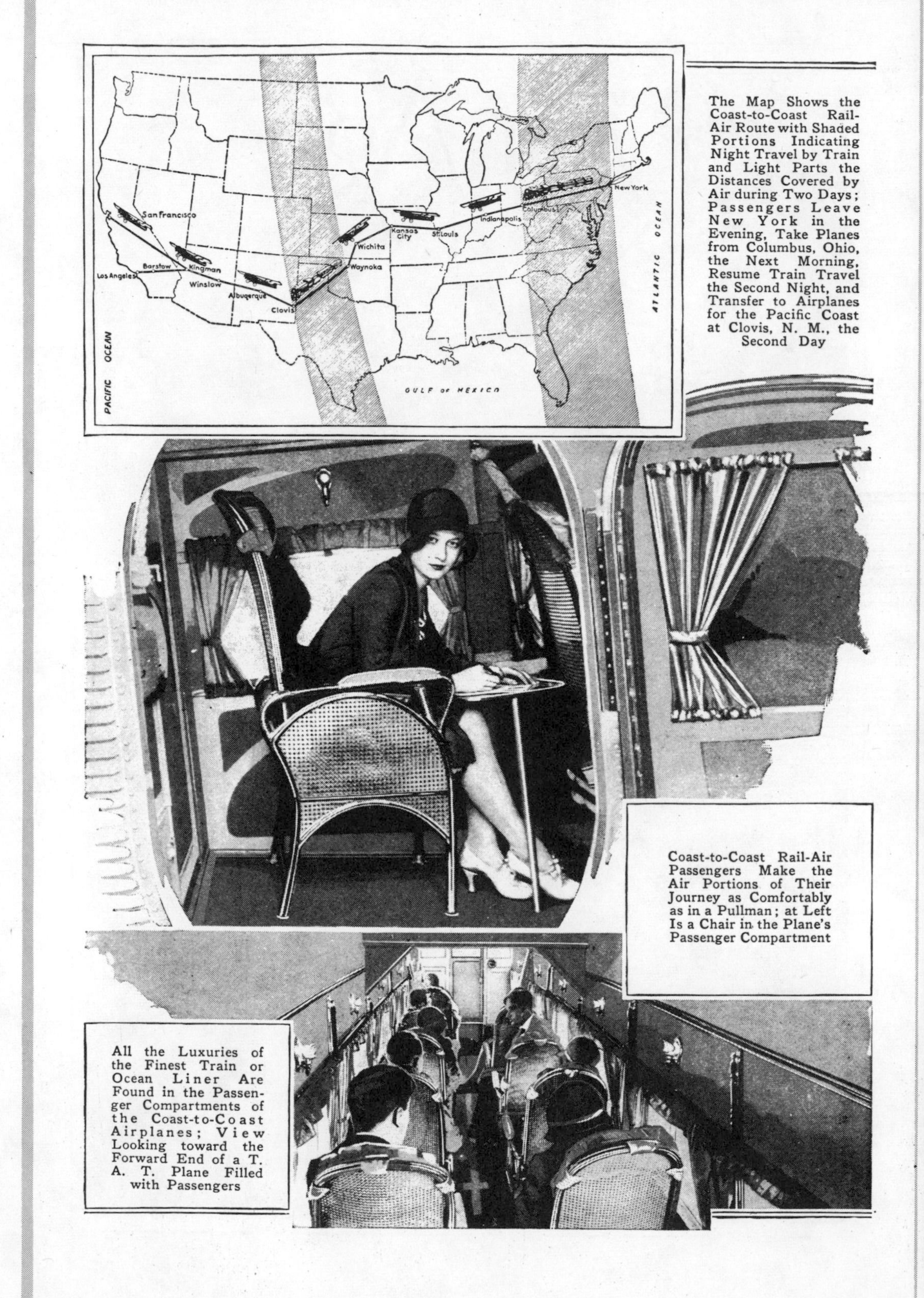

The Map Shows the Coast-to-Coast Rail-Air Route with Shaded Portions Indicating Night Travel by Train and Light Parts the Distances Covered by Air during Two Days; Passengers Leave New York in the Evening, Take Planes from Columbus, Ohio, the Next Morning, Resume Train Travel the Second Night, and Transfer to Airplanes for the Pacific Coast at Clovis, N. M., the Second Day

Coast-to-Coast Rail-Air Passengers Make the Air Portions of Their Journey as Comfortably as in a Pullman; at Left Is a Chair in the Plane's Passenger Compartment

All the Luxuries of the Finest Train or Ocean Liner Are Found in the Passenger Compartments of the Coast-to-Coast Airplanes; View Looking toward the Forward End of a T. A. T. Plane Filled with Passengers

GANGSTER CAR FITTED WITH BULLET-PROOF GLASS

Upper Left, Mark of High-Velocity Rifle Bullet on Bullet-Proof Auto Glass; Center, Pock Marks of Buckshot and Large-Caliber Pistol; Right, Hole Drilled by .30-.30 Rifle; Below, Officer Testing the Glass

In New York, Chicago, San Francisco, Detroit and even smaller cities, gangs in 1930 were highly organized and heavily armed. Warring among themselves for control of the rich profits in illegal liquor, prostitution and other vice, they used highly developed techniques of attack and defense. Their arms included submachine guns, bombs, sawed-off shotguns and high-powered rifles

Two gangsters arrested in California recently traveled in an automobile behind a protecting shield of glass. Glass in the windshield was more than three-quarters of an inch thick and that in the windows was one and one-eighth inch in thickness. Visibility was unimpaired except when looking through the thick plates at a decided angle. The body of the automobile itself was not armored, the owners frankly explaining that bullets were aimed at the windows and not the body. The glass itself was of the non-shattering kind, built up of layers alternated with other layers of transparent material to hold the sections together, and was not in the least different from any other windshield or motor-car glass, so that it would fool even the astute gunmen of an opposing gang into thinking it nothing out of the ordinary. Before removing the bullet-proof glass from the car, the police submitted it to tests and found that it required a medium-power deer rifle, shooting a high-velocity bullet, to penetrate the windowpanes. Buckshot made a scarcely noticeable freckle on the glass, and pistol bullets likewise failed to do more than leave a mark and start star-shaped cracks until two bullets from a large-caliber pistol were placed in exactly the same place.

BEST COLORS FOR SIGNBOARDS

To investigate the visibility of various colors for use in outdoor advertising, an English company recently erected a huge signboard on which advertisements were displayed in an open field for comparison under expert supervision. In general, the tests showed, that black print on a yellow background or green on white gave best visibility. Then followed red on white, blue on white and white on blue. Black on white, the common form of printing, came next, revealing that its visibility stands far down on the list. Still less effective were yellow on black, white on red and white on black. Red print on yellow, green on red and red on green all proved to be entirely unsatisfactory.

The completion of the Empire State Building in New York City was the climax of the skyscraper era in architecture. It began with Chicago's 10-story Home Insurance Company Building in 1885, and was pioneered by Frank Lloyd Wright's great teacher, Louis Sullivan. The first of the giant skyscrapers was New York's 66-story Woolworth Building, finished in 1913. "As tall as the Woolworth Building" became for years an American exaggeration for emphasis. The Empire State's 102 stories and beacon still make it the tallest structure in the world

Workman Gazing over Manhattan from the Eighty-Eighth Floor of the Empire State Building; When Completed, This Building Will Be the Tallest Man-Made Structure in the World

VISIBLE fifty miles out at sea, 100 miles from an airplane and seventy miles north of New York, a $50,000,000 miracle of glass, steel, chromium, aluminum, limestone and granite commands the horizon and staggers the imagination.

Not a mirage, but a colossus of modernity, is this, the highest structure ever reared by mankind, fulfilling myriad prophecies on time, space and infinity.

The Empire State building, 1,250 feet from sidewalk to aviation beacon, ushers in the age of Babylonian pinnacles and presages severe restrictions on the term "skyscraper." One thousand feet above Fifth avenue, on the eighty-fifth story, you can see how this new Goliath dwarfs so-called skyscrapers of twenty stories.

Beginning at the ground floor, the Empire State occupies a site of 83,725 square feet, or 197 by 425 feet. The main setback, sixty feet, occurs above the fifth story. From the sixth story, there is a sheer rise of almost 1,000 feet, all surmounted by an airship mooring mast 200 feet high. The total volume is 37,000,000 cubic feet, 2,000,000 square feet of rentable space for 20,000 tenants, and enough spare room for 15,000 visitors.

These mammoth proportions fade, however, before the distinction of being the first building constructed to accommodate aircraft and their passengers. The Empire State's mooring mast may not be used for three years, but everything will soon be in readiness. Exhaustive studies are now being made of various types of mooring machinery. The 200-foot mast is faced with glass and chrome-nickel steel. The framework is reinforced and fastened rigidly to the main building skeleton. A fifty-ton jolt would not injure the mast or substructure, and it is doubtful whether any dirigible at ease could jar this anchorage.

R. H. Shreve, the architect, intends to follow new developments in mooring machinery. He referred to the graphic il-

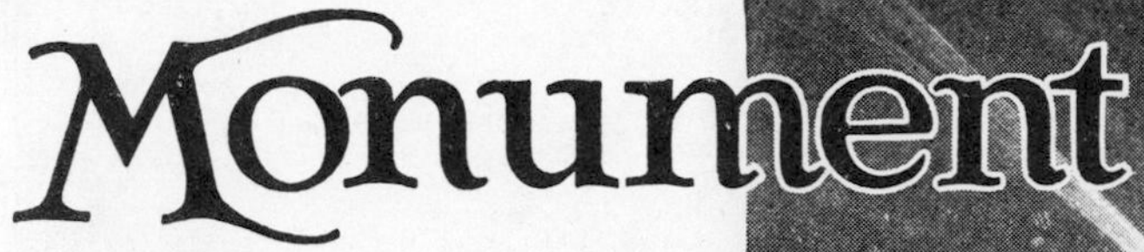

lustration of the mooring-tower head at St. Hubert's airport, Canada, which appeared in the October issue of Popular Mechanics, saying that it would be installed if no improvements are made while the choice is pending. Meanwhile, the tip of the mast will be an aviation beacon, which will be discarded when the type of mooring apparatus is selected and installed.

The building's elevator contracts involve an expenditure of $3,000,000. No firm ever before attempted a 1,000-foot elevator altitude in a building, and the project necessitates elaborate experimental work. Certain phases of construction will cost the elevator builders three times what they receive, the difference being charged to laboratory overhead. What must they do? Construct electrical equipment for sixty-six high-speed signal-controlled self-leveling elevators. One battery of express cars will make no stops below the sixtieth story, and it will reach that height in less than one minute! The main shafts will not go above the eightieth story. A separate battery will serve floors above.

The Empire State's steel frame weighs in excess of 58,000 tons, the largest single order ever placed in building construction. Loads on individual columns also break all previous records. Several columns bear 10,000,000 pounds each.

Weight is one of the principal factors in skyscraper construction, and in this case the architects were driven to a new type of exterior construction. For the first time, they made extensive use of aluminum and chrome-nickel

Architect's Drawing of the Empire State Building, Which Will Be 1,250 Feet High to Tip of the Aviation Beacon

The Empire State Building could have gone much higher without overloading the foundation or straining the skeleton. By using metal on the exterior, the builders had reduced the weight of the walls by 50 per cent. The 6400 windows were almost made integral parts of the walls. Space was saved by building radiators into the walls. Ventilating ducts were also concealed

Five thousand men were employed when Empire State construction was at its peak, with total expenses $10,000 a day. Some 290 bricklayers, 384 helpers and 225 carpenters were used. In all, the building consumed 58,000 tons of steel, 10,000,000 bricks and 200,000 cubic feet of stone. Daily deliveries were made of 5000 bags of cement, 450 cubic yards of sand and 300 bags of lime. A hundred trucks approached the building at one time every day, and the construction men had to work out a method similar to a railroad dispatch system to handle them

Drawing Showing Comparative Heights of the Empire State Building, Which Will Be the Tallest Man-Made Edifice, and Other Tall Structures of the World, Including the Pyramid of Khufu

By CRAG DALE

LOOK at it!—the humble gasoline filling station, ready to serve any automobile with fuel.

If this filling system of distribution works with the automobile, why not extend it to staple articles of food and clothing? Already power is sold that way. Light sockets are electrical filling stations, maintained by a central-power unit.

In the opinion of Frank Lloyd Wright, an architectural pioneer of international fame, the gasoline-filling station rapidly is becoming a symbol of a trend away from Main Street—a centralization made necessary in the past by the inefficiency of individual transportation.

At every crossroads, and between them, stand gasoline-filling stations ready to serve any automobile with fuel. Since this system of distribution works so well with the automobile, suggests Mr. Wright, why not extend it to staple articles of food and clothing? And indeed in many places throughout the country Mr. Wright's idea already has been translated into action.

Government statistics show that there now are 110,000 roadside-stand owners, almost all of whom expanded from filling stations. Of that number, 45,000 are permanent year-around operators, serving not only their own communities but tourists as well.

The 16,609 retail-store operators who went into bankruptcy during the first eleven months of 1930, with liabilities of $244,578,-

Artist's Drawing of One of California's Marketing Centers, Where Even Theater Tickets Are Sold; It Has Grown Up around the Easily Accessible Filling Station

Filling stations now were strung along the highways like red, yellow and orange beads. For miles, signs informed the driver that he soon would be at Joe's filling station where Highway 54 met Route 6. The gasoline pump was the heart of the station, but oil was also sold, and drivers came to expect other services from the attendant. Soon they were offering battery recharges, parts and repairs

The spotless, inspected rest rooms made for longer stops, and soon the customers could purchase candy, sandwiches and "red-hot" chili. The filling station had come a long way since Sylvanus P. Bowser set up the first gas pump at Fort Wayne, Ind., in 1885. This pump, using wooden plungers and marble valves, dispensed gasoline from a barrel

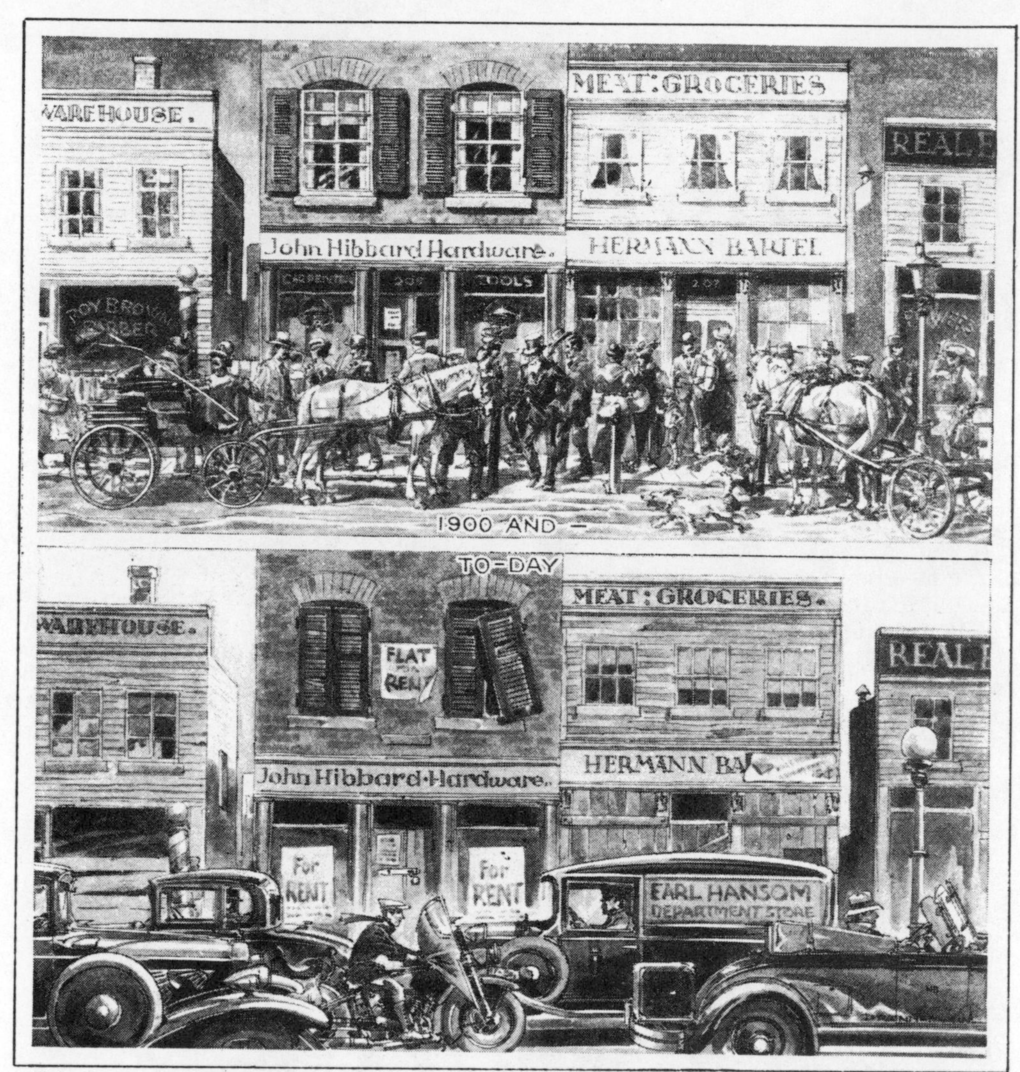

This Changing World and What Has Happened to Shop Keepers Since the Man on Foot Has Taken to the Crowded Roadway with Its Ever-Present "No Parking" Signs

000, face department of commerce figures showing that roadside marketing in 1930 took from the ordinary retail business of the country $500,000,000. In other words, it would seem that the business taken from retail stores last year by gasoline-filling stations and their accompanying roadside-marketing facilities more than doubled the total losses of the 16,609 retail bankruptcies.

A movement now is on foot, and has made great headway, to bring about a co-operative organization of filling stations engaged in selling commodities other than gas and oil. The latest census of gasoline-filling stations shows 317,000 in operation. That figure includes 6,000 owned and operated by the larger oil-producing companies, such as the Standard Oil company, which already is engaged in distributing tires through the service stations it owns or controls. An equal number is owned by the larger oil-producing companies but operated under lease. Independently organized companies operate 8,000, while individual oil producers and private operators maintain 105,000 filling stations. The remainder are run in connection with garages or are maintained as roadside pumps.

It is Mr. Wright's opinion, and in this he is supported by industrial leaders, that the trek to the city is about to be given the "to the rear—march" order by the very force of economic pressure, and the change which has been brought about in society by the use of the automobile. Mr. Wright holds that the automobile and the filling-station system have made possible man's accommodation to the country. The city, he thinks, served its purpose in a day when transportation and communication were undeveloped. But now, he believes, homes and industries might better establish themselves near public highways far from present congested areas. Mr. Wright's ideas are borne out by the latest estimates of the government, which show a larger population on American farms at the beginning of 1931 than at the beginning of the previous year. For the first time in ten years, according to these estimates, farm residents have increased in number. More than 1,500,000 left the farms last year for the cities and 1,392,000 moved back to them. This would seem to show a small difference in favor of the cityward movement, but the normal increase by births in the farming communities makes the net result of 208,000 more souls living on farms now than a year ago.

Three Types of Quaint Roadside Stands That Attract California Motorists

Added to that might be considered, in connection with the development of commodity distribution by filling stations, the fact that last year, according to the American Tourist Camp association, there were 6,000,000 campers using 2,000,000 automobiles on the highways spending an aggregate average of forty-six camping days at an expense of $7 a day per car. The Hotel Men's association estimates that in 1930 tourists other than campers contributed $12,000,000 to the revenues of hotel keepers in the nation.

Other statistics show that in the east and middle west the regular trade habit of farm homes is in the nearest town.

Wright's prophecy for the filling station was never fulfilled, however. The number of stations in the United States dropped from 317,000 in 1930 to about 200,000 in 1950, due to larger gas tanks and fewer breakdowns on the road. The volume of filling-station business for the same period rose from half a billion dollars to about 6½ billion a year

1932-1941

Fix it up and make it do

THE nation was in the depths of the worst economic depression in history. The people were interested in making things last . . . in learning how to adapt worn-out things to new uses . . . in how to save money or earn extra money by doing things themselves. The burden of most newspapers and periodicals of the period was pessimism, even hopelessness—but *Popular Mechanics* told its readers there were things one could do, and how one should do them.

The nation as a whole was in a "do something" mood. The jobless walked aimlessly past the factories where they used to work—and many of those factories were as silent and gloomy as the men who walked by. There were almost 15 million of these unemployed—men who used to work the idle mines, or manned the ships tied up and rotting at the wharves, or filled the freight cars now rusting in empty lines in the railroad yards. Farmers were desperate as they watched the produce they grew and the animals they tended sell for prices that would hardly pay for seed and feed. Angry farmers halted trucks and dumped milk into the roads so that it would not be sold at depression prices, and stood in grim-faced bands, cradling shotguns, to prevent the sale of farms in mortgage foreclosures.

When the depression showed no signs of ending itself as such hard times had in the past, the government began to intervene in the nation's economy. President Herbert Hoover set up the Reconstruction Finance Corporation in January of 1932, and a program of public works was begun. Before his program of "priming the pump" of industry could be fairly tested, however, Hoover was voted out of office by a public clamoring for a change in the political as well as the economic climate.

On the eve of the inauguration of Franklin D. Roosevelt, most of the banks in the nation closed their doors. A national bank holiday was declared, and Congress was called to special session to adopt the Emergency Banking Act of 1932. There followed the bewildering era of the New Deal—the social and economic experiments conducted by the "alphabetical agencies"—some of them successful, others admittedly errors, and some so controversial that economists with time to assess their value argue bitterly about them to this day.

The PWA and the WPA

But for the man in the street the era of hopelessness at least was gone. At the peak of government assistance in March, 1934, more than seven million families, involving 26 million persons (or one of every five Americans) were receiving direct aid in one form or another from the government. The leaf-raking days of the Public Works Administration were gone—and those employed on Works Projects Administration jobs for the most part could take pride in the things they were doing—building 650,000 miles of surfaced roads, 78,000 bridges, 35,000 public buildings, even projects as grand as New York's Triborough Bridge. Government loans became available to save mortgage-threatened farms and homes.

By 1936, although lagging behind Europe, the degree of American recovery was measurable—national income rose from 30 billion dollars in 1933 to 71 billion dollars, and the value of manufactures for this period had about doubled. But the recovery applied chiefly to industries making consumer goods; the heavy industries and the building trades lagged behind, and there continued to be about 10 million unemployed. In 1937 every phase of economic activity declined again, but conditions had improved somewhat by the summer of 1938.

The literature of the period for the most part reflected the depression years. Erskine Caldwell's *Tobacco Road* and John Steinbeck's *The Grapes of Wrath* mirrored the lives of the destitute; so did plays like Clifford Odets' *Waiting for Lefty* and the poetry of Carl Sandburg, Archibald MacLeish and Edna St. Vincent Millay. There were outstanding exceptions to the social theme: Margaret Mitchell's *Gone With the Wind* and Dale Carnegie's *How to Win Friends and Influence People*. New American schools of art developed around Thomas Hart Benton, Grant Wood and John Steuart Curry. Foreign opera stars gave way to such American names as Grace Moore, Lawrence Tibbett, Richard Crooks, John Charles Thomas and Helen Jepson.

As in every decade, the public took up, and then put down, new fads and fancies. A kaleidoscope of these: long skirts . . . open-toed sandals . . . "bank nights" and free dishes at the movies . . . bingo . . . contract bridge . . . jigsaw puzzles . . . pinball machines . . . miniature golf. People talked about: the Dionne quintuplets . . . Technicolor . . . the "Gas House Gang" of the St. Louis Cardinals . . . John Dillinger . . . college boys swallowing goldfish . . . Edward VIII and Mrs. Wallis Warfield Simpson of Baltimore . . . Mrs. Roosevelt.

Emilie, Yvonne, Cecile, Marie and Annette

It was a decade rich in world's fairs—A Century of Progress (Chicago, 1933-34), California Pacific International Exposition (San Diego, 1935-36), Great Lakes Exposition (Cleveland, 1936-37), Golden Gate International Exposition (San Francisco, 1939-40), New York World's Fair (1939-40). The Olympic Games were held in the United States for the first time at Los Angeles in 1932.

The uneasy peace that had prevailed since 1918 was broken when Japanese troops marched into Manchuria in 1932. The League of Nations and the United States, which had not joined, sent stiff protest notes—but that was all. Mussolini's troops raped Ethiopia, and in Germany Adolf Hitler rattled his saber and screamed demands of western Europe. Austria became the victim of *Anschluss;* Czechoslovakia was swallowed in two gulps, and in 1939 the pretenses were dropped and the Nazi *blitzkrieg* knifed into Poland. World War II was on.

The United States again was determined to stay out—but again was irresistibly drawn into the whirlpool by moral obligations and the threat to American security. To give aid to Great Britain and France, the arms embargo was lifted in 1939, and a lend-lease program began with the exchange of 50 overage U.S. destroyers for naval and air bases on British-controlled islands in the Atlantic.

The day that lives in infamy

Meanwhile, relations with Japan had grown steadily worse. War came with shocking suddenness on Dec. 7, 1941, with the Japanese surprise attack on Pearl Harbor. Declarations of war on Japan, Germany and Italy followed in rapid order.

The cover story told of Army Air Corps tests of a master parachute that would float cabin and passengers to earth when a plane met disaster in flight. Experiments showed that individual parachutes were safer, since there was danger of injury to the passengers when the cabin struck and was dragged over the ground. The air services have tested the practicality of many devices intended primarily for commercial aviation

One-Wheel Auto Carries Passengers in "Tire"

The One-Wheel Auto Rolling Along beside a Car of Ordinary Size; It Has Room for Two Passengers and Can Make a Speed of Thirty Miles an Hour on Smooth Highways

Resembling huge automobile tires in general appearance, motor-driven cages, ten feet high, recently rolled over the highways in England at thirty miles an hour in the initial tests of a form of vehicle termed the "dynasphere." In effect, it is a one-wheel automobile with room for two passengers inside the "tire." The wheel is of metal latticework with a bulging rim like an inflated tire. Inside is a circular track on which rests the set of wheels supporting the driver's seat. These wheels are operated by a small gasoline or electric motor.

Racing Auto and Golf Ball in a Speed Duel

Gene Sarazen Driving a Golf Ball in a Speed Contest with an Automobile; at 120 Miles an Hour, the Car Passed the Ball after the First 100 Yards of the Race

How fast does a hard-driven golf ball travel? The answer is: about 120 miles per hour—but you've got to be a champion to drive them that hard. This deduction was reached recently following a speed duel on the Packard proving ground between a high-powered speedster driven by Col. J. G. Vincent and a golf ball "driven" by Gene Sarazen, holder of various of golf's most coveted titles. The motor car was given the handicap of a flying start. As it flashed by, Sarazen swung and the race was on. For the first few yards, the speed of the ball was slightly faster than the automobile's 120 miles per hour. Then gradually, the car overcame the lead, drew even and, at 100 yards, passed the flying pellet.

In spite of the fact that four seems to be the logical number of wheels for an automobile, inventors have come up again and again with cars having all sorts of weird suspension arrangements. In addition to the four-wheeled, there have been cars with one, two, three, six and eight wheels. Probably the most fantastic of them all is the Bi-Autogo, a two-wheeled, three-passenger roadster built in 1912 by James Scripps Booth. It has a 140-inch wheelbase, is powered by a large V-8 engine and looks like a huge, enclosed motorcycle. An odd feature is the radiator, which consists of a mass of copper tubing draped like limp noodles over the front portion and down along the sides. It cost $25,000 of good 1912 money to build and was driven 635 miles. It is now in James Melton's Museum in Connecticut

Winston Churchill was on an American lecture tour when he wrote this article which reveals some amazingly accurate predictions and Churchill's sure grasp of a wide field of information. At the time the article was written, Churchill was a member of the British House of Commons, having retired from the cabinet when the Conservative Party, then led by Stanley Baldwin, lost the general elections of 1929. His future then, he has since admitted, looked very dismal indeed

FIFTY YEARS

Winston Churchill, Former British Chancellor of the Exchequer

THE great mass of human beings absorbed in the toils, cares and activities of life, are only dimly conscious of the pace at which mankind has begun to travel. We look back one hundred years and see that great changes have taken place. We look back fifty years and see that the speed is constantly quickening. This present century has witnessed an enormous revolution in material things, in scientific appliances, in political institutions, in manners and customs.

The greatest change of all is the least perceptible by individuals; it is the far greater numbers which in every civilized country participate in the fuller life of man. "In those days," said Disraeli, writing at the beginning of the nineteenth century, "England was for the few and for the very few." "The twice two thousand for whom," wrote Byron, "the world is made," have given place to many millions for whom existence has become larger, safer, more varied, more full of hope and choice. In the United States, scores of millions have lifted themselves above primary necessities and comforts, and aspire to culture—at least for their children. Europe, though stunned and lacerated by Armageddon, presents a similar, if less general, advance. We all take the modern conveniences and facilities as they are offered to us, without being grateful or consciously happier. But we simply could not live if they were taken away. We assume that progress will be constant.

"This 'ere progress," Mr. Wells makes one of his characters remark, "keeps going on. It's wonderful 'ow it keeps going on." It is also very fortunate; for if it stopped, or were reversed, there would be a catastrophe of unimaginable horror. Mankind has gone too far to go back, and is moving too fast to stop. There are too many people not merely whose comfort, but whose very existence is maintained by processes unknown a century ago, for us to afford even a temporary check, still less

HENCE

by WINSTON CHURCHILL
Former British Chancellor of the Exchequer

a general setback, without experiencing calamity in its most frightful forms. When we look back beyond one hundred years over the long trails of history, we see immediately why the age we live in differs from all other ages in human annals. Mankind has sometimes traveled forward and sometimes backward, or has stood still for hundreds of years. It remained stationary in India and in China for thousands of years. But now it is moving very fast.

What is it that has produced this new prodigious speed of man? Science is the cause. Her feeble groping fingers lifted here and there, often trampled underfoot, often frozen in isolation, have now become a vast organized, united, class-conscious army marching forward upon all the fronts toward objectives none may measure or define. It is a proud, ambitious army which cares nothing for all the laws that men have made; nothing for their most time-honored customs, or most dearly cherished beliefs, or deepest instincts. It is this power called science which has laid hold of us, conscripted us into its regiments and batteries, set us to work upon its highways and in its arsenals; rewarded us for our services, healed us when we were wounded, trained us when we were young, pensioned us when we were worn out. None of the generations of men before the last two or three were ever gripped, for good or ill, and handled like this.

Man in the earliest stages lived alone and avoided his neighbors with as much anxiety, and probably as much reason, as he avoided the fierce flesh-eating beasts that shared his forests. With the introduction of domestic animals the advantages of co-operation and division of labor became manifest. In neolithic times, when cereals were produced and agriculture developed, the bleak hungry period, whilst the seeds were germinating beneath the soil, involved some form of capitalism and the recognition of those special rights of landed proprietors the traces of which are still visible in our legislation. Each stage involved new problems, legal, sociological and moral. But progress only

Churchill's classwork at Harrow and Sandhurst, the "West Point of Britain," was undistinguished. The grasp of history and science he shows here was largely gained in spare-time reading during his service with the Fourth Hussars Regiment in Cuba and India and with Lord Kitchener's army in Egypt. He has described his favorite reading as including Plato, Aristotle, Macaulay and Darwin, with a special fondness for Gibbon's Decline and Fall of the Roman Empire

Despite the industrial basis of Communist society, Churchill was quick to see its similarity to the social structure of ancient barbarian empires. For "efficiency of despotism," Churchill gives the Soviets a higher rating than the Pharaohs, and notes the similarity of "powers at once irresistible and capable of intimate regulation." Churchill early warned of the Nazi menace, but contradictorily approved Mussolini even after the Italian conquests in Africa. An uneasy ally of Russia during World War II, Churchill startled the world in 1946 with his speech at Fulton, Mo., warning of the danger of new Soviet aggressions

crawled, and often rested for a thousand years or so.

The two ribbon states in the valleys of the Nile and the Euphrates produced civilizations as full of pomp and circumstance, and more stable than, any the world has ever known. Their autocracies and hierarchies were founded upon the control and distribution of water. The rulers held the people in an efficiency of despotism never equaled till Soviet Russia was born. They had only to cut off or stint the water in the canals to starve or subjugate rebellious provinces. This gave them powers at once as irresistible and capable of intimate regulation as the control of all food supplies gives to the Bolshevik commissars. Safe from internal trouble, they were vulnerable only to external attack.

But in these states man had not learnt to catalyze the forces of nature. The maximum power available was the sum of the muscular efforts of all the inhabitants. Later empires, scarcely less imposing but far less stable, rose and fell. In the methods of production and communication, in the modes of getting food and exchanging goods, there was less change between the time of Sargon and the time of Louis XIV, than there has been between the accession of Queen Victoria and the present day. Darius could probably send a message from Susa to Sardis faster then Philip II could transmit an order from Madrid to Brussels. Sir Robert Peel, summoned in 1834 from Rome to form a government in London, took the same time as the Emperor

Television May Be Expected to Span Oceans and Continents to Conquer Distance as Radio Has Already Done

Vespasian when he had to hasten to his province of Britain. The bathrooms of the palaces of Minos were superior to those of Versailles. A priest from Thebes would probably have felt more at home at the council of Trent, two thousand years after Thebes had vanished, than Sir Isaac Newton at a modern undergraduate physical society, or George Stephenson in the Institute of Electrical Engineers. The changes have been so sudden and so gigantic, that no period in history can be compared with the last century. The past no longer enables us even dimly to measure the future.

There are two processes which we adopt consciously or unconsciously when we try to prophesy. We can seek a period in the past whose conditions resemble as closely as possible those of our day, and presume that the sequel to that period will, save for some minor alterations, be similar. Secondly, we can survey the general course of development in our immediate past, and endeavor to prolong it into the near future. The first is the method of the historian; the second that of the scientist. Only the second is open to us now, and this only in a partial sphere. By observing all that science has achieved in modern times, and the knowledge and power now in her possession, we can predict with some assurance the inventions and discoveries which will govern our future. We can but guess, peering through a glass darkly, what reactions these discoveries and their applications will produce upon the habits, the outlook and the spirit of men.

The most wonderful of all modern prophecies is found in Tennyson's "Locksley Hall:"

For I dipt into the future, far as
 human eye could see,
Saw the Vision of the World, and all
 the wonder that would be;

Saw the heavens fill with commerce,
 argosies of magic sails,
Pilots of the purple twilight, dropping down with costly bales;

Heard the heavens fill with shouting,
 and there rain'd a ghastly dew
From the nation's airy navies grappling in the central blue;

Far along the world-wide whisper
 of the south wind rushing warm,
With the standards of the peoples
 plunging thro' the thunderstorm;

Till the war-drum throbb'd no longer,
 and the battle-flags were furl'd
In the Parliament of man, the
 federation of the world.

Slowly comes a hungry people, as a
 lion, creeping nigher,
Glares at one that nods and winks
 behind a slowly-dying fire.

Streamlining Is Being Extended to Locomotives, so It Is Not Difficult to Visualize the "Iron Horse" of the Future Like This

Churchill cites the difficulties of prophecy, declaring that since the Industrial Revolution it is no longer possible to foresee the future by looking at the past, nor by projecting what science already has accomplished into the future. He concludes that prophecy is best done by intelligent insight. Like many another, Churchill is intrigued by the prophecies of "Locksley Hall," Tennyson's famed poem which appeared in 1843

Only the first of Tennyson's prophecies—conquest of the air—has been fulfilled completely, as Churchill probably would be the first to admit today. World War I proved not to be the world's last Armageddon; the League of Nations was found impotent in its first major test—the 1935 dispute between Italy and Ethiopia—and the free world struggles still to contain the spread of Bolshevism

Hidden Cities, and Even a Lost Civilization, May Be Discovered When Exploration of the Ocean Floor Is Made Easy

These six stanzas of prediction, written eighty years ago, have already been fulfilled. The conquest of the air for commerce and war, the world struggle of Armageddon, the League of Nations, the Bolshevik revolution—all divined in their true sequence by the great Victorian, all now already in the history books and stirring the world around us today. We may search the Scriptures in vain for such precise and swiftly vindicated forecasts of the future. Jeremiah and Isaiah dealt in dark and cryptic parables, pointing to remote events and capable of many varied interpretations from time to time. A Judge, a Prophet, a Redeemer would rise to save his chosen people; and from age to age the Jews asked disputing, "Art thou he that should come? or look we for another?" But "Locksley Hall" contains an exact foretelling in their sequence of stupendous events, which many of those who knew the writer lived to see and endure! The dawn of the Victorian era opened the new period of man, and the genius of the poet cast back the curtains which veiled it.

Whereas, formerly, the utmost power that man could guide and control was a team of horses, or a galley full of slaves, or, possibly, if they could be sufficiently drilled and harnessed, a gang of laborers like the Israelites in Egypt, it is today already possible to control accurately from the bridge of a battle cruiser all the power of hundreds of thousands of men. Or to set off with one finger a mine capable in an instant of destroying the work of thousands of man-years. These changes are due to the substitution of molecular energy for muscular energy, and its direction and control by an elaborate, beautifully perfected apparatus. These immense new sources of power, and the fact that they can be wielded by a single individual, have made possible novel methods of mining and metallurgy, new modes of transport and undreamed-of machinery. These, in their turn, enable the molecular sources of power to be extended and used more efficiently. They facilitate also the improvement of ancient methods. They substitute the 100,000-kilowatt turbo-generators at Niagara for the mill wheel of our forefathers. Each invention acted and reacted on other inventions, and with ever-growing rapidity that vast structure of technical achievement was raised which separated the civilization of today from all that the past has known.

There is no doubt that this evolution will continue at an increasing rate. We know enough to be sure that the scientific achievements of the next fifty years will be far greater, more rapid, and more surprising, than those we have already experienced. The slide lathe enabled machines of precision to be made, and the power of steam rushed out upon the world. And through the steam clouds flashed the dazzling lightnings of electricity. But this is only a beginning. High authorities tell us that new sources of power, vastly more important than any we yet know, will surely be discovered. Nuclear energy is incomparably greater than the molecular energy which we use today. The coal a man can get in a day can easily do five hundred times as much work as the man himself. Nuclear energy is at least one million times more powerful still. If the hydrogen atoms in a pound of water could be prevailed upon to combine together and form helium, it would suffice to drive a 1,000-horsepower engine for a whole year. If the electrons—those tiny planets of the atomic systems—were induced to combine with the nuclei in the hydrogen, the horsepower liberated would be one hundred and twenty times greater still. There is no question among scientists that this gigantic source of energy exists. What is lacking is the match to set the bonfire alight, or it may be the detonator to cause the dynamite to explode. The scientists are looking for this.

The discovery and control of such sources of power would cause changes in human affairs incomparably greater than those produced by the steam engine four generations ago. Schemes of cosmic magnitude would become feasible. Geography and climate would obey our orders. Fifty thousand tons of water, the amount displaced by the "Berengaria," would, if exploited as described, suffice to shift Ireland into the middle of the Atlantic. The amount of rain falling yearly upon the Epsom race course would be enough to thaw all the ice at the arctic and antarctic poles. The changing of one element into another, by means of temperatures and pressures far beyond our present reach, would transform beyond all description our standards of values. Materials thirty times stronger than the best steel would create engines fit to bridle the new forms of power. Communications and transport by land, water and air would take unimaginable forms if, as is in principle possible, we could make an engine of six hundred horsepower weighing twenty pounds and carrying fuel for a thousand hours in a tank the size of a fountain pen. Wireless

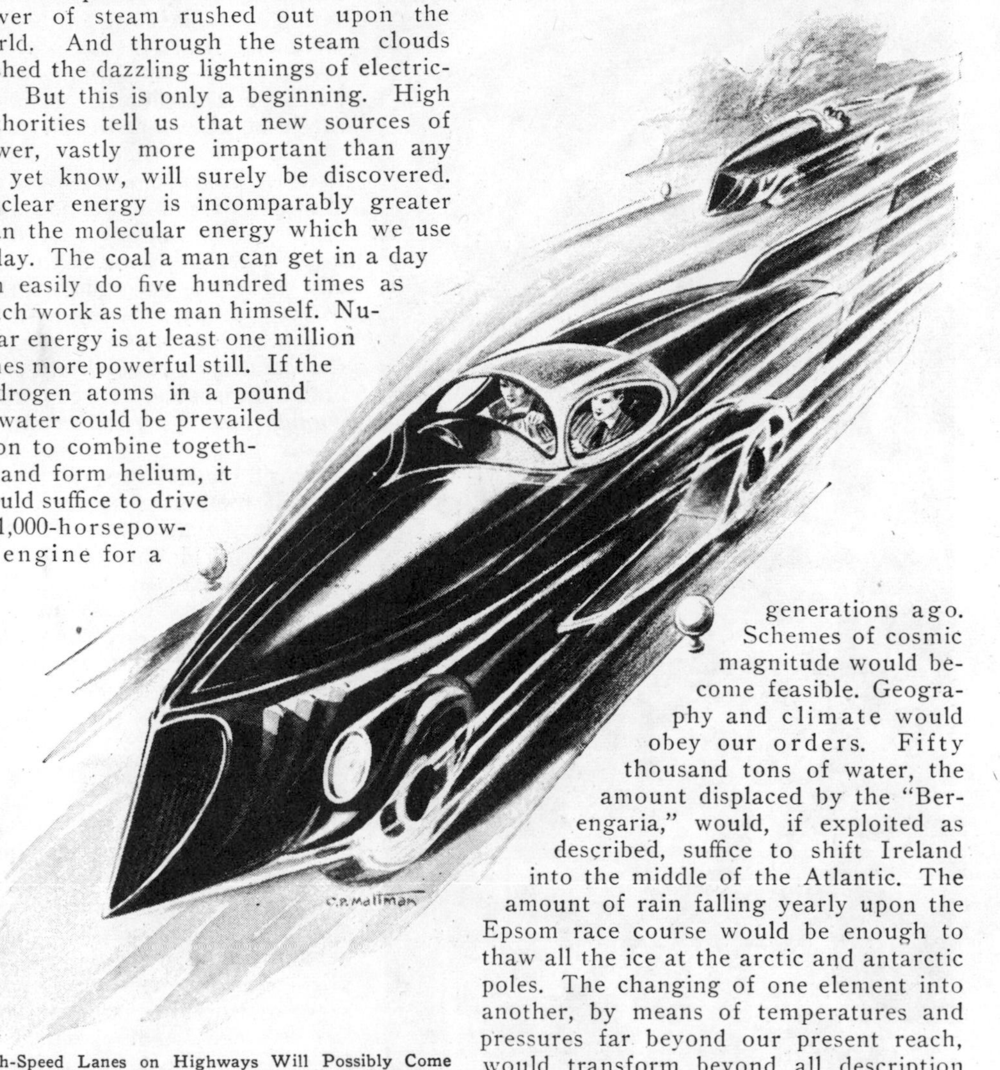

High-Speed Lanes on Highways Will Possibly Come with Further Evolution of Streamlined Cars

The reader will find it interesting to compare Churchill's predictions here with those of the article, "Miracles You'll See in the Next Fifty Years" on page 298. Waldemar Kaempffert, science editor of The New York Times, *shows there that science still shares some of the convictions about technologies of the future as are expressed here by Churchill*

Even before the threat of atomic war, the decentralization of urban life had been suggested by many sociologists. Waldemar Kaempffert's 1950 article suggests almost the same trend for decentralization as does Churchill here

The Metropolis of the Future May Contain Set-Back Structures Like These and Elevated Streets

telephones and television, following naturally upon their present path of development, would enable their owner to connect up to any room similarly equipped and hear and take part in the conversation as well as if he put his head in through the window. The congregation of men in cities would become superfluous. It would rarely be necessary to call in person on any but the most intimate friends; but if so, excessively rapid means of communication would be at hand. There would be no more object in living in the same city with one's neighbor than there is today in living with him in the same house. The cities and the countryside would become indistinguishable. Every home would have its garden and its glade.

Up till recent times, the production of food has been the prime struggle of man. That war is won. There is no doubt that the civilized races can produce or procure all the food they require. Indeed, some of the problems which vex us today are due to the production of wheat by white men having exceeded their own needs, before yellow men, brown men and black men have learned to demand and become able to purchase a diet superior to rice. But food is at present obtained almost entirely from the energy of the sunlight. The radiation from the sun produces from the carbonic acid in the air more or less complicated carbon compounds which serve us in plants and vegetables. We use the latent chemical energy of these to keep our bodies warm, we convert it into muscular effort. We employ it in the complicated processes of digestion to repair and replace the wasted cells of our bodies. Many people, of course, prefer food in what the vegetarians call "the secondhand form," i.e., after it has been digested and converted into meat for us by domestic animals kept for this purpose. In all these processes, however, ninety-nine parts of the solar energy are wasted for every part used.

Even without the new sources of power great improvements are probable here. Microbes, which at present convert the nitrogen of the air into the proteins by which animals live, will be fostered and made to work under controlled conditions, just as yeast is now. New strains of microbes will be developed and made to do a great deal of our chemistry for us. With a greater knowledge of what are called hormones, i.e., the chemical messengers in our blood, it will be possible to control growth. We shall escape the absurdity of growing a whole chicken in order to eat the breast or wing, by growing these parts separately under a suitable medium. Synthetic food will, of course, also be used in the future. Nor need the pleasures of the table be banished. That gloomy Utopia of tabloid meals need never be invaded. The new foods will be practically indistinguishable from the natural products from the outset, and any changes will be so gradual as to escape observation.

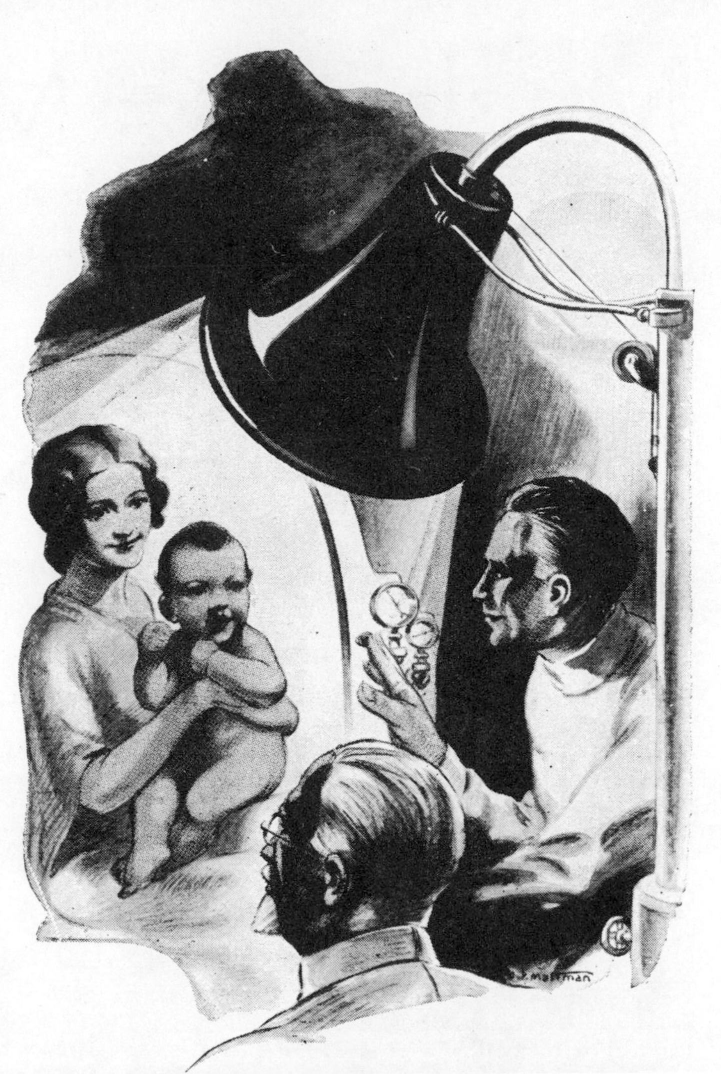

Ultraviolet Light May Result in Many Changes in Life Processes Just as It Already Aids in the Treatment of Disease

If the gigantic sources of power become available, food would be produced without recourse to sunlight. Vast cellars, in which artificial radiation is generated, may replace the cornfields and potato patches of the world. Parks and gardens will cover our pastures and plowed fields. When the time comes, there will be plenty of room for the cities to spread themselves.

But equally startling developments lie already just beyond our fingertips in the breeding of human beings and the shaping of human nature. It used to be said of scientific progress: "You have taught the dog more tricks; but you cannot alter the breed of the dog." But this is no longer true. A few years ago London was surprised by a play called "Rossum's Universal Robots." The production of such beings may well be possible within fifty years. They will not be made, but grown under glass. There seems little doubt that it will be possible to carry out the entire cycle which now leads to the birth of a child, in artificial surroundings. Interference with the mental development of such beings, expert suggestion and treatment in the earlier years, would produce beings specialized to thought or toil.

Churchill's prophecy about solar energy still holds interesting possibilities. In the first flush of speculations about atomic energy, many scientists thought it would obviate the necessity for further research into solar energy. Later, however, as the magnitude and expense of atomic energy plants became apparent, solar energy re-entered the picture as a possible source of cheap power. Chemical experiments with hormones have since been made in the direction Churchill indicates here

Machines—*Masters*

By GEORGE W. GRAY

Dr. Karl T. Compton

William Green

In 1932, the worst year of the world-wide depression, there were many who blamed the machine for creating unemployment by piling up huge inventories of goods which in turn led to falling prices and declining wages. There were others who believed that the problem was not quite so simple. This article covers every major aspect of the great debate then going on about the machine and its responsibility for the industrial depression

MACHINES, which owe existence to their power to serve human wants, are now accused of turning the tables on man. They are held responsible for unemployment and all the ills which today afflict the world.

A recent suggestion of this point of view comes from Dr. Raymond B. Fosdick, of the Rockefeller Foundation. "Our machines," he says, "have fastened themselves on every detail of our lives. They have called into being millions of people who otherwise would not have been born. For these hundreds of millions they are the sole means of support. Stop the machines, and half the people in the world would perish in a month."

But what do the scientists and engineers, the creators and builders of the machines, say? Recently a leader in the physical sciences, Dr. C. E. K. Mees, expressed doubt as to the human value of mechanical improvements. Doctor Mees is an eminent chemist, director of research for the Eastman Kodak company, and his laboratory has been a prolific incubator of contributions to the machine age. Yet, save in checking disease, he does not think that science and engineering have benefited man.

"Will any student of history agree that the inhabitants of an American city are on the whole happier than those of a Greek or a Babylonian city of the past?" asks Doctor Mees. In those days there was more leisure, less pressure, more opportunity for the exchange of ideas, less emphasis on material things. There is little that a man can get today which he could not have had in Athens."

But the taint of slavery is smudged over the Athenian glory. The only people who could get "things" and enjoy them in ancient Athens were the aristocrats.

or Slaves?

Left, Dr. James Henry Breasted; Right, Dr. Arthur D. Little; Below, Dr. Willis R. Whitney

During its greatest period, Greece had 12,000,000 slaves and only 5,000,000 freemen. For every hour that the small patrician class spent in comfort and leisure and enjoyment, many hours of brutish labor had to be performed by human slaves.

"The machine in itself is not an evil, but a good," said Dr. Karl T. Compton, president of the Massachusetts Institute of Technology. "Its good lies in this—that it has taken from the overloaded muscles of men and women innumerable burdens and labors, and transferred them to the steel muscles and electric nerves of machinery. It is only when the machine is exploited without thought to its human consequences, that it becomes a danger and a detriment."

If we had to abolish all machinery, and put back into the muscles of men all the labor now performed by steam, electric, gasoline, and water power, we should need at least five billion human slaves, says Dr. W. E. Wickenden, of the Case School of Applied Science. Of course such a transfer is impossible. That's more people than the total population of the earth!

William Green, president of the American Federation of Labor, recently pointed out that within the last ten or twenty years mechanical improvements in some industries are comparable with a century of earlier progress.

"Take, for instance, the manufacture of electric-light bulbs," said Mr. Green. "In 1918, it took one man a whole day to make forty bulbs. The next year came a machine that made 73,000 bulbs in twenty-four hours. Each of these machines threw

Dr. Willis R. Whitney, director of research for the General Electric Co., said in a continuation of the article not reproduced here: "Science is at our service—it can free us or enslave us—but we ourselves must make the choice. . . . Idleness is not the goal of our mechanical improvements but leisure for new experimenting, for new experiencing, may well be"

Dr. James Henry Breasted, founder and director of the Oriental Institute of the University of Chicago, pointed out that the ancient Egyptians declined after they "came completely under the spell of their material triumphs." Popular Mechanics' *editors summed up the debate as proving that: "As an instrument of exploitation and profiteering, the machine is doomed by common sense, but as an instrument of service to mankind . . . the future of the machine may well be unending"*

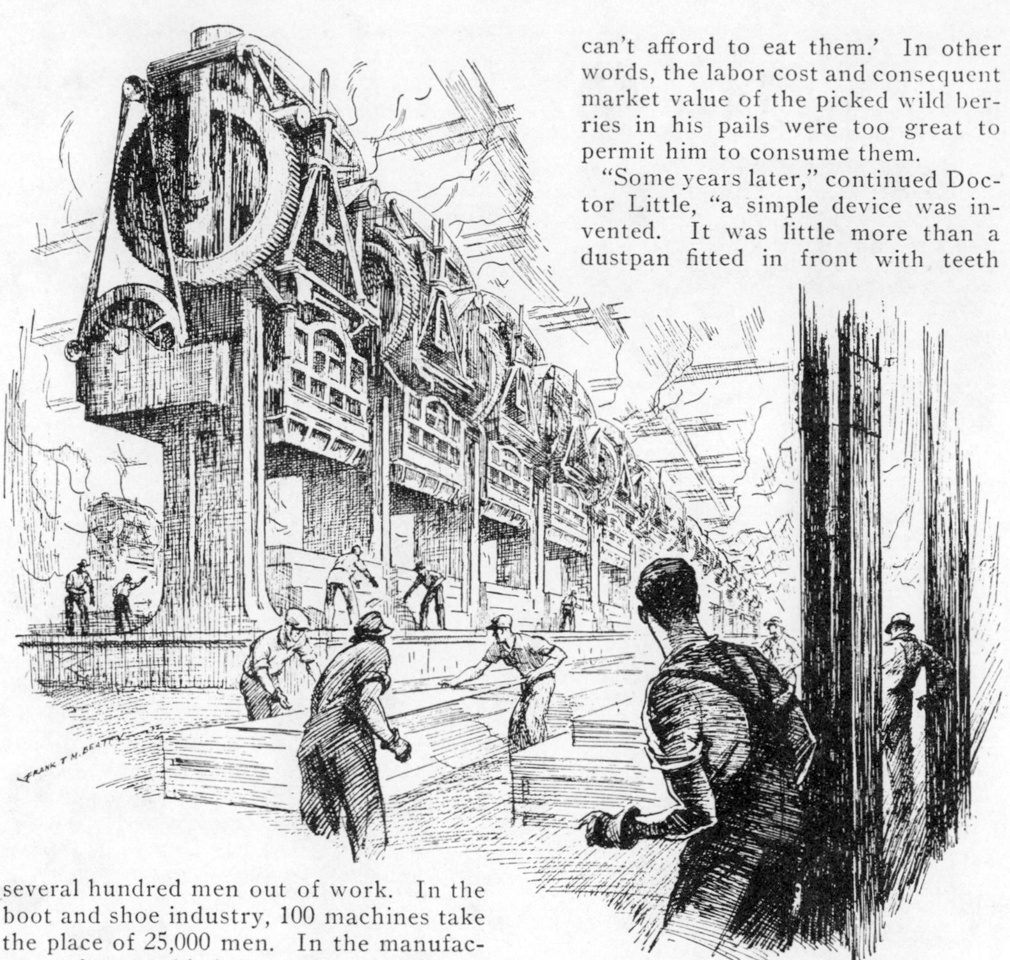

several hundred men out of work. In the boot and shoe industry, 100 machines take the place of 25,000 men. In the manufacture of razor blades, one man can now turn out 32,000 blades in the same time needed for 500 in 1913. In steel blast furnaces, seven men now do the work of sixty in casting pig iron. In machine shops, one man with a gang of semi-automatic machines replaces twenty-five skilled mechanics."

No one can deny that the machine displaces labor. Indeed is not that its chief reason for existence: to save labor and increase production per man? But there is another side to the picture. Recently I was talking with Dr. Arthur D. Little, the well-known industrial chemist, and he related this experience from his boyhood:

"I was climbing Mount Chocorua, in New Hampshire, and came upon a man who was eating a luncheon of dry bread, while beside him were several large pails heaped with blueberries. I asked him why he didn't eat the berries. He answered, 'I can't afford to eat them.' In other words, the labor cost and consequent market value of the picked wild berries in his pails were too great to permit him to consume them.

"Some years later," continued Doctor Little, "a simple device was invented. It was little more than a dustpan fitted in front with teeth like a rake, but it enabled a man to pick a bushel of blueberries in the time formerly required to pick a quart. At once the labor cost of blueberries went down. Canneries were established, many more pickers found employment, and though they received far less per quart than the hand pickers had, their daily earnings were so increased that they could have lunched on caviare sandwiches had they cared for such food."

But there are those who claim that the slavery is of another sort. The machine has cluttered up our lives with "things," it has standardized us into monotonous patterns of working and thinking, it has made man materialistic. Stuart Chase recently declared that men in a machineless country are happier, more content, than the fully machined men of the United States.

AS LOW AS

Re-Soles Shoes 4½ CENTS

Amazing New
SAVASOLE "Plastic"
Pays Agents UP TO $42 a Day

Ends costly shoe repairs—saves buying new shoes. Spreads on worn soles and heels like butter on bread. Hardens overnight. Halfsoling costs as little as 9c a pair—patches, one cent. Savasole fills in all cuts, holes, cracks, forming a smooth, flexible, waterproof, non-skid surface. New low price makes everybody buy. Agents cleaning up. Mail coupon today for Free Sample on leather and money-making agents offer showing how you can make up to $42 a day.

1001 USES Savasole also repairs auto tires and tops, boats, rubbers, harness, garden hose, tarpaulins, sporting goods. Anything made of leather, rubber or cloth can be easily, quickly and cheaply repaired with Savasole.

Mail Coupon for FREE Sample on Leather

Mail coupon and get exclusive territory offer and learn how you can have the same opportunity that made Kimura of Cal., over $60 in a day and a $500 cash bonus; that made Lewis of Kansas $30.10 his first morning. Everybody buys Savasole to save money. It's a marvelous "hard times" seller. Territories going fast. Mail coupon at once.

-in 5 Minutes This to This
BEFORE AFTER

SAVASOLE CO.
H-30 Daylight Bldg., Cincinnati, Ohio

Spreads on Soles Like Butter on Bread—Dries Hard Overnight

Mail for FREE Sample

SAVASOLE Co.,
H-30 Daylight Bldg.,
Cincinnati, Ohio.
Gentlemen: Rush Free Sample Savasole on leather and your agents proposition where I can earn up to $42 a Day. I am not obligated.

Name.........................
Address.........................
City.................. State......

WRITE ME *Your* MONEY PROBLEMS
I CAN HELP YOU

By GABRIEL ANDRE PETIT

Let me show you how you can make money *right in your own home.* An extra income of your own—full time or spare time. Write and get the new Fireside Book telling how our members everywhere are decorating Fireside Giftwares and making handsome profits without previous experience.

START EARNING IN 3 DAYS

Yes, you make money fast the Fireside way. "I sold $150.00 worth of novelties before finishing my second lesson," says Mrs. Grace Miller of Ohio. "$586.57 in two months and without experience," says Mrs. Harry Yano of New York. Here's simple, easy, pleasant and wonderfully instructive work. We teach you and supply everything. We need a new member in your community at once. Write and get our

FREE CRAFT BOOK

Even if you "can't draw a line" my 3-step method enables you to make beautiful art-craft within a few days. Seeing is believing—write and let me show you. The book is Free, address—

SPARE TIME EMPLOYMENT

FIRESIDE INDUSTRIES Dept. 66-K Adrian, Mich.

MAKES PERFECT CIGARETTES! *Automatically*

Imagine a little machine that rolls cigarettes so perfectly you can't tell 'em from ready-mades! An utterly different invention that lasts a lifetime — ROLL-O-MATIC.

TOBACCO AND PAPERS INCLUDED

ROLL-O-MATIC

THE most astounding little invention of the age. 10 years ahead of all ordinary cigarette-making devices. Sturdy, beautiful, sanitary. Simple and easy to operate—just turn the crank. It rolls and seals 20 perfect cigarettes in five minutes and pays for itself in a few days. Think of getting 30 or more cigarettes for 10c—without fuss or bother—without using special papers or wetting tongue to paper. Even women thrilled, for papers can be supplied in any shade, with gold tips if desired. Complete outfit for monogramming offered. Act at once. Write TODAY for free demonstration offer of this astonishingly different invention. Address

AGENTS
Most sensational money-maker in years. Quick profits, full time or spare time. Don't wait. Write TODAY for demonstration offer.

MARDEN MFG. CO.,
Dept. K-10., 11-15 Main St. N. E., Minneapolis, Minn.

When writing to advertisers please mention Popular Mechanics

Advertising changed its pace during the depression years. Americans walked on thin soles and tried to make every penny count. They had lost the knack of "rolling their own"—and newspapers were spread under cigarette machines on many kitchen tables. Few workers escaped wage reductions, many searched for ways to earn sparetime money

Jigsaw puzzles were a raging fad during the 1930's. Shapes and colors were the principal clues to fitting together the hundreds—sometimes thousands—of pieces into a finished picture. Millions of persons spent hours bending over such puzzles. The unkindest things you could do to a devotee were to scramble the pieces before he had finished or to hide a few key pieces of the puzzle

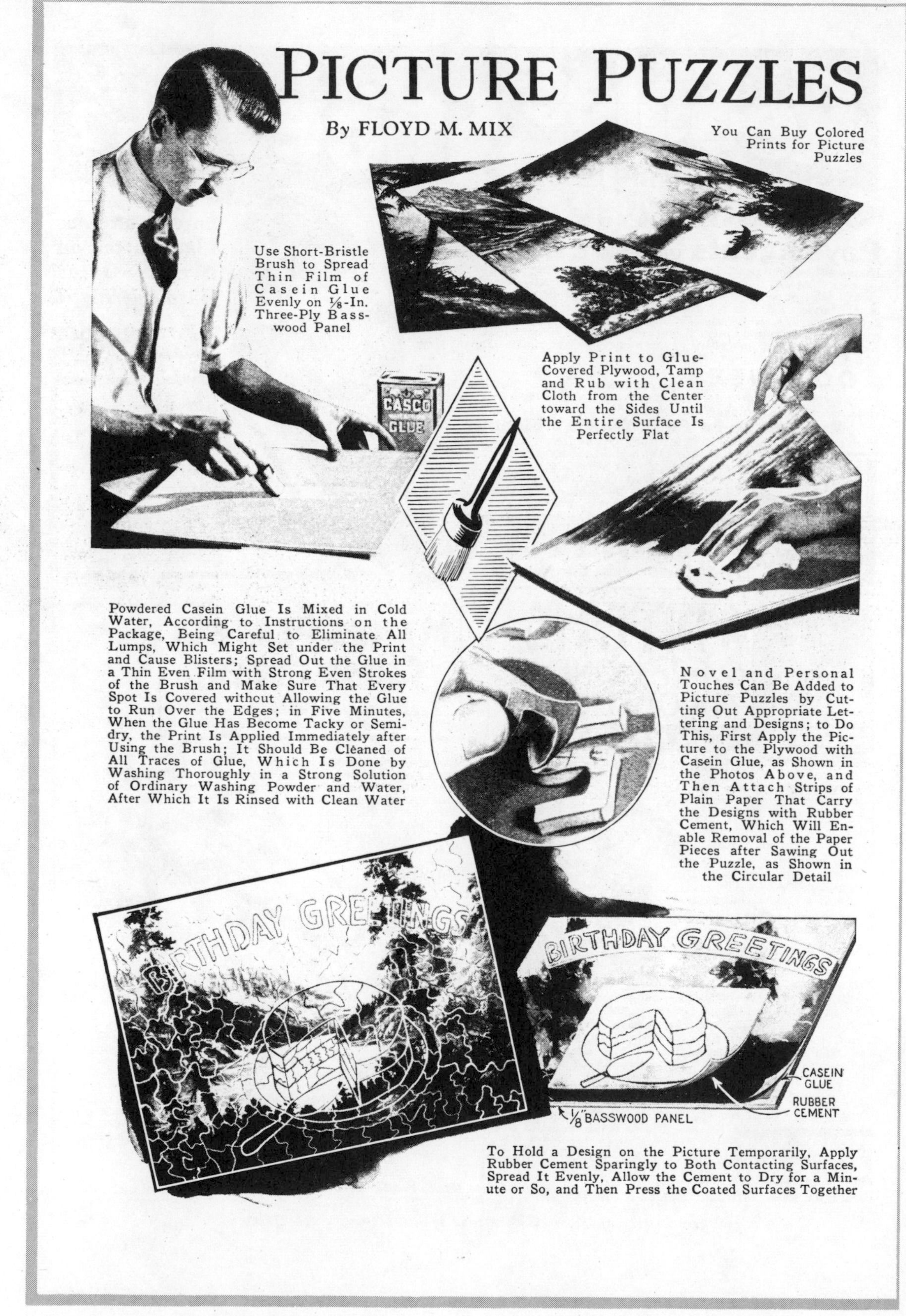

PICTURE PUZZLES

By FLOYD M. MIX

You Can Buy Colored Prints for Picture Puzzles

Use Short-Bristle Brush to Spread Thin Film of Casein Glue Evenly on ⅛-In. Three-Ply Basswood Panel

Apply Print to Glue-Covered Plywood, Tamp and Rub with Clean Cloth from the Center toward the Sides Until the Entire Surface Is Perfectly Flat

Powdered Casein Glue Is Mixed in Cold Water, According to Instructions on the Package, Being Careful to Eliminate All Lumps, Which Might Set under the Print and Cause Blisters; Spread Out the Glue in a Thin Even Film with Strong Even Strokes of the Brush and Make Sure That Every Spot Is Covered without Allowing the Glue to Run Over the Edges; in Five Minutes, When the Glue Has Become Tacky or Semi-dry, the Print Is Applied Immediately after Using the Brush; It Should Be Cleaned of All Traces of Glue, Which Is Done by Washing Thoroughly in a Strong Solution of Ordinary Washing Powder and Water, After Which It Is Rinsed with Clean Water

Novel and Personal Touches Can Be Added to Picture Puzzles by Cutting Out Appropriate Lettering and Designs; to Do This, First Apply the Picture to the Plywood with Casein Glue, as Shown in the Photos Above, and Then Attach Strips of Plain Paper That Carry the Designs with Rubber Cement, Which Will Enable Removal of the Paper Pieces after Sawing Out the Puzzle, as Shown in the Circular Detail

To Hold a Design on the Picture Temporarily, Apply Rubber Cement Sparingly to Both Contacting Surfaces, Spread It Evenly, Allow the Cement to Dry for a Minute or So, and Then Press the Coated Surfaces Together

for FUN *and* PROFIT

Photos of Your Friends or Yourself, at Work or Play, May Be Substituted for Colored Prints on the Picture Puzzles

A High-Speed Motor-Driven Scrollsaw, Fitted with a Special Fine-Tooth Blade That Gives Ample Clearance, Enables You to Cut Out the Puzzles Easily, Leaving Smooth Edges without Tearing the Paper

Here Is a Simple Method of Hand-Punching Picture Puzzles Out of Cardboard Instead of Plywood, for Those Who Have No Scrollsaw; Glue the Picture to the Cardboard and Drive a Metal Strip, Well-Sharpened and Bent as Shown Below, through the Work, Using a Hammer and a Hardwood Block; or Better Still, Use a Large Vise, as the Pressure Can Be Applied Slowly and Evenly to Make a Clean Cut

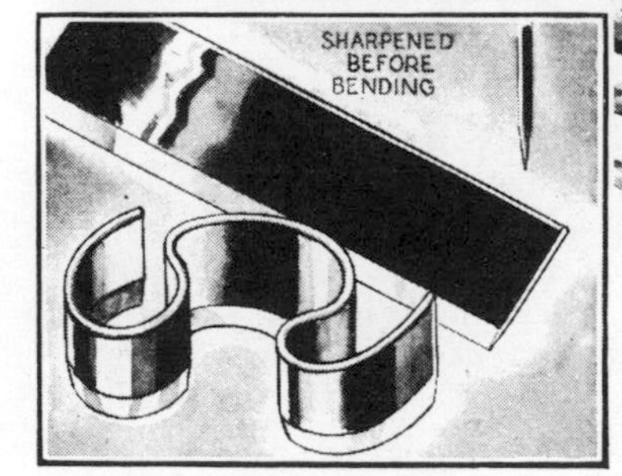

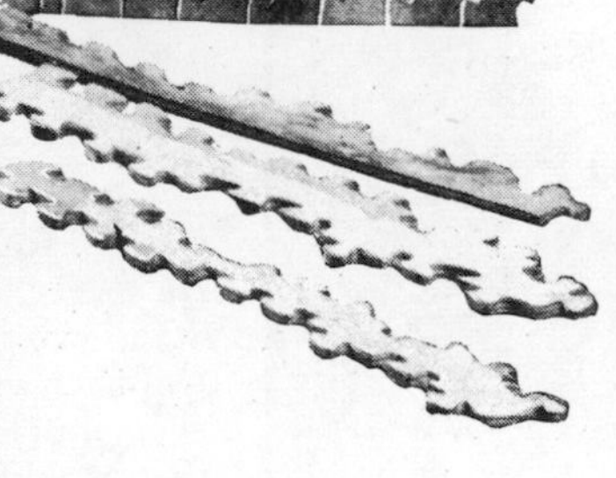

Interlocking Plywood Puzzles, Which, When Assembled, Can Readily Be Picked Up from the Table, Are Made by First Sawing Out Strips across the Length and Then across the Width, Keeping the Assembly Together While Sawing; the Detail Above Shows the Method Followed in Making the Cuts So That Each Piece Interlocks with the Adjacent Ones on Three or Four Sides

The jigsaw puzzle was an ideal project for the home craftsman. The sets were easily turned out on a jigsaw, and provided a means of earning some extra money. During the depression many craftsmen also turned their jigsaws to such easily salable projects as lawn ornaments, house numbers and small, easily assembled furniture pieces

The Popular Mechanics *Blueprint Department still receives requests for the plans for this house. At today's prices, it could not, of course, be built for $700. The original plans called for a roof of wooden shingles, which are now prohibited by the building codes and fire laws of most cities and towns. In its day, however, the house was a sound and comfortable one, and was built by many readers. Because construction is simple, yet based on good principles of carpentry, the design today would be excellent for a summer home*

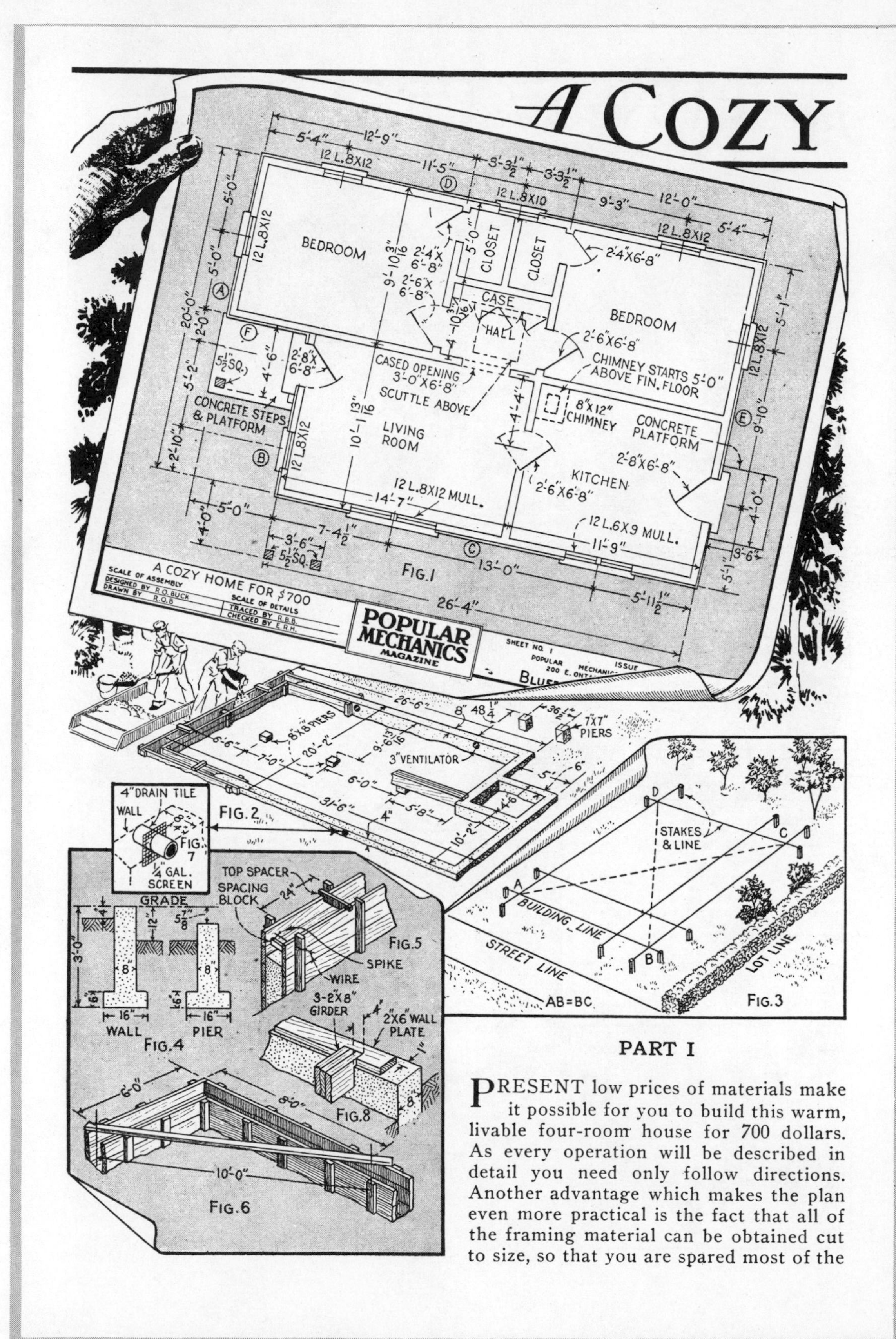

A COZY

PART I

PRESENT low prices of materials make it possible for you to build this warm, livable four-room house for 700 dollars. As every operation will be described in detail you need only follow directions. Another advantage which makes the plan even more practical is the fact that all of the framing material can be obtained cut to size, so that you are spared most of the

HOME *for* $700

Designed to be built at the lowest possible cost without sacrificing adequate strength and necessary insulation, this comfortable, four-room bungalow can be constructed by anyone who carefully follows the plans and instructions as given in this article, published in two installments. The price, between 600 and 700 dollars, depending on location, includes all material except masonry, heating plant, plumbing, and freight. If desired, you may arrange to distribute the payments over a long-term financing plan so that you can start building at once. For more particulars, write to our Small-House Editor.

R. O. BUCK
Lane Technical High School, Chicago

heavy sawing. The construction of the house is standard throughout. It is neither practical nor wise, even for the sake of economy, to resort to light or cheap construction, for such property is unsalable and often untenantable in cold weather. The floor is double, with paper between, and the outside walls are covered with ship-lap sheathing, paper and wood shingles. Wood shingles for roof and siding give the necessary insulation, wearing quality and the best appearance for the money. Another advantage is that they do not require painting. A dip coat and one brush coat of stain are sufficient to last for five or six years.

A study of the floor plan, Fig. 1, will convince you that this is a real home for year-around occupancy. The living room is of good size and well lighted, the kitchen is large enough to serve as a dining room as well, and has plenty of room for kitchen cabinets, etc. Or if the family is large, you may have a combination living and dining room. The two good-sized bedrooms are provided with adequate closet space, and in addition, a large storage case opens into the hall connecting the bedrooms. The window for the closets is placed midway between them.

This home boasted no central heating plant, but construction was such that it could be heated comfortably by a coal or oil stove. The builder had his choice of two roomy closets and no bathroom, or a bathroom with closet space to be taken by sacrificing space in the two bedrooms. A recessed front porch and overhanging-roof protection at the side entrance gave some distinction to this little home. Today, if it were placed with the broadside facing the street, a builder would call it a "four-room ranch-type house"

Glimpses of the WORLD'S FAIR

A Century of Progress Exposition was the first of a number of fairs and expositions held during the depression years in an effort to stimulate business. Chicago's fair, marking the 100th anniversary of the city's founding, covered 424 acres along three and a half miles of Lake Michigan. The fair opened June 1, 1933, and was so successful that it continued through the summer of 1934. A total attendance of 38,634,836 persons was reported

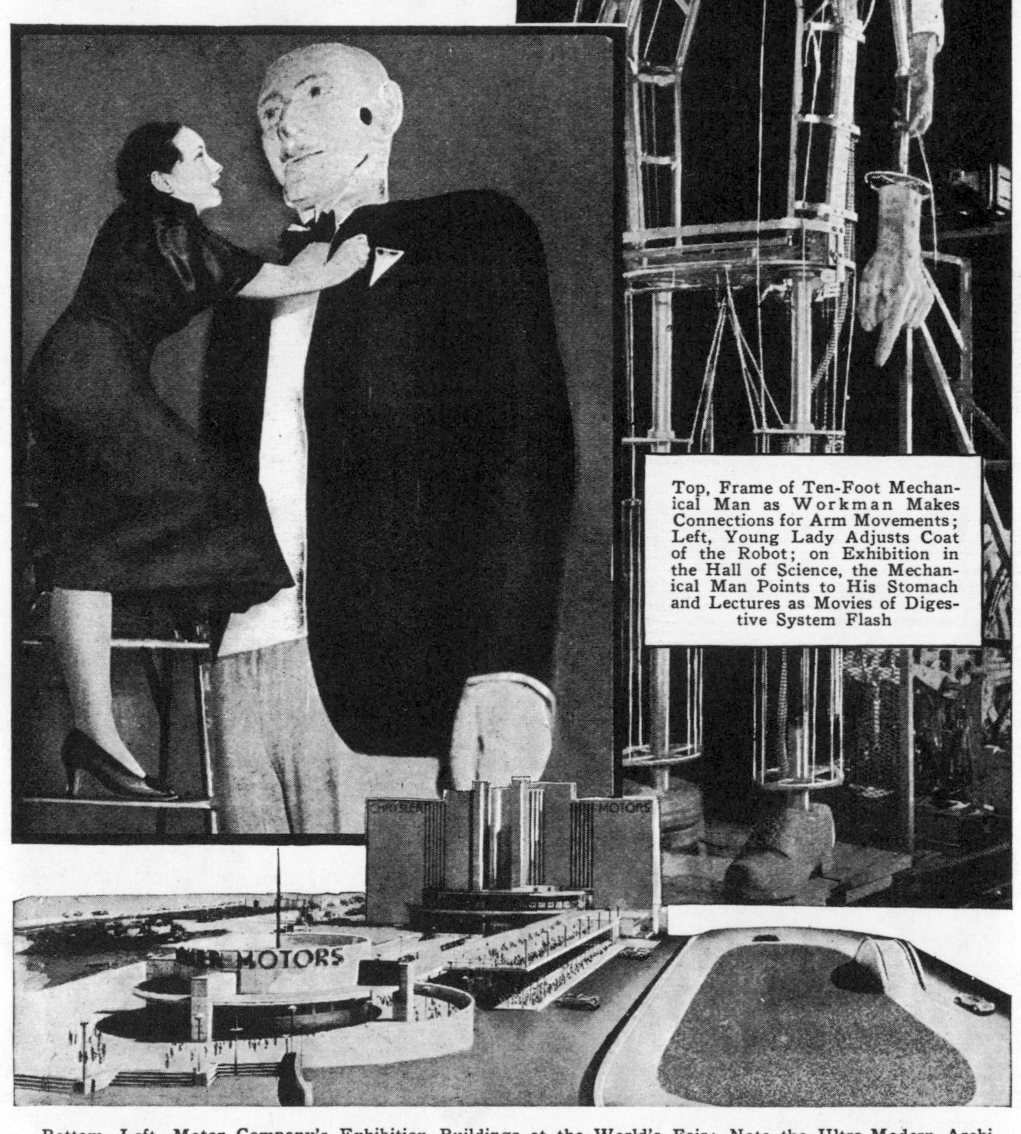

Top, Frame of Ten-Foot Mechanical Man as Workman Makes Connections for Arm Movements; Left, Young Lady Adjusts Coat of the Robot; on Exhibition in the Hall of Science, the Mechanical Man Points to His Stomach and Lectures as Movies of Digestive System Flash

Bottom, Left, Motor Company's Exhibition Buildings at the World's Fair; Note the Ultra-Modern Architecture; Bottom, Right, Quarter-Mile Hard-Surface Track on Which Automobiles Are Demonstrated Daily; Racing Drivers Subject the Cars to Unusual Tests on the Track

SHERLOCK HOLMES RETURNS

B. C. Farrer, Handwriting Expert, Who Decided from a Study of Ransom Notes That Lindbergh Kidnaper Was German Carpenter

"A METHODICAL Teutonic or German carpenter." That is the picture B. C. Farrer, handwriting expert of the treasury department, drew of the Lindbergh kidnaper even before any ransom was paid. This deduction was based on a study of the handwriting of the ransom notes.

Disclosures following the arrest of Bruno Hauptmann in the Lindbergh case seem to indicate that the famous Sherlock Holmes has been reincarnated not only in the person of the treasury department expert, but in the entire system of criminal investigation of the department of justice.

That the writer of the ransom notes was German would be apparent to the expert at a glance. That the writer was methodical is apparent

Sketch of Man Who Received Lindbergh Ransom Money Made from Description of Man Who Dealt with Him, and Photograph of Bruno Hauptmann

The Lindbergh baby, Charles, Jr., was kidnaped on the evening of March 1, 1932. The kidnaper climbed a ladder to gain entrance through an unlocked window of the second-floor nursery of the secluded house near Hopewell, N. J. In the nursery, the parents discovered a ransom note demanding $50,000 be paid to an agent selected by the kidnaper. Following instructions, the agent tossed the package of money over the wall of a cemetery. On May 12 the baby was found dead near the Lindbergh home. The most extensive man hunt in the history of the nation began

The first break in the case came two years after the kidnaping when a gasoline-station attendant jotted down the license number of a motorist who gave him a $20 gold certificate. The bill was the first of the ransom money that had turned up. Police traced the license number to the automobile of Bruno Hauptmann, German-born carpenter, and arrested him on Sept. 19, 1934

These two photographs illustrate the action of ultra-violet light in disclosing the presence of secret writings made by invisible inks

Illustrating the use of a comparison microscope. The enlarged images of the bases of two cartridges or of two bullets are thrown together on a single eyepiece

Illustrating the use of an instrument whereby the enlarged images of two separate fingerprints are thrown together on a screen in such a way that the lines of one flow into the lines of the other, if they are identical

from the deliberateness of the writing and the careful planning revealed in the text. A detailed drawing of the box in which he wanted the money delivered, together with a certain stiffness of the writing, always found in those who work with their hands, and the square holes in the ransom notes evidently punched with a file, indicated that he was a carpenter.

Observations of detectives added to and corroborated the work of the handwriting expert. The homemade ladder used in the kidnaping could only have been built by a carpenter, for the rungs were perfectly mortised, and although forty-eight nails were driven flush there was not a single hammer mark on the wood. A broken rung fixed his weight at about 160 pounds. The wood in the ladder was traced to a Bronx lumber dealer, and when the ransom money began appearing in an area with the Bronx district as its center, the search was centered in that locality. With emery dust and glycerine appearing on this money under the microscope, further proof was given that the kidnaper was a mechanic or carpenter who sharpened his own tools. A musty odor indicated that the money was kept underground.

But in spite of the accurate verbal descriptions given by Sherlock Holmes, he was never able to furnish fellow detectives with an actual likeness of his quarry. How the department of justice special agents did just this constitutes a distinct advance in scientific crime detection. James T. Berryman, sports cartoonist of the Washington Star, was called in to furnish a pictorial likeness of the man who received the ransom money. Berryman called on John

F. ("Jafsie") Condon, who passed the money through the cemetery hedge in 1932, and obtained a description of the kidnaper. Then going to the public library he requested files of illustrated German magazines. Selecting portraits of the oval Teutonic type of face he made composite sketches of the type. Returning to Condon with the sketches, the aged educator pointed out where the features of "John" differed from those of the composite—the mouth a little straighter, the droop of the left eyelid more pronounced, a line at the side of the mouth, and the cheeks a bit flatter. After four hours of erasing and redrawing, Condon pronounced the likeness as nearly perfect as his memory could direct. Berryman made finished drawings of these sketches, which were photographed and distributed to detectives working on the case. The remarkable results obtained by Berryman can be seen by comparison of the sketches, reproduced here, with photographs of the suspect now under arrest.

After a sensational trial, Hauptmann was found guilty of the kidnaping and murder of the Lindbergh child. He was electrocuted on April 3, 1936. The crime was so revolting, and kidnaping had reached such proportions, that the Lindbergh Law was adopted in 1934, making it a federal offense if the victim of such a crime was taken across state lines, and making the death penalty mandatory for conviction

cross the street and
walk to the next corner
and follow Whittemore Av
to the soud
take the money with
you. come alone
and walk
I will meet you

the boy is on Boad Nelly
it is a small Boad 28 feet
long. two person are on the
Boad. the are innosent.
you will find the Boad between
Horseneck Beach and gay Head
near Elizabeth Island.

Prisoner's signature

FOLD THIS CARD

1730 U. S. GOVERNMENT PRINTING OFFICE: 1931

Above, Map of Manhattan Which Aided in Tracing Ransom Money; Colored Pins Were Placed in Map to Indicate Points Where Money Had Been Passed; Below, Handwriting Experts Claim to See Similarity between Hauptmann's Signature and Writing in Ransom Notes

The exact occupation of the writer cannot always be told with such certainty as it was in the Lindbergh case. Telegraphers join their words together for speed, persons connected with writing and publishing usually give themselves away by their rapid but still legible writing, together with the use of carets at insertions and the placing of circles around periods or replacing them with tiny crosses.

One of the two "Zephyrs" which the Burlington introduced as twin trains set a long-distance speed record on its first run, covering 1017 miles at an average of 83.4 miles an hour, with a top speed of 116 miles an hour for one mile. Back in 1893 the New York Central's "Empire State Express" had reached 112.5 miles an hour for a short, bone-shaking run. But the new streamliners could stay at high speeds without causing discomfort for the passengers. This same year, 1934, the New York Central put a streamlined steam locomotive in operation, and the Pennsylvania introduced an electric streamliner the next year. Central Railroad of New Jersey had already used a Diesel electric engine in 1924

WINGS

Controls of the "Zephyr" and the Straight-Eight, Two-Cycle, Six-Hundred Horsepower Diesel Which Drives the Train through an Electric Generator, the Current Being Delivered to the Drive-Motors on the Forward Truck; Cooling Air Drawn in through Grill at Top of Control Car Passes through Radiator and Out Near Exhaust Ports in the Roof, Which Is Removable and Strongly Reinforced; Lower Right, Rear Observation Compartment

RACING the sun in a history-making flight from Denver to Chicago—1,015 miles in 785 minutes without a single stop—the Burlington "Zephyr" gave the railway's answer to bus, automobile and air competition.

All the safety and dependability of the rails, plus the comfort of a fireside chair and the speed of an airplane, at a passenger cost below that of the least expensive private automobile!

In its run from Denver to Chicago, the "Zephyr" used 418 gallons of fuel oil at a total cost of $16.72. On the same run a locomotive would burn $255 worth of coal.

Air conditioned throughout, with concealed lighting, individually adjustable seats and broad, curtained windows, this three-coach articulated train rides as smoothly at 112 miles an hour as the ordinary Pullman does at forty-five miles. Into its building have gone years of scientific progress and research, and at least three of its features point the way for industrial achievement in many other lines. First, the material of which it is built—stainless steel, an alloy of low-carbon steel, eight-

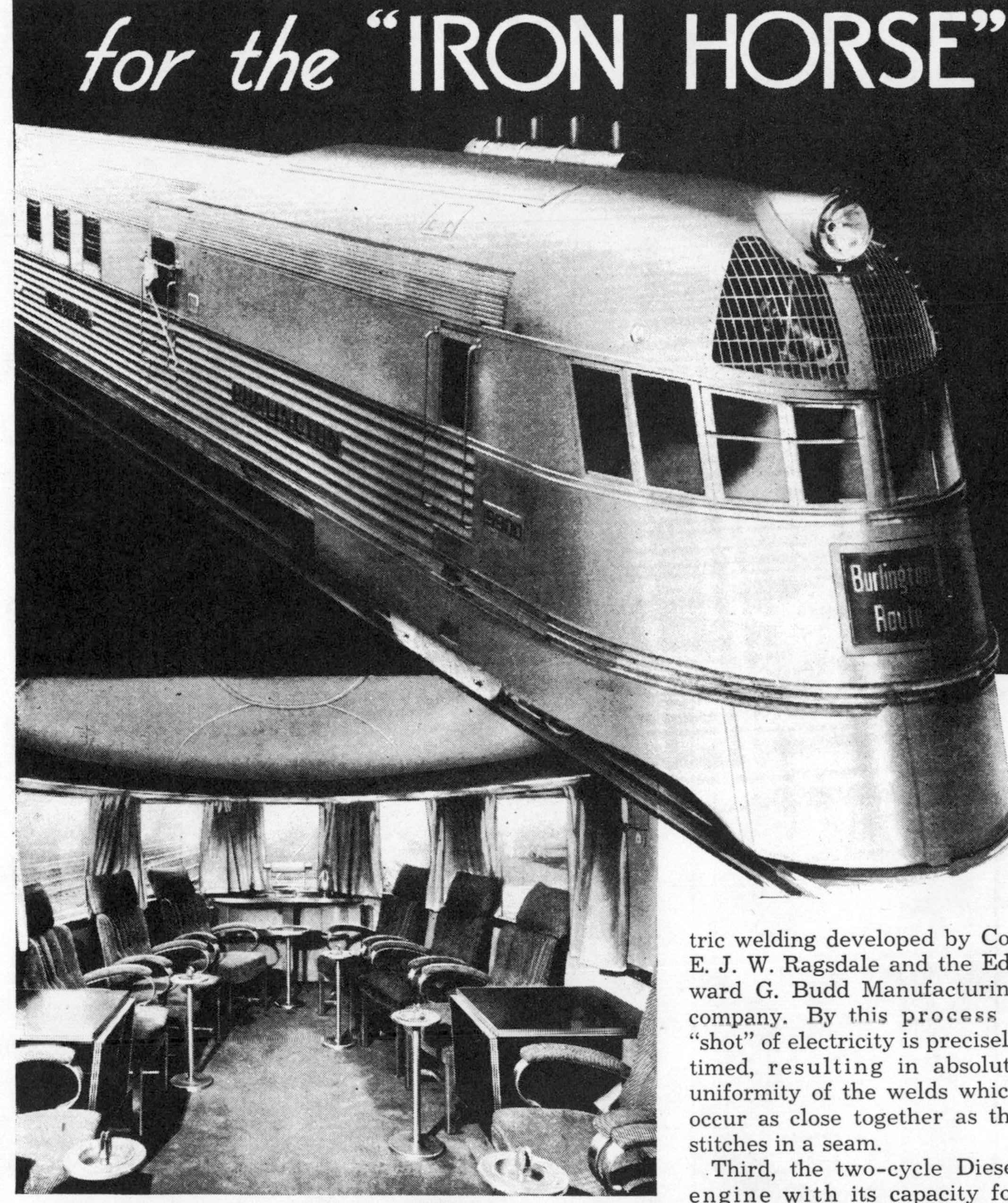

The "Zephyr" combined a number of features which already had been developed and used independently. The use of lighter, stronger steel, fused in more compact joints by electric arc welding, and the Diesel engine, with four times the efficiency of the steam engine, gave the "Zephyr" new power and speed. At the same time, new methods of "cushioning" the coaches made the speeds more comfortable for passengers. Inside, the Zephyrs had intercar telephones, wall outlets for electric appliances in dressing rooms, radios in every bedroom, drawing room and compartment, and an "air current" that shut out kitchen odors from the dining room. Streamlining, modern furniture, adjustable seats, and air conditioning added to its comfort and appearance

een per cent chromium and eight per cent nickel. Because of the greater strength of this metal and the fact that it is not subject to corrosion, tremendous savings in weight are made possible, more than compensating for its higher first cost.

Second, the "Shotwell" method of electric welding developed by Col. E. J. W. Ragsdale and the Edward G. Budd Manufacturing company. By this process a "shot" of electricity is precisely timed, resulting in absolute uniformity of the welds which occur as close together as the stitches in a seam.

Third, the two-cycle Diesel engine with its capacity for quick acceleration, dependable operation and exceedingly low operating costs. Engines of this type have made records of 600,000 miles without overhauling.

There is no gainsaying the advantages which trains like the "Zephyr" afford when compared to the conventional steam trains in service today.

Palomar's giant eye was opened to the heavens in 1948. More than a year was taken to grind and polish the 200-inch mirror, whose curvature had to be accurate within a millionth of an inch. The telescope in which the mirror was mounted is made up of 400 tons of moving parts, balanced so delicately on bearings, some of which are 48 feet in diameter, that it can be moved virtually without effort. The entire instrument weighs 540 tons

Building the WORLD'S

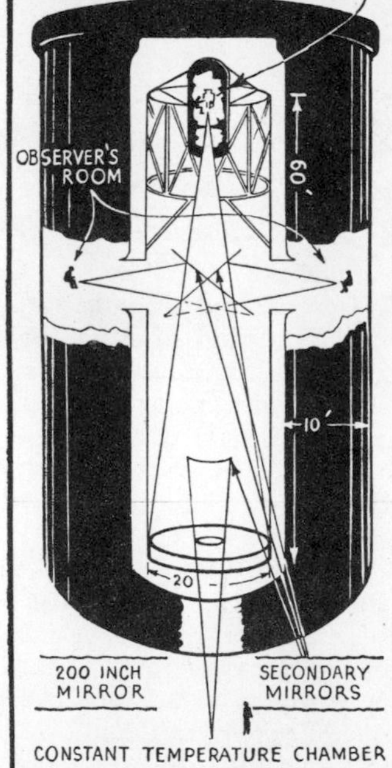

Diagram of telescope and cutaway model of observatory, showing the telescope inside

IMAGINE a telescope so powerful you could see clear across the United States. Standing in New York, you could reach past Chicago and San Francisco and watch ships moving in the Pacific, reading the names painted on the bows as easily as if they were across the street.

If you should turn the telescope eastward you might see cars chugging along English roads or watch airplanes flying above the streets of Paris. A second later you might turn south and watch people in Mexico City or reach past the Canal Zone and observe the surf on South American beaches. From Los Angeles you might peek at Honolulu and then swing northward for a close-up of Alaska.

Fantastic as it seems, that will be the power of the super-telescope under construction for the California Institute of Technology in Pasadena. Of course, it could never be used for purposes like these because clouds, mountains, and the curvature of the earth make such sight-seeing impossible. Besides, it will have much more important work to do. The closest object toward which it will ever be pointed will be the moon.

This titan of telescopes will have twice the range of the world's present largest instrument, it is expected,

BIGGEST "EYE"

Drawing showing how interior of dome will appear with giant telescope peering out at stars. Switchboard to operate telescope is in front of man on stair

and will enable astronomers to study eight times as much space as has been explored so far. Even these general figures may be revised because auxiliary instruments are being improved so rapidly no one can say exactly how powerful the mighty instrument will be.

But the telescope will be about 640,000 times as far-sighted as your own two eyes. Its 200-inch concave mirror will gather light from nebulae one billion light-years away. Multiply the speed of light, 186,000 miles per second, by sixty seconds, then by sixty minutes, then by twenty-four hours, then by 365 days, and you have the distance light travels in a year. One billion light-years amounts to about 6,000,000,000,000,000,000,000 miles.

You get an idea of that distance by reflecting that light from our sun, 92,000,000 miles away, is only eight minutes old when it reaches the earth.

A companion instrument of Palomar's eye is a 36-ton Schmidt telescope-camera, which acts as a "scout" for the big mirror. The camera has a 48-inch lens. One of the most important discoveries made with the new equipment at Mount Palomar Observatory was reported in 1951. Observers witnessed stars apparently shooting away from our solar system, giving added weight to the theory that the universe is expanding

"Moderne," an American furniture style borrowed from French and Swedish designs, first appeared at A Century of Progress in Chicago in 1933. It soon became popular because it was based on beauty gained from pleasing lines, unusual woods, and interesting finishes. After the disappearance of mission furniture in the 1900's, and before the emergence of "Moderne," there was no distinctively American style. One feature of the new style was that it could accommodate the American passion for "built-in" features without having its lines spoiled

Utility and Beauty Mark Modern Furniture

Above, quilted maple and mahogany bed of modernistic lines combines beauty and utility. Note matching stand and lamp. Below, easy chair has reading lamp built into the wings. Illumination is supplied by two twenty-five watt bulbs

Left, milady finds this full-length vanity cabinet the ultimate in convenience. It lends itself to conservation of space by folding. The wings contain shelves for many aids to beauty

Right, cabinet resembling radio when closed holds an entire kitchenette. Electric coffee pot, toaster and electric grill are in upper compartment, storage space is in lower left cabinet and an ice box using Dry Ice is in right-hand compartment. It is designed for small apartment or cottage. This and other photos on this page were taken at 1937 American Furniture Mart

Homemade WOOD LATHE *mounted on floor stand*

Self-contained unit has four-speed V-belt drive, rigid iron bed, and a quick-acting tailstock

By ALBERT C. LARSON

WITH this lathe you can swing a disk 12 in. in diameter on the headstock or turn down a full-length table leg between centers. The headstock spindle, Fig. 1, is supported on auto connecting rods bolted to a short length of channel which forms the base and is bolted to the bed. A hardwood spacer between the rods holds the whole thing rigid. The ½-in. spindle runs in Ford spindle-bolt bushings which are pressed into the upper ends of the connecting rods and then reamed to give the spindle a free-running fit. The spindle also carries two ball thrust bearings, one on each side of a four-step V-pulley. Polished flat washers are used to take out the end play, if any. The inner end of the spindle should project about ¾ in. to take a hollow-sleeve spur center of the type which locks in place with a headless set screw. This and the drive pulley, also the thrust bearings, can be purchased at little cost. Faceplates are also available.

The bed is simply two channels of the size given in Fig. 3. They are bolted together with spacers.

Herbert E. Tautz, a Milwaukee mechanic motorized a jigsaw in 1925 and started a new industry. Today, sales of light power tools total more than 100 million dollars yearly, and more than 14 million persons have workshops in their homes. For those who prefer to make their own power tools, the magazine has printed detailed instructions for the making of more than 100 different machines and special setups. The best of these have been published in a book, 40 Power Tools You Can Make, *by the Popular Mechanics Press*

Rudolph Diesel, German scientist, conceived the idea for a nonsparking high-compression engine while a student in Munich. His first such engine, built in 1893, nearly killed Diesel when it exploded, but it worked long enough to prove his theory. The first successful Diesel engine was built in 1897. Diesel had expected a thermal efficiency of 73 per cent; its actual performance of 28 to 32 per cent was greater than any other engine of the time. Diesel exhibited several of his engines at the Munich Exposition of 1898, and lectured in the United States in 1912. His death in 1913 was highly mysterious, with overtones of international intrigue, on the eve of World War I. The British Admiralty had asked him for a consultation, and he was en route to England on a German boat when he disappeared on September 30

The

TWICE as much horsepower per American. An increase of from ten to 200 per cent in efficiency of compression motors with a new accuracy of motor control. An entirely new principle of "power in a package" which eventually may cut power bills to half of present levels. Complete installation of home power units for costs as low as five dollars per kilowatt capacity. Cheap power independent of high lines and expensive copper channels.

These are some American power notes of today's and tomorrow's headline news of the new small-unit two-cycle Diesel engines which our largest manufacturer of automobiles now begins in mass production.

This year marks the forty-first birthday of a combustion engine invented by Dr. Rudolph Diesel, to whose doorway in Munich the mechanical world beat not only a footpath, but a six-lane boulevard. This year brings the Diesel hot off the assembly line, in home-sized units of twenty-two to 160 horsepower. These midget Diesels are "little brothers" of the streamline-train Diesels which have rolled up more than eight million miles of railroad service. But the new small Diesel is more than just an engine. It is a power package equipped

Top, streamline power car ready to be lowered onto its trucks. Bottom, left, steam engine built by Hero in 130 B.C. Center, two other engines. Right, Dr. Diesel's first successful engine

ADVANCE of DIESEL

Rudolph Diesel's early engines burned powdered coal. Today, Diesels operate with a petroleum distillate like that used in oil furnaces. But under proper conditions the engine could be operated with many different types of fuel, including gasoline, animal greases, glycerin, alcohol or even salad oil. This versatility could be important to future developments in motor fuels. If any major emergency should cut off the supply of gasoline, an entire structure of Diesel power could be operated using substitute fuels

Top, general view of plant building Diesel engines for railroad trains. Below, first commercial Diesel engine

with all accessories needed to start its job. In the case of the miniature stationary electric power plant the package includes the engine, generator, fuel-supply equipment, switchboard, etc.

A million square miles of our country are still beyond electrical service from central power plants or high lines. At least one million rural homes in the United States still do not have access to power lines. Power rates of different sections still range more than 700 per cent from a base average price. Though almost 37,000 miles of additional rural power lines have been built or contracted for in the past three years, studies made by the government show that no power-line mile which yields less than thirty-two dollars per year in kilowatt income can be a profitable investment. This limits the number of miles of copper channels which can be operated under present conditions.

Perfection of a small-unit Diesel generator suggests that in thousands of rural communities it may be possible to make electricity at home cheaper than it can be bought from power

Experimental Diesel-powered automobiles have been built, but results thus far have not justified their mass production. Problems of weight, fuel-feeding and strength of materials have been the three great drawbacks of the Diesel from the standpoint of everyday use. The earlier models were too heavy to be practical anywhere except as stationary engines or on large ships. Later, as stronger alloys were developed and fuel-injection methods were perfected, the Diesel became practical for locomotives, trucks, tractors and busses. Diesel-powered busses are economical to operate, giving more miles per gallon on cheaper fuel than gas busses of equal size

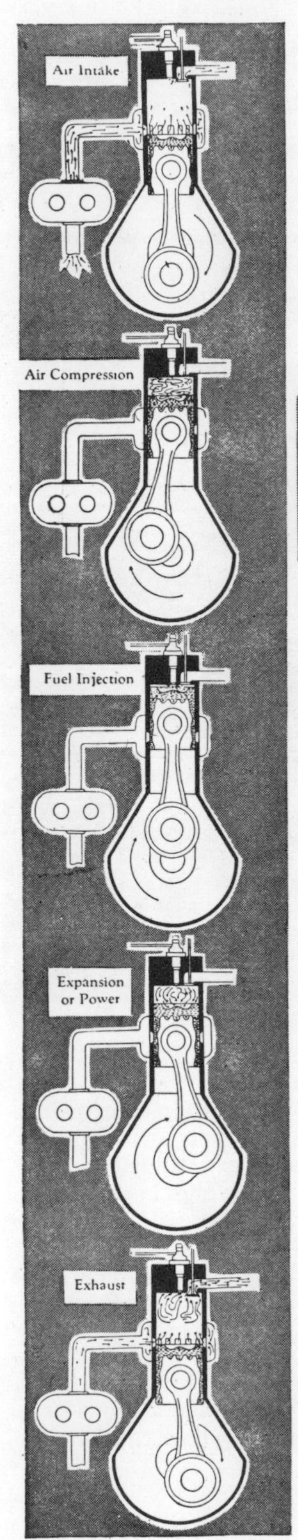

lines. Also that in remote areas power companies may be able to establish small Diesel plants to serve from one to a dozen families living beyond reach of power lines, hiring a resident farmer or workman to tend and fuel the equipment. Or an individual could install his own power plant and, if local laws allow, sell power to his neighbors.

Thus packaged power may serve to increase the uses of electrical equipment upon many thousands of farms. It may give birth to hundreds of new enterprises such as roadstands, rural amusement centers, billboard lighting, outlying theaters, parking lots, new vacation and resort projects. New progress in Diesel development unquestionably will take a still more important role in American timber industries, railroads, commercial fishing and marine shipping, as well as in further developing radio and electrical refrigeration. Almost certainly it will be of great importance to continued progress in farming, where it will power more and heavier equipment. Already city buildings are being equipped with private Diesel-generator power plants.

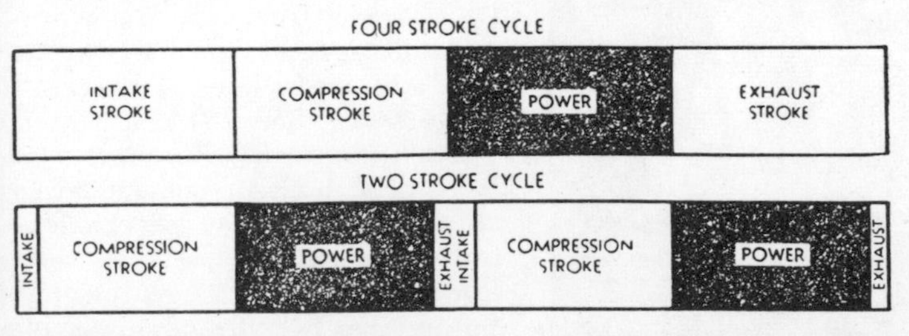

Strip at left shows how the two-cycle Diesel works. Note that it has one power impulse for each two strokes of piston. Diagram, bottom of page, compares two-stroke with four-stroke cycle, showing that two-stroke cycle produces twice as much power as the four-stroke because it has two power impulses instead of one. Photo at top, "power in package" Diesel engine

Popular Mechanics Magazine

REGISTERED IN U. S. PATENT OFFICE AND CANADA

WRITTEN SO YOU CAN UNDERSTAND IT

Vol. 70 OCTOBER, 1938 No. 4

Poor Boy Still Makes Good–CORRIGAN Proves It!

By Lowell Thomas

THERE are but few men on this earth—outside of those in high official rank—whose names require no added words of explanation. For example, if you mention Charles A. Lindbergh, everybody from Pt. Barrow, Alaska, to the "ham" radio operators at the Cape of Good Hope will know instantly what he stands for, what he has accomplished. You would hardly need all the fingers of one hand to count all the other living persons of whom this is true.

But there is one recent, overnight addition to the list. Two months ago we had never heard of him, did not know he existed. Today the name of

The $900 plane in which Douglas Corrigan flew the Atlantic and, above, Corrigan working on his ship in New York before the take-off for California by way of Dublin

As Lowell Thomas points out, Corrigan typifies the indomitable single-mindedness of the man who is mechanically inclined. Corrigan's dream of flying the Atlantic was born when, as a mechanic at the Ryan Airplane Company in San Diego, Calif., he worked on Lindbergh's Spirit of St. Louis. *Corrigan was among those chosen to prepare Lindbergh's plane for its historic flight because he was known as a natural mechanic—and one who spent extra hours at the factory tinkering with the engines for his own amusement. While others went to the movies, Corrigan read books and magazines on mechanical science*

In 1929 Douglas Corrigan had saved enough money to buy an old Curtiss Robin. The engine was beyond repair, but Corrigan obtained two old motors, and from these managed to put together one that would run soundly. He replaced other warn parts of the plane, little by little, meanwhile running up 1500 flying hours. Corrigan himself installed some elementary navigating instruments, but they did not include an earth-inductor compass, blind-flying equipment or even a radio. To prepare the plane for its long flight, Corrigan put extra gasoline tanks in front of the cabin, which meant he had to tilt his plane and look from a side window to check his bearings ahead

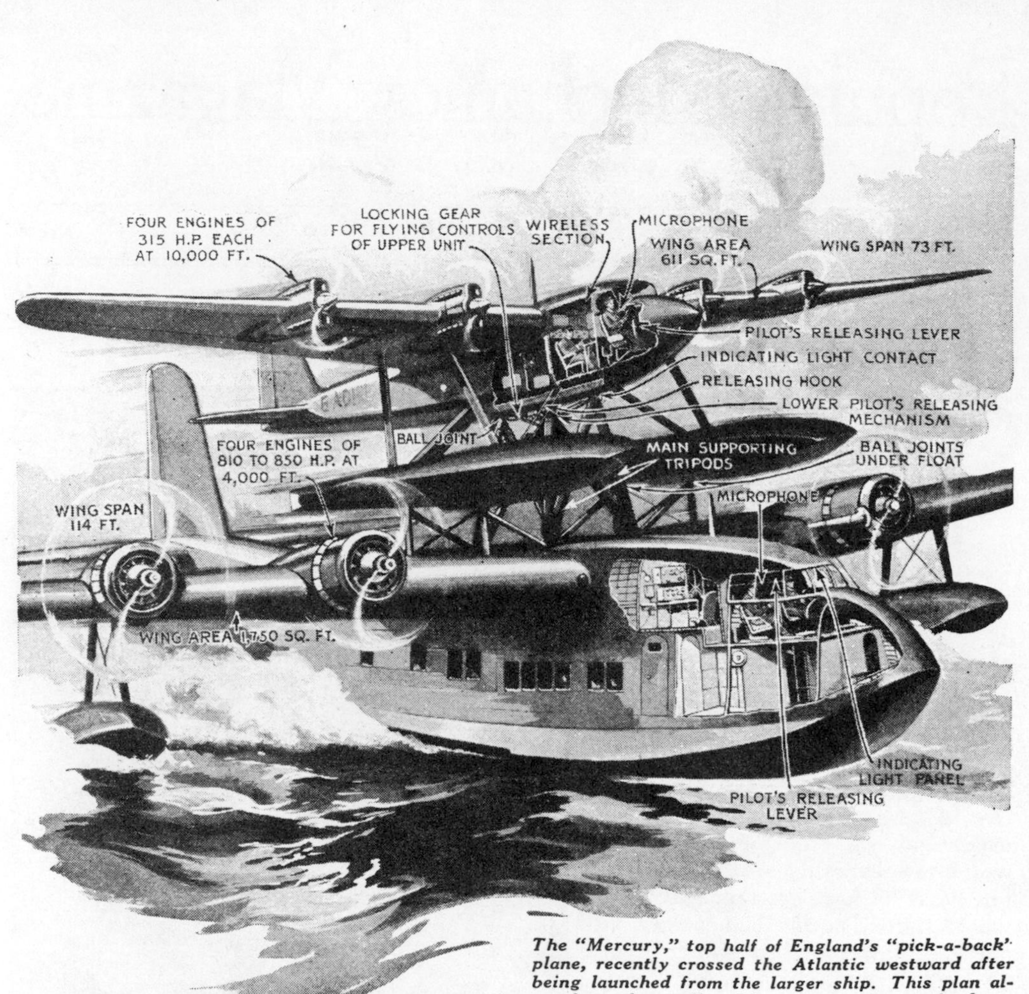

The "Mercury," top half of England's "pick-a-back" plane, recently crossed the Atlantic westward after being launched from the larger ship. This plan allows the smaller ship to carry more payload

young Douglas Corrigan is on the lips of all, young and old. Physically he flew, completely without benefit of publicity, from New York unaided and alone to Dublin. Actually he flew in twenty-eight hours, swiftly and surely, into the hearts of everybody with eyes to read or ears to listen. And that is putting the case mildly.

Now the first, fine, careless rapture of excitement and amazement is over. So let's examine what lies behind the exploit that has made Corrigan famous.

One fact that captured the world's admiration was the Lindberghlike precision with which the flight was executed. Corrigan had none of the instruments with which Howard Hughes was equipped. An ordinary compass and an inclinometer, which he had installed himself at a cost of $60, represented virtually the whole of his scientific apparatus. Nevertheless he reached his goal easily and surely. Insofar he quite earned the admiration and respect that have been showered upon him.

But Corrigan achieved more than that. He illustrated with graphic and unmistakable clarity the capacity and resourcefulness of the mechanical mind. He became the latest personification of the type of mentality that has lifted mankind within three centuries from a race of crawlers to a generation of fliers, the kind of mind which has given us modern surgery, modern plumbing and the ability to talk to one another though separated by thousands of miles of space.

Since it first began to function, the mechanical mind has been up against a long,

Cockpit of Hughes' round-the-world ship and, above, the German catapult seaplane, "Nordmeer," after her Atlantic crossing

unvarying, endless struggle, not merely the struggle to acquire knowledge, to overcome difficulties, to express its ideas in elaborate machines and instruments. Its toughest struggle has been the conflict with scepticism. Its worst enemy has been the Brahmin mind. The Brahmins say: "Thus and so is the world, thus and so it must remain." They have said: "It is impossible to travel faster than fifteen miles an hour. Nay more, it is wrong." The mechanics replied "Is that so? Then take a look at this." Whereupon they produced the steam locomotive. There is not a single modern appliance, whether telegraph instrument, motorcar or radio set that was not developed in the teeth of similar hostility.

Probably it was experienced by the genius who invented the wheel and thus laid the foundation for all the swift means of locomotion on land. Every schoolboy knows it was the fate of Galileo Galilei who established that the planets move around the sun, then was tortured until he made his lip-service recantation. Didn't somebody nickname the first steamboat in America "Fulton's Folly?" And in the Smithsonian Institution is an antique flying machine known as "Langley's Folly."

What about the two bicycle mechanics at Dayton, O., who worked independently of Prof. Langley and who beat him to it by being the first to demonstrate concretely and beyond dispute that man can fly? The Wright brothers encountered even more scepticism and jeers than attended the experiments of Langley.

Douglas Corrigan has no diploma from any famous technical school. He has in short, no academic background whatsoever. But he is a born mechanic. Working at it has been not merely his means of earning a livelihood. It has been his passion, the best fun he knows, his life. Not only his hours in the factory but his spare time—playtime to other men—has been given up to mechanics. The only pastime he has known, sailing, he made a means to the end he accomplished.

When he considered the plane ready, Corrigan flew from Long Beach, Calif., to Long Island, N.Y., in 28 hours. But when he applied for permission to fly the Atlantic, Bureau of Air Commerce officials refused, ruling his plane was unsafe. Corrigan then said he would fly back West, and on July 16, 1938, he loaded his ancient plane with gas and took off. Observers noted his plane rose with difficulty, flying low—and in the wrong direction! He disappeared over the mist-shrouded Atlantic. Just 28 hours and 24 minutes later, the willful young flier landed at the airport at Dublin, Ireland, where he was greeted by angry customs guards. Unperturbed, Corrigan greeted them with the exclamation: "Where am I?" Then he explained: "I thought I was headed for California."

An intermediate step between the floor-type gearshift and today's automatic transmission, the steering-post gearshift became standard equipment on most American automobiles after 1939. Most motorists welcomed the easier, faster means of shifting gears. But there were many habit-ruled motorists who drove for months before they stopped "reaching for the floor," a reflex built up by years of shifting gears with the conventional stick

WRITTEN SO YOU CAN UNDERSTAND IT

Vol. 70 DECEMBER, 1938 No. 6

GOOD-BY *to the* "WOBBLE-STICK"

By Julian Leggett

AMERICAN automobile manufacturers are agreed that the "wobble-stick" must go. As a result, the 1939 models are equipped with, or offer at small extra cost, handy little gear shifters located on the steering post to replace the long lever that stuck out of the floor in the driving compartment.

Few times in automotive history have the makers been in such accord. Perhaps other manufacturers took a tip from the favorable response which greeted the steering-post shifter introduced in 1938 by LaSalle, Cadillac and Pontiac, but more probably, they recognized it as the answer to two problems: first, how to clear the front compartment without using an expensive automatic transmission, and, second, how to eliminate noise conducted into the car by the old type lever, or wobble-stick.

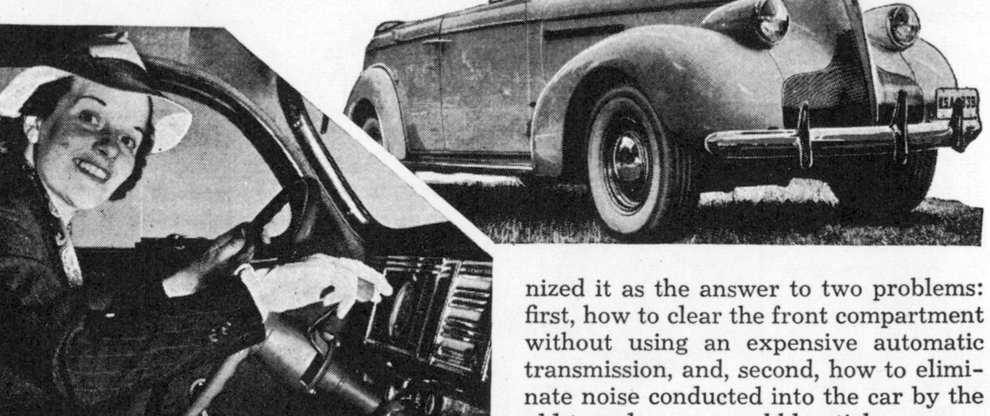

Cadillac-LaSalle "Sunshine" top; front of Buick, and Plymouth's gear shift

This substitute for the gear lever has none of the complicated mechanisms of automatic transmission or clutch. That makes it easy for the owner, because he

Even as auto makers introduced the steering-post gearshift, they were experimenting with the automatic transmission of the future. Hudson had a "selective" shift which was semiautomatic, and Cord had an electric shift operated by push-buttons. The principles of the hydraulic drive were known, but had to await tougher steel alloys before the automatic transmission could be fully perfected

doesn't have to learn how to drive all over again. It does the same job of changing gears and it does it in the same way, in conjunction with the clutch, as did the wobble-stick. From the maker's standpoint, it is so inexpensive that in most cases it can be included without increasing the price of the automobile. However, on some cars, particularly those in the lowest price field, it can be offered only as optional equipment. Chevrolet presents the shift, with a vacuum booster that takes eighty per cent of the work out of gear changing, for ten dollars extra. Deluxe models of Plymouth, and all models of DeSoto, Dodge and Chrysler have the feature as standard equipment.

Pontiac found the shifter popular as an extra-cost item last year.

Top, left, Buick's rear signal control, located on gear lever. Right, De Soto's substitute for "wobble-stick"; Center, left, front of new Chevrolet, and (just below) new Pontiac Six; Right, "lateral airfoil" design of Plymouth's front end. Note headlamps in fenders. Bottom, Packard's rear spring suspension

Electric power rates have risen about 40 per cent since 1939. Your 13 "servants," therefore, would now draw a wage of about seven cents an hour—still a bargain. And Americans are putting more electrical servants to work all the time—electric power output has more than doubled the rate for 1939

THIRTEEN SLAVES

YOU thought slavery was abolished long ago. You look back with a twinge of envy to Mount Vernon, and lament that the ease and splendor of that graceful period of American life are vanished forever.

Don't feel sorry for yourself. You're a bigger slave-owner than George Washington. True, the master of Mount Vernon did not have to pay wages to the scores of negroes, men, women and children, who tilled his fields and cooked his meals, hewed his firelogs and tended loom and spinning wheel, washhouse and stable. But he had to clothe them, house them, to deal out daily rations to them all.

Washington's slaves cost plenty more than yours. You do have to pay yours, but you don't feed nor clothe them, nor build them living quarters. And you probably pay less than two-fifths of a cent for every hard hour's work put in by any one of your husky, versatile and willing slaves. You really can't complain.

Your slaves are kilowatts. Put a kilowatt to work for one hour and it does the work of thirteen strong men. Flick the switch of your thousand-watt electric iron, use it to press clothes for sixty minutes and you have hired the labor of thirteen men for a nickel or less.

Compare the back-breaking old way of ironing with modern way at top. Bottom, putting electrical slaves to work in a moth-prevention treatment of furniture

Meals at Mount Vernon came from separate cookhouse. You can prepare breakfast right on the table with electric toaster, griddle and coffee urn. Drawings contrast old and new way of doing household chores

It all adds up close to 156 servant-hours a day, and all for about thirty cents!

Whether they turned a fruit juicer or pumped oil into a furnace or rang the doorbell chimes or boiled the breakfast eggs, these electrical servants toiled at the same "muscular" rate. But they didn't all draw the same pay. This householder, living in a small city in New York state, hired the equivalent of 4,797 servants for one hour each month; the first 156 servants cost him one-half cent each; the next 585 worked an hour for one-third of a cent; the next 1,850 for one-fourth cent, and the remaining 2,206 collected one-ninth cent each.

Washington would have liked to be rid of his slaves. Of course, he could not dream that the lightning with which his friend Benjamin Franklin was experimenting would one day furnish homes throughout America with more slaves than ever served Mount Vernon. But he was pointing in the right direction when he wrote:

"We must encourage introduction of new and useful inventions from abroad as well as exertion of skill and genius in producing them at home."

George Washington had more than an academic interest in new inventions. The icehouse he built at Mount Vernon was something new to the Virginia of his day. General Washington was one of the first Virginians to have a "smokejack," a flywheel built into the kitchen chimney to turn the meat spit by means of the chimney air currents. In 1787, Washington mentioned in his diary a trip to Philadelphia during which he "visited a machine at Dr. Franklin's for pressing, in place of ironing clothes from the wash"

Antoine Laurent Lavoisier, "father of modern chemistry," died under the guillotine. But his close friend, Pierre Samuel Du Pont de Nemours, also arrested by the French Revolutionary Tribunal, was saved by the death of Robespierre. In 1799, Pierre and his family fled to the United States. All returned in 1800 except a son, Eleuthère Iréné Du Pont de Nemours. He remained in the new country to establish, in 1802, a powder mill on the Brandywine River near Wilmington, Del. From this small mill grew the largest manufacturers of chemical products in the world, still controlled by Pierre's descendants

Popular Mechanics Magazine
REGISTERED IN U. S. PATENT OFFICE AND CANADA
WRITTEN SO YOU CAN UNDERSTAND IT
Vol. 71 JUNE, 1939 No. 6

From TEST TUBE to YOU

Above, storage vault where giant rolls of film are kept befo being sensitized. Right, testing plastic for safety glass

By LAMMOT DU PONT
President, E. I. du Pont de Nemours & Company

IT HAPPENED May 7, 1794, in Paris. Antoine Laurent Lavoisier, France's most talented chemist, stood before the Revolutionary Tribunal to receive the death sentence. "The Republic has no need of scientists," said the court in passing sentence.

Lavoisier died, but the spirit of science lived. Chemistry, especially, was destined to bring immeasurable benefits to humanity, developing progressively in Europe in the century that followed the execution of Lavoisier and advancing phenomenally in this country in the last twenty

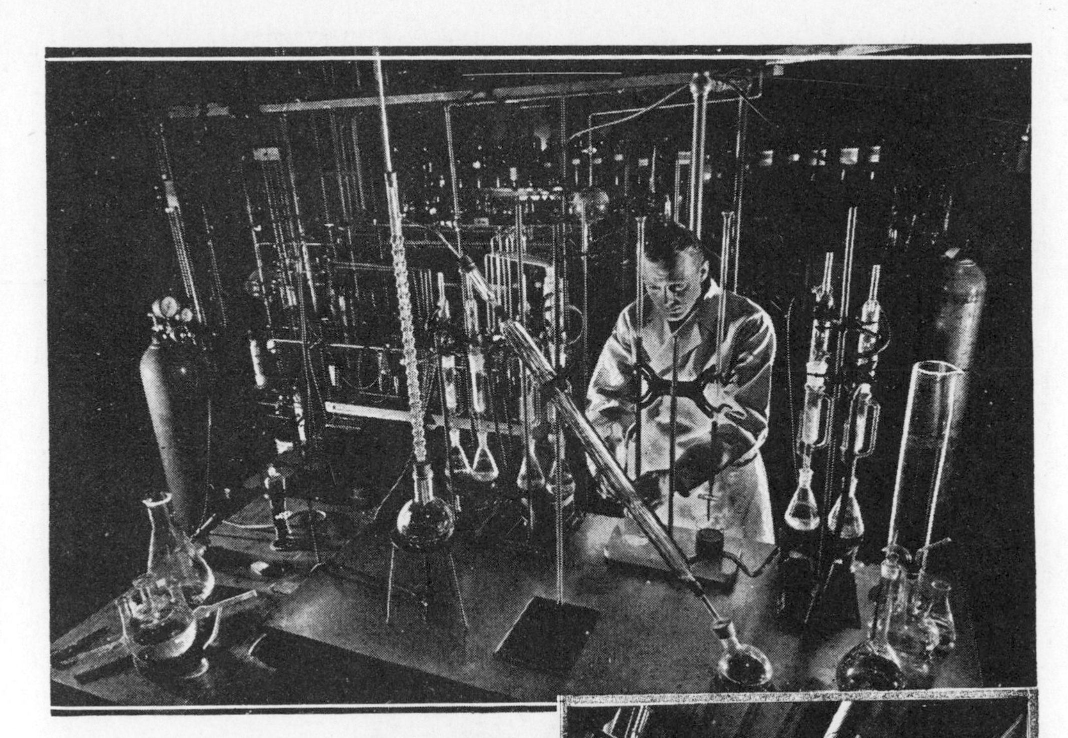

years. Today, American chemical industry and industries based on chemistry have become so important that they employ one-fifth of all factory workers and one-fourth of all industrial capital investments.

Chemistry underlies not only such patently chemical industries as the manufacture of acids, alkalis, dyestuffs, explosives, and plastics, but also such giant industries as leather tanning, petroleum refining, pulp and papermaking, the smelting of metals, and soapmaking.

How does chemistry work? If you expect magic, you will be disappointed. Rather, the chemist pursues his work methodically, carefully investigating one possibility after another, much as a salesman calls on a list of prospective customers.

Day after day, perhaps month after month, he seemingly makes no progress. Finally, he comes upon an idea that

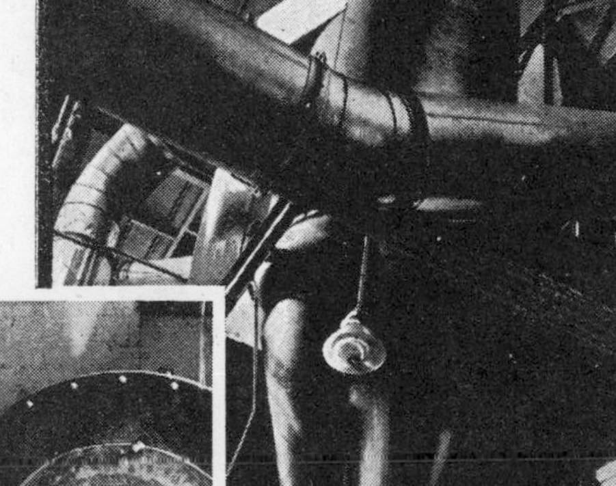

Top, the chemist at work in U. S. Rubber company laboratories. Center, "cyclones" used to recover powdered vinyl acetal resin from the air. Bottom, kiln for firing decorated glass and pottery

In its early days, the Du Pont company made only black powder. In 1875, Alfred Nobel improved dynamite gelatin, and Du Pont began making high explosives. The first step into a wider field came in 1922 when the firm bought North American rights to Cellophane, which the Swiss chemist, Jacques Brandenberg, had been trying to get into commercial production since 1908. The first large roll was produced in 1924. It was found that foods packaged in the new materials increased sales from 400 to as much as 1500 per cent. Meanwhile, the field of industrial chemistry was being widened by research in X-ray crystallography, which revealed the atomic arrangement of molecules and made possible the creation of synthetic materials

By the end of the 1930's, synthetic materials were being widely used in American production. Synthetic plastics were being molded into thousands of familiar forms—tableware, jewelry, buttons, dental plates, radio cabinets, automobile accessories, etc.—while laminated plastic sheets were being used for interior paneling. Cheap synthetic musk replaced animal musk, costing $40,000 a pound in its pure state, as a perfume fixative. Rayon made it possible for America's low-income wives and daughters to look more attractive. Chemists learned to take nitrogen from the air, and the resultant fertilizer sharply increased the yield of America's farms. World monopolies over such things as dyes, camphor and potash were smashed by the dual efforts of the chemists who developed new processes for the extraction of basic materials and the means to make synthetic products from common substances like wood and coal

seems worth while. It is only an idea, however, proved solely in the test tube. The idea must be developed on progressively larger scales, until it can be operated as a factory process. Supplies of raw material must be assured; outlets determined; and the product introduced to the public.

In a few instances, such developments require only a year or two; in other instances sometimes ten, twenty or even more years elapse. For example, Count de Chardonnet's first experiments with rayon were recorded in 1884. It was not until 1911, however, that the first American plant produced rayon. Knowledge, materials and manpower are not sufficient. Money equally is needed. Usually the amount runs into the hundreds of thousands, sometimes millions of dollars, before a commercially suitable product is achieved.

Most of us are aware that the chemist has produced new products and has improved existing products. We are conscious of beautiful chemical plastics, the durable lacquer finishes on the automobile and refrigerator, the gleaming transparent wrapping material, the rainbow of man-made colors from coal tar, and fabrics fashioned from rayon.

But what of the significance of these things to the nation?

Consider our natural resources. The chemist has aided in conserving natural resources by developing synthetic products to supplement or wholly replace natural products.

By heat cracking, approximately twice as much gasoline is obtained from crude oil as formerly by distillation which means the doubling of our oil reserves so far as gasoline is concerned.

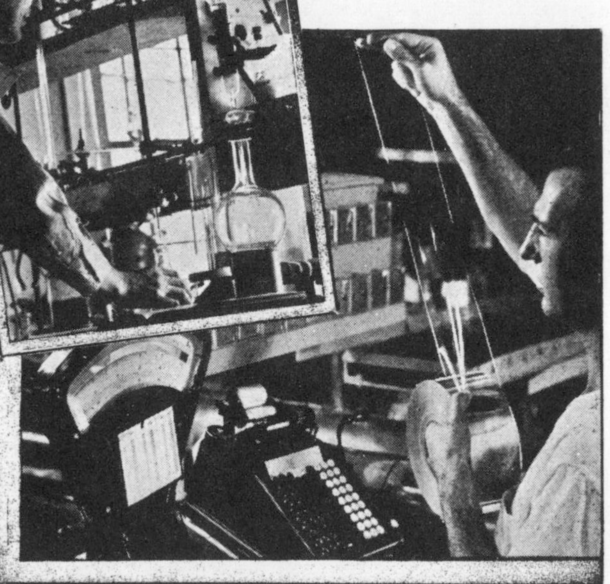

Top, lathe-turning operation on "Lucite," one of the newer plastics. Center, research laboratory of Krebs Pigments department of the du Pont company. Bottom, roll of "Cellophane" cellulose film being inspected and weighed after being prepared according to customer's specifications

Flashes from the world of chemistry. Top, machine drills holes in toothbrush handles, inserts bristles and anchors them automatically. Center, liquid viscose dripping from white tube. Right, incandescent coke being pushed out of ovens. Bottom, left, aging tanks used in manufacture of "Cellophane" cellulose film. Right, porcelain pots, glass rods and textile yarns in dye bath

Chemists have learned how to extract magnesium, a vital raw material which faced exhaustion, from sea water. New problems in research are given to the chemical laboratories every day—an instance is the extraction of aluminum, known to be present in some amount in every clay and almost every rock. Today, synthetic fibers, led by Du Pont's nylon and orlon, account for one fifth of American textile production. About 1½ billion tons of synthetic ammonia are made in the United States every year. As the synthetic materials get into mass production, they usually cost less. As Lammot Du Pont said in 1939: "Progressive elements of business have long recognized that the cure for many of our economic ills lies in a consistent and honest application of the doctrine of giving more for less"

All of the 16 hints on these two pages have one thing in common—they help a person to do vexatious tasks easier, better and at very little expense

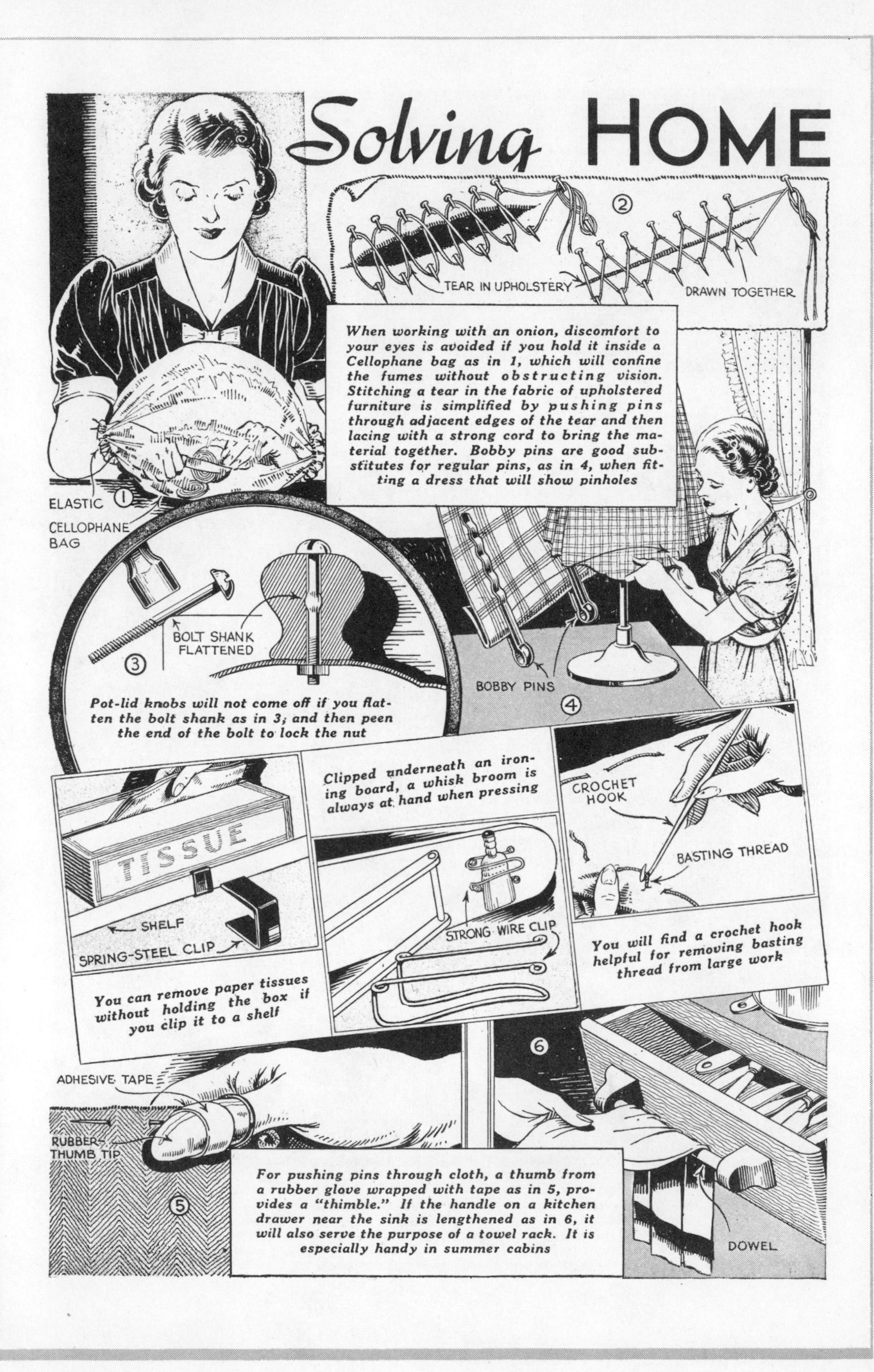

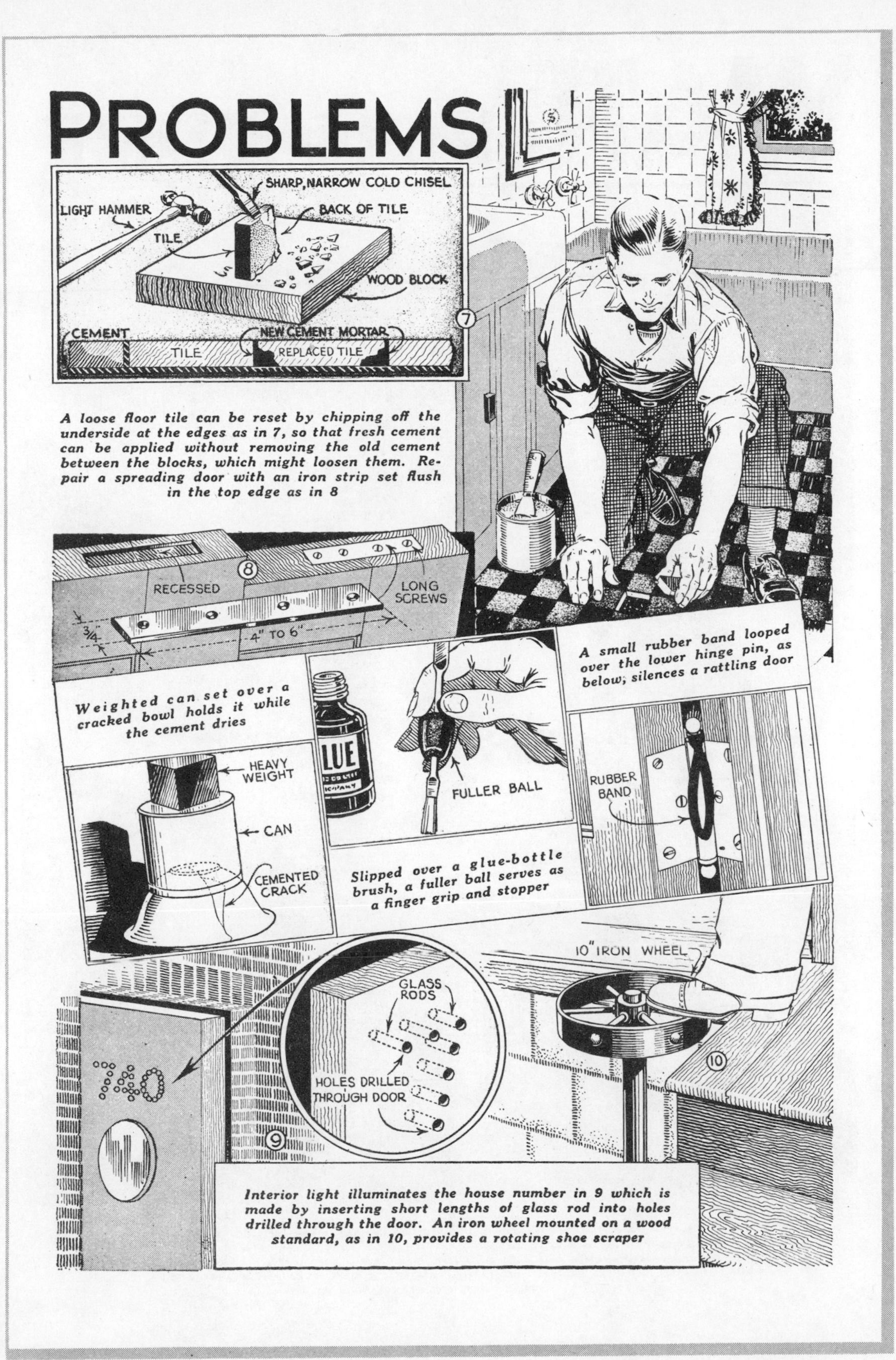

Making the ordinary object perform the unusual task is a forte of the household hints section. Popular Mechanics *has reported more than a score of unusual uses for spring-type clothespins, and has discovered 31 ways in which nail polish can be used besides glorifying feminine fingernails*

Again Americans watched the world go to war, and debated whether the nation would be drawn into the conflict. Hitler, after wresting much territory without the use of arms from a world desperately seeking to keep the peace, invaded Poland on Sept. 1, 1939. England, France and the British Commonwealth of Nations declared war. Although on paper the antagonists seemed well-matched, actually the Allies began the war with antiquated fighting equipment. The ships and planes shown here were not representative of the average overage bombers and destroyers of the British. Hitler's air force, while small, was fast and maneuverable, and the Nazi ground forces were models of military efficiency

Outbreak of war in Europe turned loose fighting machines far more terrible in striking power, far stronger in defense than any hitherto used. On these pages are some of the modern instruments of battle. At top, a British bombing plane. Left, 5.25-inch guns in twin turret on Britain's newest battleship (center); guns can be elevated to sixty-degree angle. Bottom, latest high-speed German tank

# of LAND, SEA and AIR

MAIN FIRE CONTROL TOP
MAIN DIRECTOR TOWER
POM-POMS
NAVIGATING BRIDGE
4.7 HIGH ANGLE GUN
AFT CONTROL TOWER
POM-POMS
AFT 5.25-INCH SECONDARY ARMAMENT
CATAPULT
PORT AIRCRAFT HANGAR
FORWARD PORT 5.25 IN. SECONDARY ARMAMENT

The H.M.S. King George V *was a classic of the dreadnaught era of fighting ships. The ship was heavily armed and heavily armored, with steel plates as much as 16 inches thick. Air power sharply reduced the effectiveness of the dreadnaught, however. Before World War II was ended, fleets were built around aircraft carriers, which were protected by light, fast battle cruisers*

Across the pages, a drawing of the "King George V," first of six 35,000-ton dreadnaughts under construction; they will be Britain's mightiest fortresses afloat

No big gun at all but an aircraft spotter, the range finder at left is a "big brother" of the focusing device on your camera. Above, anti-aircraft crew mans its highly mobile 3.7-inch gun, which can be pointed skyward at an angle of nearly ninety degrees

One of the weapons shown on this page—the coastal defense gun—has been outmoded by the advances in military air power. Howitzers and antitank guns remain modern arms, having re-proved their worth during the Korean campaign. Jet motors now propel fighter planes at speeds faster than sound. In 1951 the United States had developed atomic war heads for torpedoes, mines and artillery shells

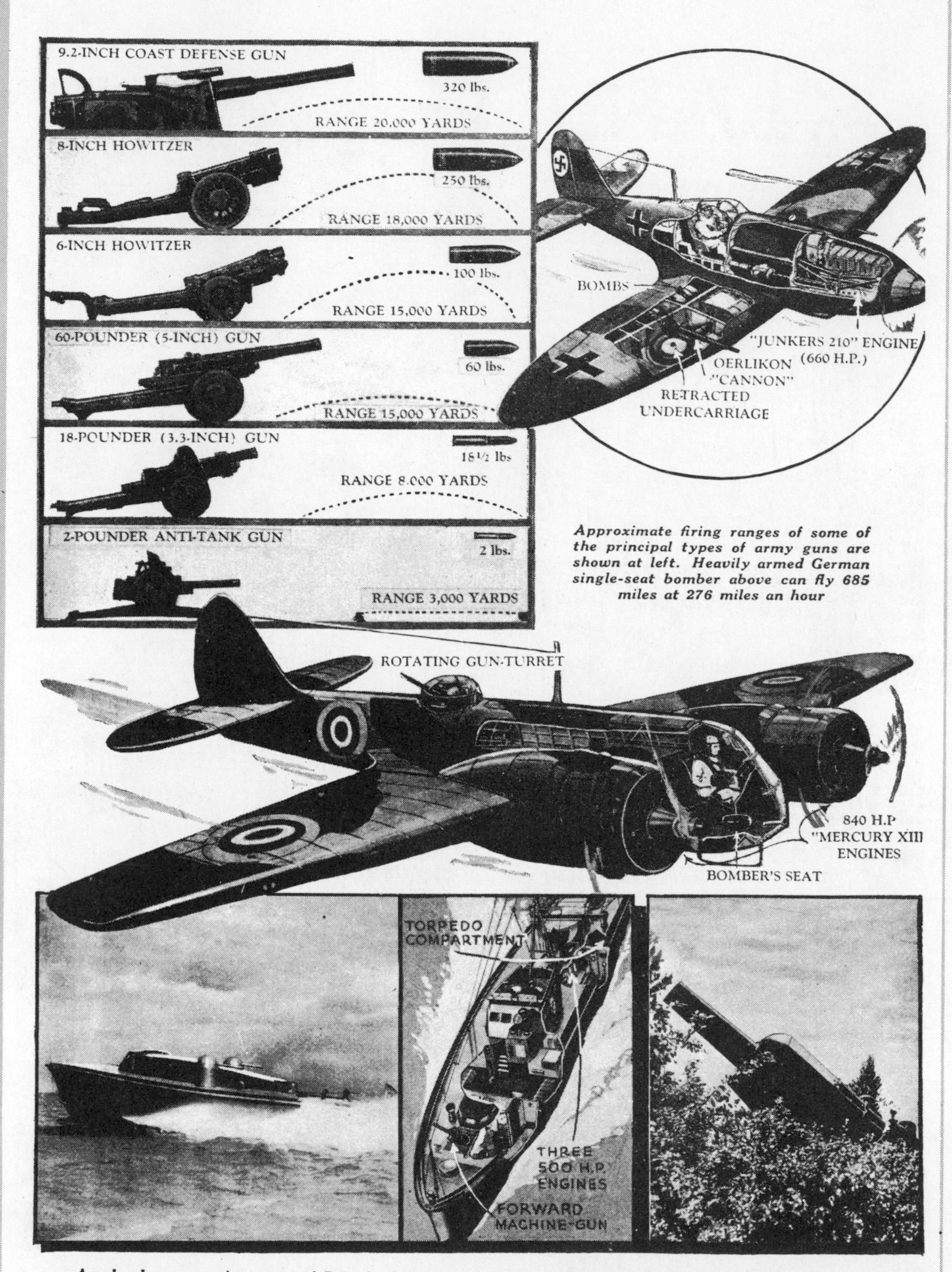

Approximate firing ranges of some of the principal types of army guns are shown at left. Heavily armed German single-seat bomber above can fly 685 miles at 276 miles an hour

Ample glass area gives crew of British plane (center) clear visibility in all directions. Below, left, forty-two-knot British boat carries four torpedoes, depth charges and armor-piercing guns in turrets; center, another torpedo boat with anti-aircraft gun; right, big German gun hidden in brush

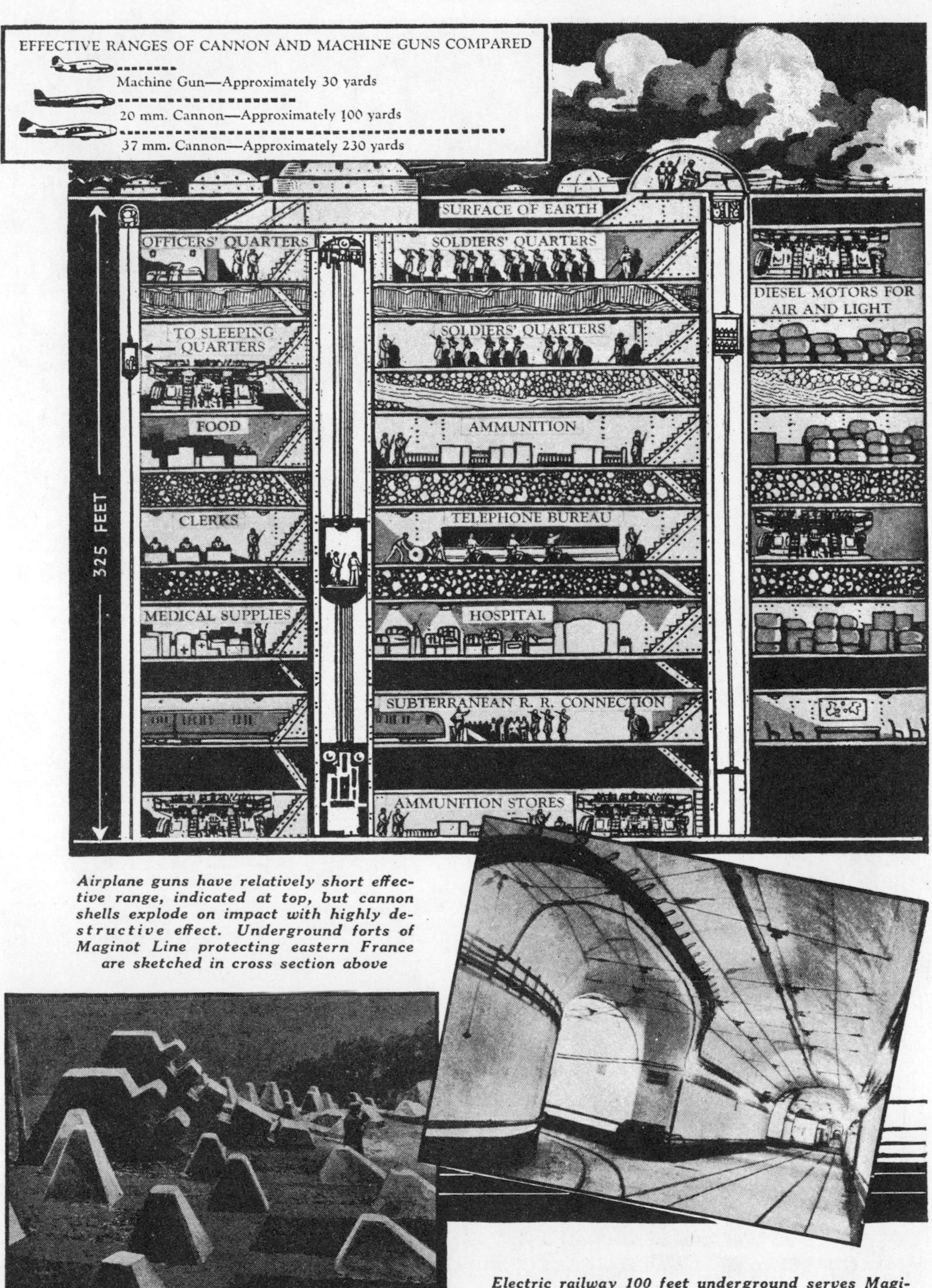

Airplane guns have relatively short effective range, indicated at top, but cannon shells explode on impact with highly destructive effect. Underground forts of Maginot Line protecting eastern France are sketched in cross section above

Electric railway 100 feet underground serves Maginot Line, above. Left, concrete traps built to keep enemy tanks from piercing Germany's Siegfried Line

This was the Maginot Line, a 125-mile chain of concrete and steel underground fortresses, stretched along their eastern frontier, on which the French placed their hopes for resisting German invasion. In the face of mechanized war, the Maginot Line proved as worthless as the Great Wall of China. In 1940 the Nazi blitzkrieg skirted the line at Sedan, then took the fortress from its vulnerable rear. The long bastion cost $500,000,000 to build and used 1,600,000 cubic yards of concrete and 50,000 tons of steel plate. There was enough food and ammunition in the underground forts to last 250,000 men a year. After taking the Maginot Line, the Nazis systematically dismantled it

"Form follows function," said Louis Henri Sullivan, the father of modern architecture in America. Sullivan, who died in 1924, left to his pupils, the most brilliant of whom was Frank Lloyd Wright, the task of carrying out his precept. Sullivan would have been proud of some of the results. New office buildings no longer imitated castles of the Middle Ages. A warehouse looked like a warehouse—but pleasantly so. Steel, glass and concrete were used quite unabashably in their naked forms, and gained beauty by such use

Building TOMORROW'S WORLD TODAY

The world of tomorrow is here. You need not travel to a world's fair to see it. True, it had a start in Chicago's 1933 exposition and gained impetus in fairs of '39, but industry is already at home in the future, in buildings shaped to perform functions efficiently instead of following tradition. Top, Hollywood studios of N.B.C., made of tinted concrete with aluminum canopy. Center, research laboratories of American Rolling Mills have porcelain enamel, stainless steel and glass walls. Below, simple lines characterize Campana company plant at Batavia, Ill.

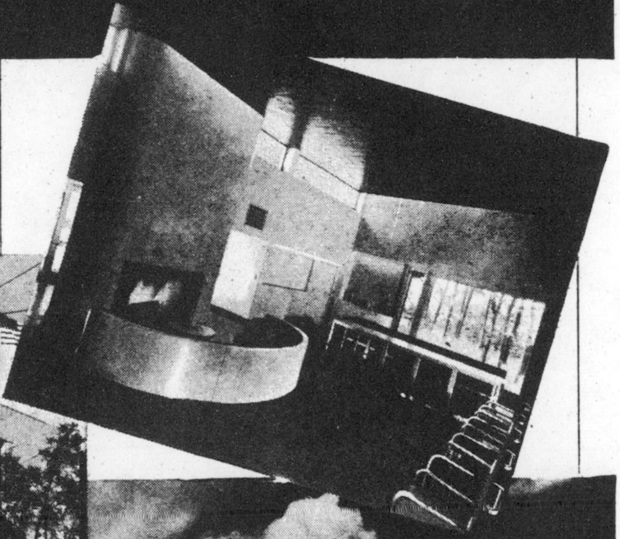

The International Style of architecture, intended by Sullivan primarily for public buildings, was extended to factories, stores and homes. The style stressed efficiency of use and simplicity of line in planning, and let decoration and pleasing effect grow naturally from the design and materials. The modern home had fewer rooms, but a great deal more care went into their arrangement. Homes were designed not only for themselves, but also in relation to their surroundings

Above, night view of home designed by Architect George F. Keck, Chicago, in answer to demand for a "house of day after tomorrow." Right, living room, with dining table against window. The house has exterior Venetian blinds, rubber-tile floors, and is arranged for minimum housekeeping effort

Windows are abolished in the modern store and factory. Scientific lighting, often with the new fluorescent tubes and with daylight coming through glass-block walls, saves maximum space for sales display and machinery. Environment is under complete control, air-conditioning systems providing optimum "weather" for work. Above, windowless Sears, Roebuck & Co. store in Baltimore. Right, model of factory just completed for Church & Dwight, soda manufacturers

The CHEMIST SPINS

For the first time, man had made a fiber—had not transformed a raw material into a fiber, as in fiberglas, but had truly created a fiber from such basic elements as coal, air and water. And a miraculous fiber it was —possessing properties not found together in any natural fiber. Nylon was tough, strong, light in weight, elastic, stable, washable and quick-drying, elastic and resistant to flame, abrasion, mildew and insects. And it was versatile—could be spun into thread or yarn, or molded into plastic forms

Bristles of hairbrush, left, are made of nylon; tough, resilient, they outwear any natural bristle. Below, processing nylon yarn; here the machines twist a "bundle" of filaments into thread. Bottom, brushes with nylon bristles used for cleaning bottles in bottling plant

IF YOU say there are no frontiers left for Americans to explore, you haven't heard about nylon.

Columbus wasn't hunting for America when he discovered it, and the research chemists who pioneered the way to nylon weren't looking for a magic yarn that would revolutionize the textile industry and a few others besides. They were not interested in stockings nor toothbrushes, but in superpolymers. Wondering, as the "pure research" scientist does, why and how certain of nature's tiny building blocks, the molecules, united to form the giant molecules called superpolymers, they developed a new type of synthetic material from which fibers of remarkable strength and elasticity could be spun. They called it nylon.

Nylon fibers have a higher strength-elasticity factor than corresponding fibers of cotton, linen, wool, silk or rayon. Truly elastic nylon yarn will return to approximately its original length after being stretched for days. Water can't hurt it, and it dries quickly; most chemicals and oils are harmless to nylon. It's no home

a NEW YARN

for moths, nor for the fungi that start mildew. The nylon family has some admirable traits, and while it has practically no past its future is bound to be brilliant.

Perhaps you haven't made the acquaintance of nylon, but you can't escape it long. It was announced at the du Pont laboratories October 27, 1938. Commercial production of the yarn has just begun. But in its first year of life, nylon, produced in a "pilot" factory of the du Pont company, has been launched on a versatile career in the forms of fishing lines and leaders; surgical sutures; bristles for toothbrushes,

Sheer hosiery of nylon yarn, top. Drawing in center indicates random arrangement of molecules in section of undrawn nylon fiber (left) and orderly lineup of molecules after drawing (right). Bottom, control panel which maintains precision in nylon processing

hair and clothes brushes; thread and hosiery. Tomorrow you may find it in rugs and bathing suits, upholstery and parachutes, sweaters, insulation, linings of men's suits—in fact, almost anywhere that silk can go, nylon can go and last longer.

Will it displace silk entirely? That's what some predicted of rayon, back in 1911; but in 1938, when the United States produced 288,000,000 pounds of rayon, twice as much silk was consumed as in 1911.

In the simplest terms, nylon is a combination of coal, air and water. It is a protein-like chemical, somewhat resembling silk, hair and wool in composition, but actually unlike anything in nature.

Americans had to wait until after World War II to enjoy the wonders of nylon. By the time production was adequate, the entire output of the new material was needed for such war uses as parachutes and surgical thread. After the war, the uses for nylon were myriad. By 1951, nearly 200 million pounds were being manufactured every year. Nylon has virtually supplanted silk, and has caused sharp reductions in the amount of cotton, wool and rayon yarn used by the textile industry

Edward Uhler Condon, now director of the U.S. Bureau of Standards, was one of the American physicists who helped unravel the mystery of atomic energy. While he was associate director of the Westinghouse research laboratories (1937-45), Condon served on various atom-splitting projects for the government. Atom-splitting was a prelude to the actual release of atomic energy. The problem for the atom-smashers was to find out how the protons and the neutrons hung together inside the tiny nucleus of the atom. At the time this article was written, physicists had already learned there were two kinds of uranium atoms—U-235 and U-238. This means that an atom of each, respectively, is 235 and 238 times as heavy as one hydrogen atom

Popular Mechanics Magazine

REGISTERED IN U. S. PATENT OFFICE AND CANADA

WRITTEN SO YOU CAN UNDERSTAND IT

Vol. 74 **JULY, 1940** **No. 1**

SHARPSHOOTING at the ATOM

By Dr. E. U. Condon
Associate Director, Westinghouse Research Laboratories

RESEARCH physicists in universities and in at least one large industrial laboratory are busy smashing the atom. Why? What for? And just what does it mean to smash the atom? And how is it done?

Ten years ago we did not even know what basic parts made up an atom. Chemists knew that all matter was made of some ninety chemically distinct kinds of atoms. Physicists knew these atoms were made of electrified particles; that there was a heavy central part, called the nucleus and charged positively, surrounded by little particles of negative electricity, called electrons. Different elements are known to be made of atoms which differ with regard to the number of electrons in the atom. Thus the hydrogen atom

Dr. John A. Hipple, Jr., assembles vacuum tube of spherical mass spectrometer designed to sort molecules and atoms so scientists may have definite target at which to direct "bullets" of atom-smashing machines

contains one electron, the iron atom contains twenty-six, the lead atom eighty-two, the list ending with the uranium atom having ninety-two electrons.

Eight years ago a new fundamental building block of matter was discovered, the neutron. It was given this name since it is electrically neutral. It has about the same mass or weight as a single hydrogen atom. It is now known that the central heavy nucleus of all atoms (except the simplest, hydrogen) is a little aggregate of protons and neutrons stuck together. The proton is the smallest unit of positive electricity we know—having the same electric charge as an electron, but weighing 1840 times as much. We are

Above, assembling porcelain insulating columns which support giant electrode at top of sixty-five foot "atom-smasher." Below, Dr. William H. Wells measuring voltage of giant machine with electroscope. This instrument calibrates voltage by measuring gamma rays emitted by fluorine under bombardment by protons, the hearts of hydrogen. Right, details of Westinghouse atom bombarding machine

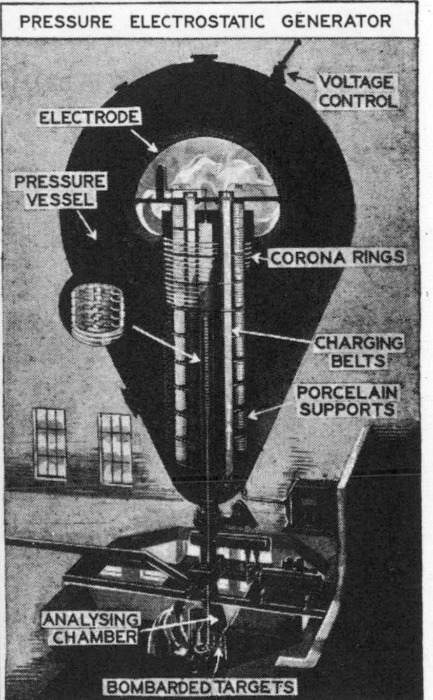

now quite sure that all matter is made up of these three things: Electrons, negatively charged, small weight; protons, same charge, 1840 times electron weight; neutrons, no electric charge, about same weight as proton.

Condon only hinted at the possibility of atomic energy, but an editor's note at the conclusion of his article, expanded the point by saying: "Discovery that 'U-235' explodes with tremendous force, coupled with the feat of finding a way to separate the two kinds of uranium atoms, is regarded by some scientists as pointing the way to release of atomic power. . . . Some scientists think that the discovery eventually may revolutionize the world, that it promises to make all other sources of power mere child's toys by comparison." The note was based on research by Prof. John R. Dunning of Columbia University, who identified the 235 atom as the one which released energy when bombarded with neutrons

"Blitzkrieg" is the German word for "lightning war." Armies had combined surprise with speed before, but never at the pace set by the Nazi columns in 1939-1940. Low-flying, strafing planes swept ahead of the German columns of swiftly moving tanks and armored cars. In such fashion the Nazis overran Poland in 10 days, swept through the Lowlands in five days, and swerved around the Maginot Line to capture Paris in less than 40 days. In Poland the blitzkrieg columns stabbed through the main Polish army, then turned on it from the rear, trapping the Poles between two strong Nazi forces

Mechanics Magazine
TERED IN U. S. PATENT OFFICE AND CANADA
YOU CAN UNDERSTAND IT
Vol. 74 — T, 1940 — No. 2

German dive bombers of the type pictured above played a big part in forcing Dutch and Belgian capitulation and in fighting Allied navies. German tanks that threw a stream of flames seventy yards were used in the march to the channel; at left is an Italian army flame thrower

By R. Ernest Dupuy
Major, U. S. Field Artillery

LESS than a year ago a siren voice was heard: "Stay on the defensive—modern weapons are so murderous that whoever takes the offensive is doomed." A part of the world believed; another part—professional soldiers these—disbelieving, found themselves without an audience.

Distrust history, sang the siren. Forget Genghis Khan, Frederick the Great, Washington's sweep to Yorktown, Napoleon's 1805 campaign to Austerlitz, Robert E. Lee in the Shenandoah Valley, Grant before Vicksburg and again at Appomattox, Allenby in Palestine. Forget that surprise, speed and striking power offensively used have won every previous campaign. Today that siren is silent. An amazed world prates

In warfare of old the spy and the cavalry worked behind enemy lines and made forays into enemy country. Today parachute troops (top) bail out of big transports with guns, supplies, even bicycles to sabotage and prepare the way for the army. Below, timetable of German blitzkrieg

of blitzkrieg, the lightning war, as something new under the sun.

This is an error. What is new is the technique, the utilization of scientific advances —mainly the internal-combustion engine and everything it made possible—which has geared warfare to a heretofore unthinkable rapidity of movement. The basic elements of success in war remain the same; an offensive plan which chooses the terrain to fight on, which takes advantage of every opportunity, and which has the punch to crash through.

Here, of course, an aggressor has initial advantage, unless a peacefully inclined nation be fully prepared for every eventuality. For only if prepared in theory, fact and training, can a peacefully inclined nation parry the thrust and launch a counterattack, the return blow which means so much.

The essence of the first move, then, is surprise. Surprise brings uncertainty and disorder in its wake, disrupts all the normal life of the invaded country. To be stronger than the attacked, particularly in the air, is essential. You don't make a blitzkrieg unless this is reasonably certain. The strongest body is powerless if its nerve-centers be cut.

Dupuy, a colonel in charge of Army public relations during World War II, summed up the weaknesses of the blitzkrieg: "The success of a blitz is definitely dependent upon ability to follow up the mechanized spearheads with the main body of troops. . . .
Once the other fellow has time to draw breath, the initiative has been yielded by the attacker. And the essence of it all is time. A counterattack cannot be launched until the direction and extent of the blow be definitely known. One must first parry, get set, then return the blow. Better still, and certainly less nerve-racking, is not only to match the other fellow ship for ship, gun for gun, trained man for trained man, in the air, on the land and on the sea, but also to raise the ante. The pleasant thing about that is that there probably won't be any blitzkrieg"

$E = Mc^2$ (energy equals the mass times the speed of light squared). When Albert Einstein offered that formula to physicists in 1908, they were certain that powerful energy must lie in the nuclei of atoms. In 1938, chemical tests by Lisè Meitner and her German associates indicated the uranium atom could be split. In 1939, Alfred A. O. Nier separated the two isotopes of uranium, U-238 and U-235. The following year John R. Dunning exploded pure U-235. Then it was that scientists began serious speculation on the future of atomic energy

Popular Mechanics Magazine
REGISTERED IN U. S. PATENT OFFICE AND CANADA
WRITTEN SO YOU CAN UNDERSTAND IT

Vol. 75 **JANUARY, 1941** **No. 1**

The MIRACLE of U-235

By Dr. R. M. Langer

***Editor's Note*—One of the country's eminent physicists in this article paints a picture of the world as he visualizes it when U-235, a possible new source of power, emerges from the laboratory. Dr. Langer, now at the California Institute of Technology, has been doing uranium atom research and has been connected with leading laboratories in this country and abroad**

SEVERAL months ago you read in Popular Mechanics that the secret of atomic power is close to solution and that possibly within a decade civilization will be using the tremendous amounts of energy contained in U-235, an isotope of uranium.

Since then, additional research has opened up greater possibilities than ever. At first we thought that a heavy power plant weighing tons would be required to extract the power; now it appears that a pound or even a single ounce of

Top, author's idea of U-235 plane, a flying wing with propelling jets at rear and lifting jets underneath. Cross-section treatment gives view of interior. Bottom, giant electron microscope developed as result of atomic studies

Only six months before, the editors of Popular Mechanics *had indicated in a general way some of the possibilities of atomic energy (see page 258). In this article, Dr. R. M. Langer of the California Institute of Technology makes some specific predictions. They are based on the future development of a uranium-fired steam-turbine motor. Another prediction by Dr. Langer: "The readers of* Popular Mechanics *will play an important part in putting U-235 to use. There is no end to the practical applications that amateurs can work out once the energy source is available"*

Above, assembling plastic plane. Bottom of page, left, examining spring suspension in pendulum railway car shown in cutaway sketch at right. Auto of uranium age will be constructed similarly, the author believes

U-235 can be made to deliver energy. A power plant the size of a typewriter will be available. Its heart will be a one-pound package of uranium that contains the same amount of power that we extract from 250,000 gallons of gasoline. With such a power pack in a car you could drive 5,000,000 miles without refueling. Obviously, at $1,000 a pound, U-235 will be cheap.

But more miles per dollar is only one minor advantage foreseen for the uranium age. We can look forward to universal comfort, practically free transportation, and unlimited supplies of materials. Power will be cheap in every home and factory, without distribution lines, and electricity will cost less than one-tenth of a cent per kilowatt-hour.

It is not too early today to consider the changes that this power source suggests. Jet propulsion will free the airplane from earth. For both local low-altitude trips and long-range flights at high altitudes we will probably always use the simple airfoil or flying-wing design. We will use the principle of rocket power but there will be no need to employ the bullet shape of present rockets. We will fly several thousand miles per hour at several hundred thousand feet above the surface and will have to slow down in descending to the surface

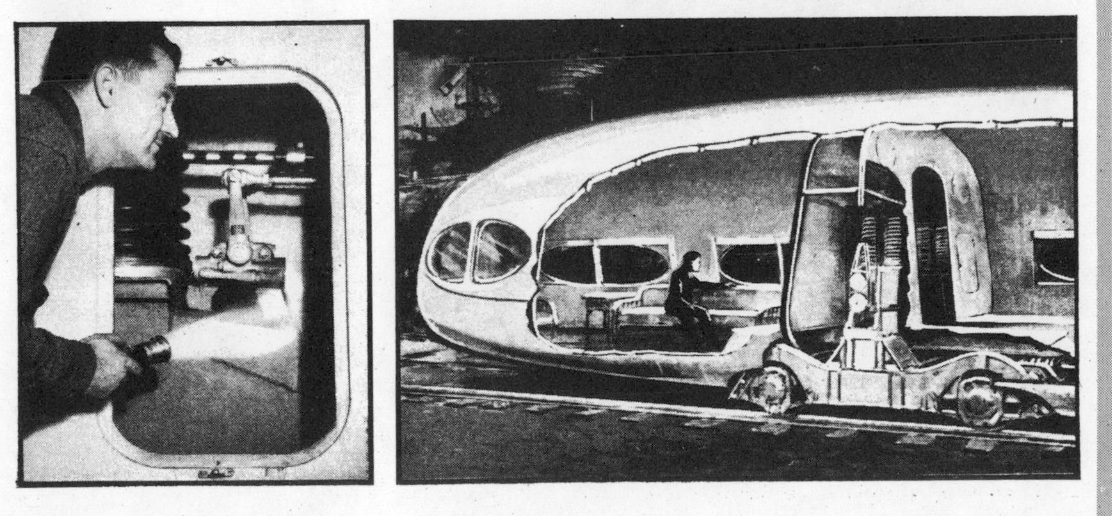

In November, 1941, Popular Mechanics *published its last major article on atomic energy until after World War II. Shortly after this article appeared, the United States began the famed Manhattan Project which culminated in the atomic bomb, and a cloak of silence necessarily descended over all developments in atomic research. After the war, the troubled international situation forced continued caution in the release of atomic information. In 1946 Congress placed all atomic research under the charge of the Atomic Energy Commission*

to avoid being burned up like a meteor.

The flying-wing driver will have a gyroscope, the main propulsion jets, and a few directable control jets at his command. Compressed air or steam for the jets might do for landing or leaving the ground but for greater efficiency we might very well use steel vapor for propulsion at higher altitudes. Vapor from boiling steel would have powerful thrust and would condense as fine harmless dust.

U-235 at $1,000 per pound would be the same as buying aviation gasoline at 250 gallons per dollar, not including taxes. Really the efficiency of uranium power is much greater than this comparison indicates.

When the present war ends, things may begin to happen that will make this article seem unimaginative. Until then the best we can do is to see that science continues to be free, that men have time and freedom to follow hobbies and that whatever truths are discovered are given to the public without distortion as a help to preserving freedom.

Popular Mechanics Magazine

REGISTERED IN U. S. PATENT OFFICE AND CANADA

WRITTEN SO YOU CAN UNDERSTAND IT

Vol. 76 JULY, 1941 No. 1

The SEARCH for SUBSTITUTES

MR. AND MRS. AMERICA soon will be using many commonplace things made of "ersatz" materials—substitutes for certain metals, rubber, silk, cork and special woods that must be conserved to insure adequate supplies for national defense purposes.

Governmental agencies and private research experts are in the midst of an intensive hunt for "ersatz," a hunt that already is yielding important results. The good news for the consumer is that in spite of the sweeping changes ahead he most likely will be as pleased with the substitute products as he was with those made from the materials replaced. In some cases, he may not even be aware that changes have been made.

From the field of plastics are coming substitutes from which hundreds of articles, formerly composed wholly or in part of aluminum, magnesium, tin, chromium and zinc, can be made. Already it has been found possible to employ plastics as housings for vacuum cleaners, household machinery of all kinds and business machines. Fan blades,

Above, reflectometer in General Electric laboratory tests plastics which are in demand as substitutes for defense materials

Right, H. M. Richardson, plastics engineer, studying articles that may be produced economically in plastic materials. Among the articles on desk are fan blades, hair-drier hoods, soap dispensers, vacuum-cleaner nozzles, business machines and a gunstock

By now, one of every four Americans worked in an industry that hadn't existed in the 1900's. Most of these industries were founded on chemical research. Man had added a fourth kingdom—the kingdom of synthetics—to those of animal, vegetable and mineral matter. The first synthetic compound, urea, was developed by Friedrich Wöhler of Germany in 1828. Another step was the derivation of violet aniline dye from coal tar by Sir William Perkin (1856). Dmitri Mendelyeev's periodic table of the elements (1859), and William Roentgen's X-ray (1895), were other tools which chemists used to study the structure of matter and develop synthetic compounds

The broad base on which the chemical industry was already established in the United States at the outbreak of World War II made it possible for this country to provide a suitable substitute for every vital war material from which normal supplies were cut off—silk was replaced by nylon and synthetic rubber and quinine were derived from coal tar. While war needs were met, civilians had to do without some things they had been used to—aluminum cooking ware disappeared from the market, and metal articles were in short supply or were made of plastic or wood for the duration

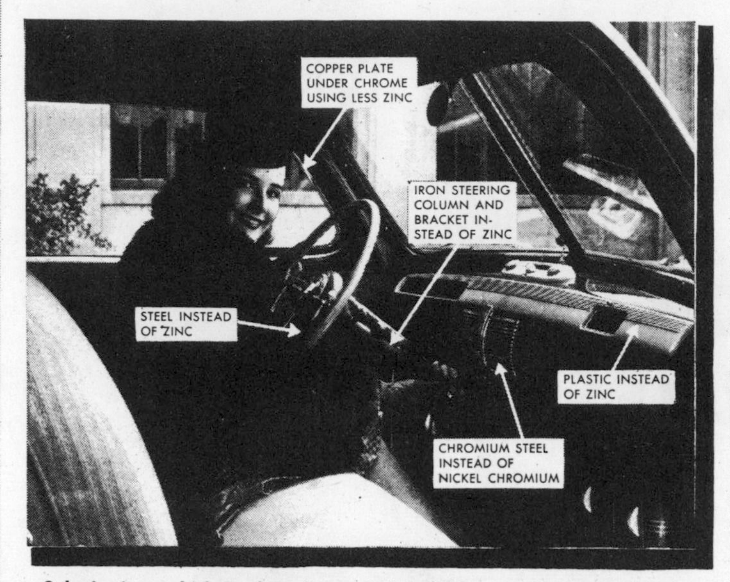

Substitutions which Ford engineers find possible to make in interior of automobile to release materials vital to national defense

camera cases, cosmetic cases and vanity cases, airplane parts, hair-drier hoods and instrument handles and cases are just a few of the more common articles in whose manufacture metals are being replaced by plastics. In the refrigerator industry, plastics can be substituted for large areas of thin-gauge aluminum and steel in making freezer doors, panel and drawer fronts, knobs and control panels.

A trend to increasing use of plastics in the automobile is being encouraged heartily by the necessity for conserving materials vital to defense. The 1941 models display instrument panels, door handles, control knobs and interior trim made of plastics, and E. I. du Pont de Nemours & Company reports there are at least 50 possible uses for plastics in automobiles. Not far in the future may be the car with body panels made of plastics. The Ford Motor Company is in the midst of a development pointed in that direction. Prospects are good, too, that airplane fuselages and wings may be molded of plastics, thus releasing large supplies of aluminum and stainless steel for other purposes.

A plastic finish for containers has been announced by the Reynolds Metals Corporation as a substitute for aluminum foil on the outside of packages of tea, coffee and other products that are easily contaminated. Oiled paper, glassine, lead foil and Cellophane also may be used.

Synthetic resin enamels are being tested as substitutes for tin in coating certain types of cans. A committee of the National Academy of Sciences estimates that 12,000 long tons of tin might be recovered annually from old tin cans.

Rubber blocks cushion path of army tanks, therefore rubber conservation is important. These tank blocks are pictured in Goodyear plant

Also essential to defense is rubber for making flotation bags, shown in Goodyear factory, which protect land planes forced down on water

CONVOY

Protection of merchant ships from enemy submarines and bombing planes has been one of England's big problems in the present war. Almost everything England needs—food, materials and finished war-making goods—must come from overseas. The convoy system, in which from 20 to 100 ships gather at a specified port and proceed under guard of planes and warships, seems the best means of accomplishing the task of moving goods in comparative safety. Latest loss figures are low—about one ship out of 50 or 60. Left, bristling guns of a British warship on patrol duty, one phase of keeping the seas clear of raiders

Typical convoy scene as viewed from patrol bombing plane engaged in guarding the ships in danger zone. Part of the plane is shown at left. Note spacing of ships in this convoy

The convoy was a relatively safe way to ship war goods, since it was virtually suicide for a submarine to attack with a warship so close at hand. But the necessity for using convoys was in a sense a mark of success for the Nazi submarine campaign. Convoys had to travel at the speed of the slowest ship in the group, and loaded ships sometimes had to lie in port for days awaiting an armed escort. Thus the amount of shipping was greatly reduced as compared to what was sent before the submarines became active

1942-1951

THERE was no breathing spell for America in World War II. Suddenly we were in it—for keeps—all over the globe. On Jan. 26, 1942, less than 60 days after Pearl Harbor, U.S. troops landed in northern Ireland. Manila, Bataan and Corregidor fell to the Japanese, but on Jan. 31 the first U.S. Navy task-force attack was launched on the Marshall and Gilbert Islands. Quickly the armed services of the United States mushroomed to 12 million men and split into theaters of war in the Pacific, North Africa, Europe, Italy and the Mediterranean, Alaska and The British Isles.

An avalanche of war production

At home, American industry retooled for war and performed the impossible—production lines spilled out planes, tanks, guns, shells and ships not only for our own armed forces but for those of our allies as well. Women donned overalls, slipped welder's helmets over their tresses and worked side by side with men on the B-26's and the Liberty ships. Lawyers and architects performed their professional duties, then worked a shift on a lathe in a machine shop. Farmers plowed their back acres, putting under cultivation the largest crops and tending the largest livestock herds in U.S. history. Harassed housewives treasured red meat tokens above money as they stood in line for scarce items. In backyards and vacant lots, some 20 million victory gardens were cultivated to help produce food.

A half million Americans manned civilian-defense posts to conduct practice black-outs and maintain an alert for enemy planes. Other volunteer workers rallied for ration and draft boards, Red Cross blood-donor service, scrap drives and USO centers. The grip of government strengthened on every facet of American life—laid down the rules for industry and individual, controlled prices, wages, rents.

Fed by the stream of American arms and men, the Allies slowly but surely carried the fight to the enemy on all fronts—victory came in the African campaign, then Italy, then, island by island, the Japanese were cut off from their empire. In Europe, Adolf Hitler split his legions with a fanatical drive into the Soviet Union. For months the world awaited a "second front"—on June 6, 1944, "D-Day" finally dawned, and Allied troops poured onto the Normandy coast from the greatest invasion armada the world had ever seen. Inexorably, the Allies advanced from east and west—the west wave breaking only once in the bloody "Battle of the Bulge." In April, 1945, Yanks and Russians met on the banks of the Elbe. Hitler was reported dead in the ruins of Berlin, and the remnants of his "thousand year" Reich surrendered unconditionally on May 8, 1945.

$E = Mc^2$

In the Pacific, meanwhile, the Philippines had been freed, U.S. troops had captured Iwo Jima and Okinawa, and bombs were being dropped on Japanese cities. On Aug. 5, 1945, a new kind of bomb was dropped on Hiroshima. A beautiful mushroom column of smoke rose from the flash of a man-made inferno of blast, heat and deadly radiations that killed 78,000 Japanese and devastated 60 per cent of the city. Three days later another atomic bomb flattened a third of Nagasaki and killed 40,000 people. On August 10 the Japanese surrendered.

Just a few weeks before victory in Europe, Americans had been stunned by the death of Franklin Delano Roosevelt, serving his fourth term as President. Vice-President Harry S. Truman took up the burdens of the last months of war and the peace.

The birth of the United Nations

It was an uneasy peace from the beginning. As early as 1942 Roosevelt and Churchill had proclaimed the brave new postwar world, and laid the foundations for the United Nations. On April 25, 1945, the United Nations held its charter meeting in San Francisco, attended by representatives of the United States, Great Britain, China, the Soviet Union and 26 other governments who had fought the Axis. But the Soviet bloc of nations proved unco-operative from the first, and began a series of intrigues and aggressions against their neighbors. The phrase "cold war" came into the language to describe the tension building up between the United States and the Soviet Union.

To bolster her allies, America poured relief into postwar Europe, then set up the Marshall Plan to aid the rehabilitation. The Balkan countries fell into the Soviet net, and the United States announced the Truman doctrine to halt Communist aspirations in Turkey and Greece. In China, efforts to bolster the Nationalist government failed, and the Communists took over. The occupation of Japan was successful, but the four-power occupation of Germany brought tensions characterized by the Soviet blockade of Berlin; broken finally by the American air-lift.

At home the nation adjusted surprisingly well to peace. A widely expected decline in business activity did not materialize. More than 60 million persons were employed by 1947, and industrial production was 50 per cent higher than 1939 levels. By 1951 the gross national production was about 285 billion dollars, and personal income totaled 217 billion dollars. Shadows on this prosperity were skyrocketing prices and a serious housing shortage.

The 1950 census counted 150,697,361 Americans, the greatest numerical growth of any decade in our history having taken place between 1940 and 1950. New "wonder drugs" and other advances in medicine had put the death rate at a new low of 9.6 deaths per thousand persons, and the average life expectancy now was 67½ years.

Further tests and research were conducted into atomic energy, and the possibility of a hydrogen bomb, many times more powerful than the atomic bomb, was announced. Jet planes were the step of the decade for aviation, and military research developed rockets and guided missiles which could be equipped with atomic war heads.

The cold-war tension finally snapped in Korea, divided into zones of Russian and American influence. Communist North Korea invaded the south on June 25, 1950. The United Nations quickly authorized a "police action," and American troops, aided by token forces from other nations, went into action against the aggressors. For more than a year, during which time Chinese Communist forces entered the fighting against the United Nations, bloody campaigns waged back and forth across the 38th parallel. In July, 1951, the Communists and United Nations forces agreed to discuss a cease-fire proposal made by the Soviet Union.

In January, 1952, *Popular Mechanics* published its golden anniversary edition. It looked back over five decades to the first 16-page issue, reporting on the era of "sky-cycles" and the horseless carriage. And it looked forward as far as the future is predictable. The anniversary came at an appropriate moment in history. America had passed through 50 years of tremendous changes, and now stood on the threshold of the atomic age—an age that promised much if man could only survive its inherent dangers. Into the same skies that the Wrights had labored with their unwieldy biplane, sleek jets roared up and out of sight before the thunder of the engines could be heard. Over the same roadbeds that the early locomotives puffed and clacked, streamlined Diesels and turbine-powered trains sped swiftly and almost silently.

An age of high promise—if we can manage it

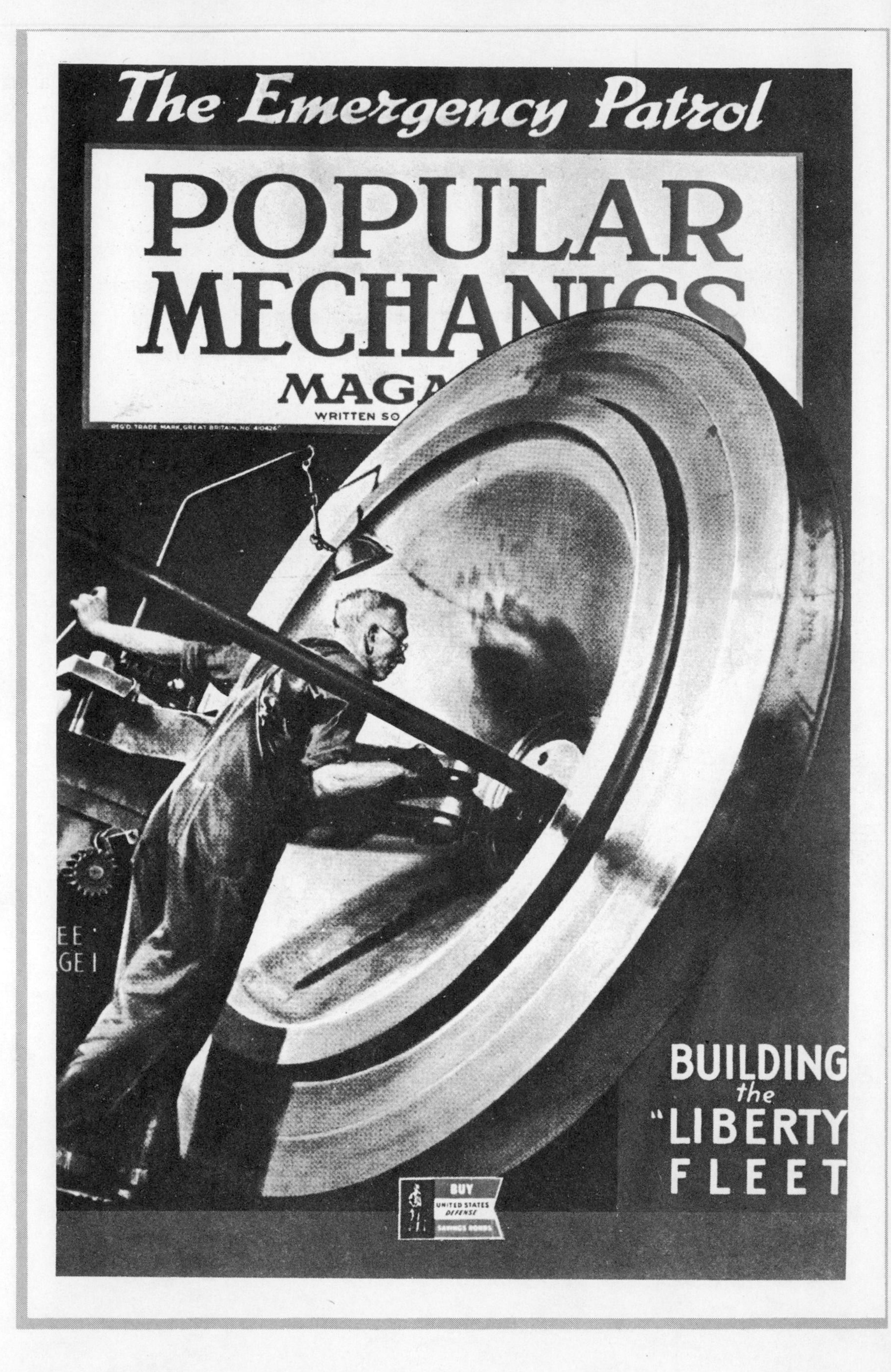

The cover pictured the shaft flange of a generator capable of producing 36 million watts of electricity in the Tennessee Valley. It illustrated a story on solar energy by Prof. C. C. Furnas of the Yale University School of Engineering. Professor Furnas urged there be thorough research into solar energy, declaring that "if we wait too long to start working on the problem, we may be caught short as other supplies of energy dwindle"

In the days of the Model T, Popular Mechanics' *hints for motorists were of the simple variety—such as how to make an emergency repair on a fan belt with a strip of bacon rind. As the automobile became more complicated, readers were kept abreast of such repairs as they could safely make themselves*

HELPFUL HINTS for the MOTORIST

1—If you can raise your car hood from the outside, the carburetor air cleaner is a good place to carry a spare ignition key. 2—Slipped over the switch of a flashlight, a wide rubber band will help prevent the light from being turned on accidentally

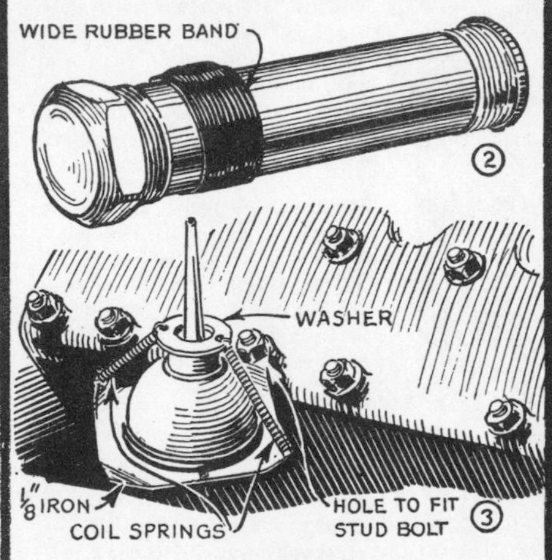

3—Clamped under one of the cylinder-head bolts of the motor, this holder permits an oilcan to be carried under the hood where it is conveniently at hand. 4—Your road map is always ready for instant viewing if it is kept on the inside surface of the glove-compartment door. Four small spring clips soldered at the corners of the door will keep the map in place

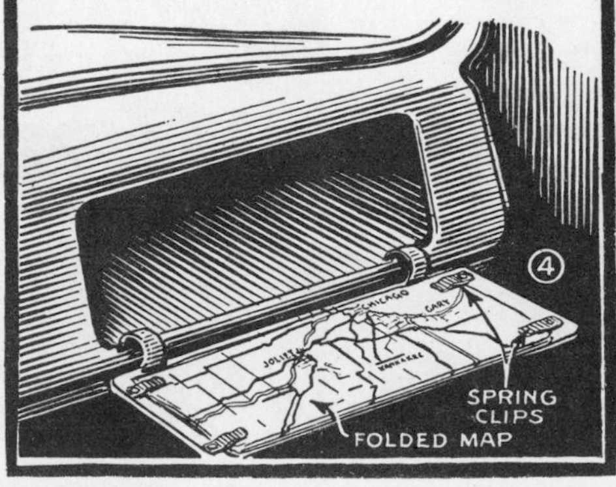

5—Recovery of nuts, washers, wrenches and other small parts is a simple matter with this tool if they have been dropped around a hot motor or in other places difficult or impossible to reach with the hand. The spring-wire jaws, which pass through a small ring soldered to the lower end of the choke wire, are opened or closed when the latter is moved up or down by the finger ring soldered to the upper end of the choke wire. 6—Instead of lowering a window all the way so your dog can put its feet on the frame to look out and maybe scratch the finish, slit a piece of hose to fit over the edge of the glass, which is then left raised slightly. This is comfortable for the dog and keeps its feet off the finish. If your telescoping antenna works hard, moisture probably has collected in the lower half and caused the parts to rust. A drain hole in the lower end of the antenna usually will stop the trouble. Wiping the sliding parts with vaseline will help also

The bombs never materialized except for a few Japanese incendiaries which drifted harmlessly on balloons into West Coast forests. But the very threat of being bombed was a new prospect for the citizens of a nation which previously had regarded itself as safely isolated from the rest of the world by two oceans. Modern aviation made the danger real, however, and to meet it the Office of Civilian Defense was formed on May 20, 1941. Half a million citizens enrolled as air-raid wardens, block captains, airplane spotters, fire fighters and members of bomb demolition squads. The American Red Cross, whose major effort was the collection of blood for wounded servicemen, also assisted the civilian defense effort with first-aid classes

IF *the* AIR RAID SIREN

↑ Coastal areas of the United States, at least, are in peril of bombing and the citizenry must be prepared. It is well to fill the bathtub with water, and bottle some drinking water, lest city water mains be broken

Stock up the room you select for your air-raid "shelter" with the necessities—jugs of ← water, Thermos bottle, flashlight, candles and matches, a first-aid kit, chocolate, magazines and cards for diversion

Gas burners should be turned off during raid; it may be wise to cut off gas at meter, but consult utility office first

To be ready for the incendiary bomb, keep a hose attached to the water faucet. On the bomb itself use a fine spray, since a heavy stream of water will make the magnesium flare explosively ↓

First thing to do in a blackout is to blanket all the windows. Don't wait ↓ until the emergency comes to plan this

SHRIEKS

In the small house, safest place is the basement (right), since upper floors will probably stop incendiary bombs. There should be a safe exit in case of fire. Get the family downstairs quietly at the first alarm. Avoid appearance of panic, for children learn fear from their elders. Stay away from windows, which should be taped to prevent shattering

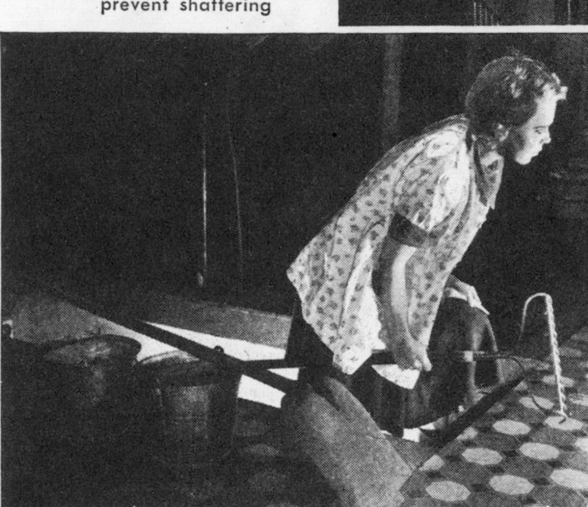

In the attic, left, where most incendiaries lodge, keep buckets of sand, a shovel and a rake or other tool for handling flaming bomb. Dry sand, graphite and similar inert powders will smother a magnesium bomb in a few minutes, but beware of wet sand and ordinary extinguishers

When bombs fall, get under a sturdy table in the basement. There, in the event of a near hit, you will be protected from debris or even a cave-in of the floor above. These suggestions are based on experiences of London; for advice on peculiar local conditions look to your community civilian defense board

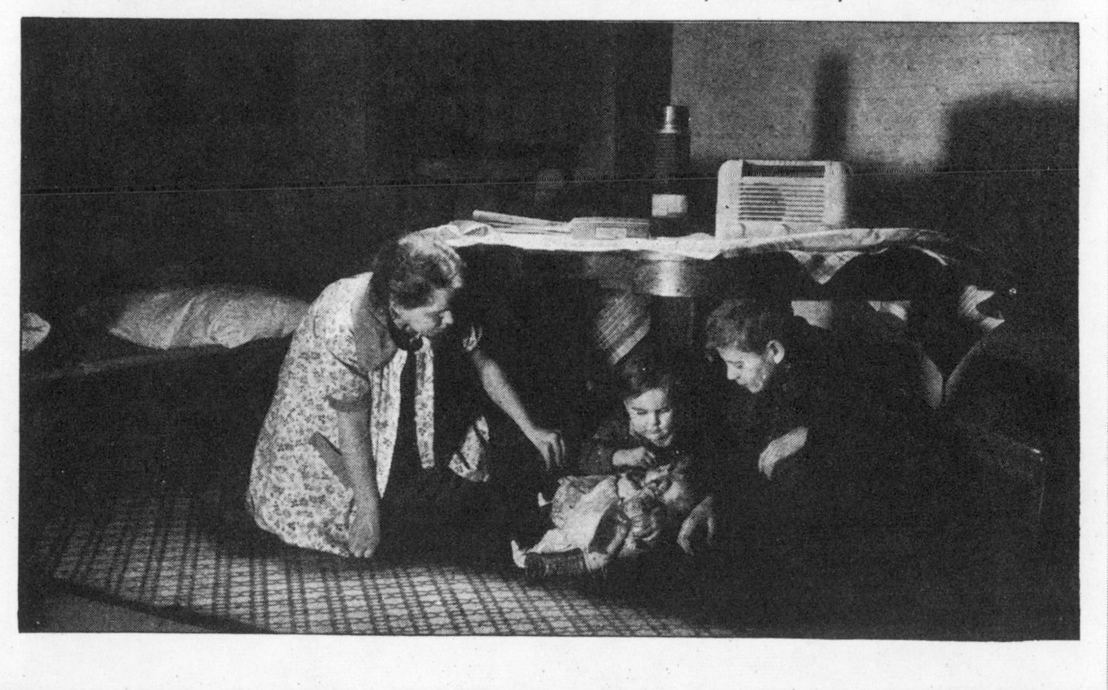

Practice black-outs were staged in every American community to test the air-raid sirens and the efficiency of the Civilian Defense Corps. Department stores advertised black-out curtains, or you could make your own. There was little hysteria—the embattled citizens of London already had set the world an example of rare courage and aplomb in the face of devastating Nazi bombings

MAKE THEM LAST LONGER!

Prodigal Americans, used to trading appliances in on a new model when they showed signs of wear, had to learn to make things last during World War II. With practically all industry turned to war production, there were few appliances, supplies or materials to be had on the civilian market

IT'S more important now than ever before to make equipment used around your home last as long as possible. Regular attention to simple precautions often will double the useful life of accessories and appliances. For example, cut in half the number of times you open the refrigerator by removing all the things you need at one time and you'll be surprised at the saving of both wear and operating expense of the vital mechanism. Leaving the door standing open as in Fig. 2, and infrequent defrosting are costly habits. Don't neglect the rubber door gasket. A weekly washing and dusting with talcum, to prevent sticking, will go a long way to make it last.

Never allow an electric extension cord to lie about doubled in a series of short bends which are the cause of breaks in the rubber covering. If you store the cord, wrap it loosely around a large mailing tube, as in Fig. 3, and place it in a drawer or dark closet. When you remove a cord from a wall receptacle, grasp the plug as in Fig. 1.

Paint the inside surfaces of eave gutters, Fig. 4, with ordinary house paint over a metal primer, or an asphalt roof coating. A galvanized wire clothesline will stay bright years longer if you wipe it with an oily rag after using, Fig. 5. The oil is wiped off

ASPHALT ROOF COATING
4
PAINT INSIDE OF GUTTERS

WIPE CLOTHESLINE WITH OILY RAG
WIRE
5
CLEAN SMOKEPIPE AND STORE IN A DRY PLACE
6
WIRE FLUE BRUSH

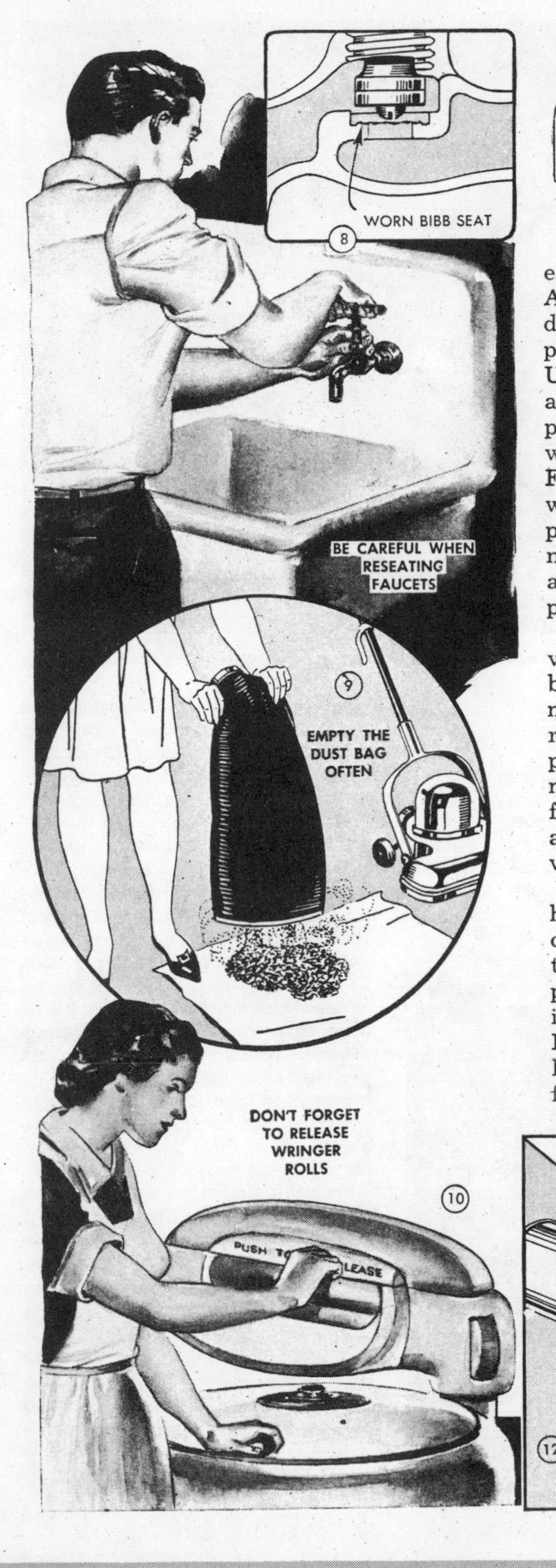

STORE PAINT "LEFTOVERS" IN FRUIT JARS

easily when you're ready to use the line. After the firing season has passed, take down the smokepipe of your heating plant and give it a thorough cleaning. Use a wire flue brush to loosen the soot and scale as in Fig. 6. Then store the pipe in a dry place. Be extra careful when you reseat compression faucets, Fig. 8. The bibb seat may have become worn from long use or cut thin from previous reseatings. Salvage all used nails and screws which are still serviceable, put them in a can or fruit jar and pour oil over them, Fig. 12.

A dust bag half full of dirt makes your vacuum cleaner far less efficient. The bag should be kept clean, Fig. 9, and the motor bearings should be lubricated at regular intervals. Be sure to release the pressure on the rolls of a washing-machine wringer, even if it stands idle for only a short time, Fig. 10. There is always the danger that the rubber rolls will stick together.

Garden sprayers and other appliances having a direct-attached hose or cord often are fitted with a spring to protect the cord or hose from sharp bends at the point where it is attached. If the spring is broken or missing renew it, Fig. 11. Leftover paint, Fig. 7, can be kept for a long time if you seal it in small glass fruit jars.

11 GARDEN SPRAYER COIL SPRING OIL NAILS FRUIT JAR 12

Almost everything, the hardware customer was told, had gone to war. The War Production Board allocated nearly all raw materials to the makers of arms and military supplies. Either banned or drastically restricted was the making of radios, plumbing fixtures, electrical equipment, luggage, cosmetics, garden tools, automobiles, zippers and thousands of other articles Americans had come to take for granted

To many Americans, accustomed to buying whatever foods their fancy dictated and their purses could afford, the food rationing during World War II seemed stringent. But these rationed meals would have made most Europeans think they were in the lap of luxury. Meat, butter, sugar and coffee were the things in scarcest supply. There was plenty of wheat and lots of vegetables, the farm supplies of the latter being reinforced by the more than 20 million victory gardens planted during the war years

WHAT YOU CAN DO ABOUT FOOD RATIONING

Your own chickens can provide a steady supply of meat. Raise them in sanitary wire pens with individual cages

THERE'S plenty of food in this land of plenty, but you can't always have what you want.

Food rationing is here to make the coffee and canned goods go 'round. Butter arrives in fractional pounds, roast beef is as rare as a day in June and when you pay for some varieties of canned fish you wonder whether they're charging for a pearl.

Does it make sense?

"In the last few years we have raised more food than ever before," says Dr. Joseph S. Davis, director of the Food Research Institute of Stanford University.

"At the same time, the men in our army are eating more than they did in civil life. Next, we are shipping tremendous quantities of food abroad to feed civil populations. This outward flow of food will increase with the growth of our merchant fleet, though we can expect to receive more foreign commodities in return. Finally, higher wages caused more people to buy more food than they once did. Prices are up because farm labor, as well as labor along the line, is being paid more.

"What we actually have, instead of a food shortage, is a shortage in variety or selection. This may increase, and you can expect to carry more ration books before the war is over. The foods that are scarcest and highest in price are the ones most obviously due for rationing, which is here for the duration.

"Great Britain is on a wartime diet much more stringent than we are apt to experience. Yet no one there is suffering from mal-

These big plants are rooted in gravel flooded regularly with nutrient solution

nutrition. We shall have plenty of nourishing food to eat."

Still, is there anything you can do about food rationing and the higher prices you are paying for food? There certainly is.

To begin with, don't hoard foods. The purpose of rationing is simply to make sure that you get your share without hoarding.

What you can do is to start raising some of your own food, even if you live in a city. That helps out in many ways. It slashes your grocery bill, provides you with the kinds of fruits and vegetables you like to eat, reduces the load on our transportation system, and allows more commercially grown food to bé available for the army and lend-lease. The Victory garden program stresses three things: home production of fruits and vegetables, meats and meat products, and food preservation. By the latter is meant home canning and drying.

Millions of Americans pitched in and planted war gardens in 1917, then their enthusiasm diminished. Most of the gardens were dismal failures. The untrained amateur gardeners didn't learn their job, just as most of us have much to learn today. But tested information is available at little or no cost. The Department of Agriculture and

The vegetables above are being grown in controlled water baths to test the amount of minerals necessary for all-around growth

Left, measuring 26-inch leaves of a new rhubarb-like chard, an excellent source of minerals and vitamins, like most greens

The ornamental chicken house sketched below takes up little room in the back yard and is an efficient home meat factory

Victory-garden produce added to the yield of small-farm and truck-garden crops totaled about eight million tons during 1943. At the same time the nation's big farmers put a record 380 million acres under cultivation and grew a billion bushels of wheat. Although meat was rationed, beef production climbed from eight to nine billion pounds annually from 1941 to 1944

The machinery for food rationing was set up Aug. 28, 1941, and prices were controlled under an emergency act of Jan. 30, 1942. Coupons and colored ration tokens accompanied the money handed to the butcher and grocer. The year 1943 was the tightest in food rationing. But black markets and price profiteering did not become flagrant until the end of hostilities in 1945. Controls were gradually lifted during that year

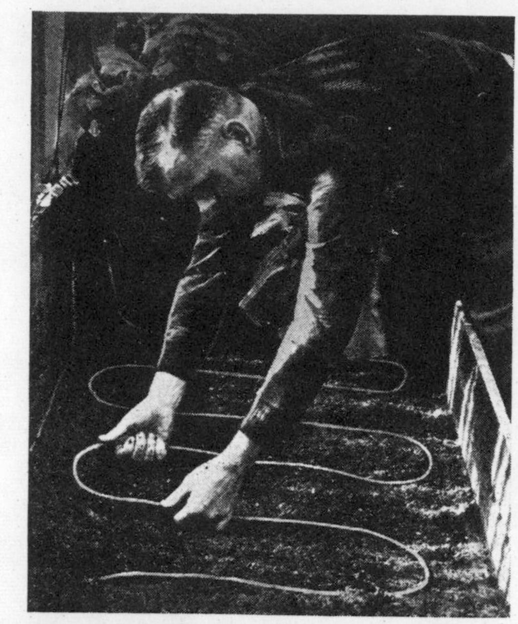

Electrical heating wires buried in subsoil of vegetable bed force plant growth by keeping soil warm

EFFICIENCY OF FOOD CROPS

High Efficiency Crops				Low Efficiency Crops			
Crop	Days in ground	Food yield in lbs. per acre	Man-hrs. per acre	Crop	Days in ground	Food yield in lbs. per acre	Man-hrs. per acre
1. Spinach	50	9,618	117	1. Snap Beans	55	4,144	133
2. Carrots	80	17,496	243	2. Cantaloupe	160	5,868	195
3. Onions	110	18,650	239	3. Asparagus	365	3,330	188
4. Irish Potatoes	120	12,751	130	4. Radish	30	5,880	273
5. Celery	120	20,189	300	5 Cucumber	130	5,893	190
6 Winter Squash	180	12,580	58	6. Market Peas	70	1,107	143
7 Cabbage	90	9,987	111	7 Watermelons	150	4,783	110
8. Broccoli	150	3,450	176	8. Lima Beans	80	545	140
9 Cauliflower	75	6,180	151				

Vitamin and mineral content of crops, which helped determine their relative efficiency as foods, are not shown

Chart is based on tables prepared by Truck Crops Division. University of California

The chart above will help plan a garden according to time, labor and food value of the various crops. At right, setting a new type of mole and gopher trap

many of the universities have pamphlets that tell you what fruits and vegetables flourish in your community, when and how to prepare the soil and plant the seed, and what to do about cultivation and pest control. The University of California agricultural extension service, for instance, will send you information on spring and summer gardens, home canning, home rabbit production, and other subjects for a few cents per pamphlet. No matter whether you want to plant your entire back yard to vegetables or you merely try your hand at water culture in a few tanks near your apartment window, there's one important thing to remember—gardening requires more or less constant attention. It takes a little work at frequent intervals.

If the shortage of farm labor continues, the chances are that only vegetables that have high nutritional value will be grown

commercially. Truck farmers will be asked to specialize on such crops as potatoes, cabbages, and onions. Unnecessary crops will be curtailed or abandoned, so if you feel that radishes or watermelons will increase your satisfaction, you'd better raise them yourself.

Some surprising facts about vegetable "efficiency" were discovered in a survey made by John H. MacGillivray, G. C. Hanna, and P. A. Minges of the University of California. They found that spinach is our most efficient crop. Mustard, kale, and similar greens are in the same category, if you don't care for spinach.

The survey measures the efficiency of 26 major vegetable crops on the basis of mineral and vitamin content, man-hours of labor required per acre, and the time it takes to grow a crop.

Radishes are the fastest crop to grow, since they are in the ground only 30 days. But an acre of radishes yields less than 6,000 pounds of edible material and requires 273 man-hours of work. Irish potatoes, on the other hand, must stay in the ground four times as long but they are a much more desirable crop. They yield twice the edible weight of radishes at half the labor, and have a much greater nutritive value.

Wonder Drug Made From Mold Aids Wounded

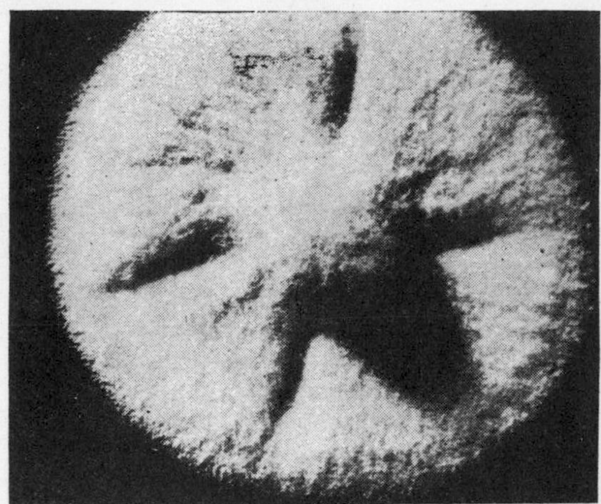

Penicillium notatum mold (left), similar to that found in bread, secretes the new lifesaving drug known as penicillin. It grows in glass culture bottles (below) and it takes about 500 quarts of fluid to make one ounce of microbe-killing powder

Photos courtesy E. R. Squibb & Sons

Penicillin, hailed as the miracle drug of 1943, is so potent that one part in 25 million parts of water will stop the growth of bacteria. This new microbe killer, which promises to surpass the phenomenal family of sulfa drugs, is made from a mold similar to that found in bread. It was discovered accidentally in 1929 by Dr. Alexander Fleming in the University of London laboratory. One morning he discovered that a secretion from mold had killed all the bacteria in a culture dish. The greenish-brown powder made from this secretion is today fighting infection on battlefields. Penicillium notatum mold grows on a liquid concoction of mineral salts and sugar. As it grows in glass culture bottles, the penicillin diffuses into the liquid beneath from which it is harvested by high vacuum evaporation. It takes about 500 quarts of culture fluid to make one ounce of the drug—one reason why all present production is allocated to the armed forces. Tests show it is superior to the sulfa drugs for infections produced by staphyloccus aureus. It is also used to fight pneumonia, gonorrhea, osteomyelitis, and streptococcus infections. There are no unpleasant after effects for the patient. Penicillin acts faster than sulfa drugs and cures certain infections those drugs cannot touch. While the limited supply of this drug is already at work saving the lives of fighting men, efforts are being made to increase production on a vast scale.

Penicillin was the first of the antibiotics—among the medical wonders of our age. From 30 to 50 per cent of all medical treatment now includes the use of one of the antibiotics. Besides penicillin, the most commonly used are streptomycin, chloromycetin, aureomycin and terramycin

Superfuel Gives U. S. Warplanes 50 Percent More Power

Triptane, a supergas that raises engine power half again over that of motors burning 100-octane gasoline, can now be produced in quantity. Known for seven years, the hydrocarbon was made in only limited amounts, and at costs ranging up to $3,000 a gallon. By a new process developed by scientists of Universal Oil Products Company, the fuel can be made commercially at an estimated selling price of less than $1 a gallon. Antiknock qualities of pure triptane, called "the most powerful hydrocarbon known for use in internal combustion engines," are so great that no commercial engine has been built that can utilize its full power value. Added to aviation gasoline, it makes possible future engines of even greater power and efficiency.

About 18 million women joined the labor force during the war. Some two million of these were directly involved in war production, for it was learned that women could perform about four fifths of all the necessary operations in 21 key industries

This month, Popular Mechanics Magazine joins other publications throughout the nation in paying tribute to America's women war workers. Some of the thousands of jobs they are performing to help beat the Axis are pictured here. Many of these jobs, such as locomotive engineer, (A) are normally man's work. In B, two young women are putting the finishing touches on the glass nose of a Flying Fortress, an operation similar to that shown on the cover of this magazine. The girl at the lathe (C) is machining parts

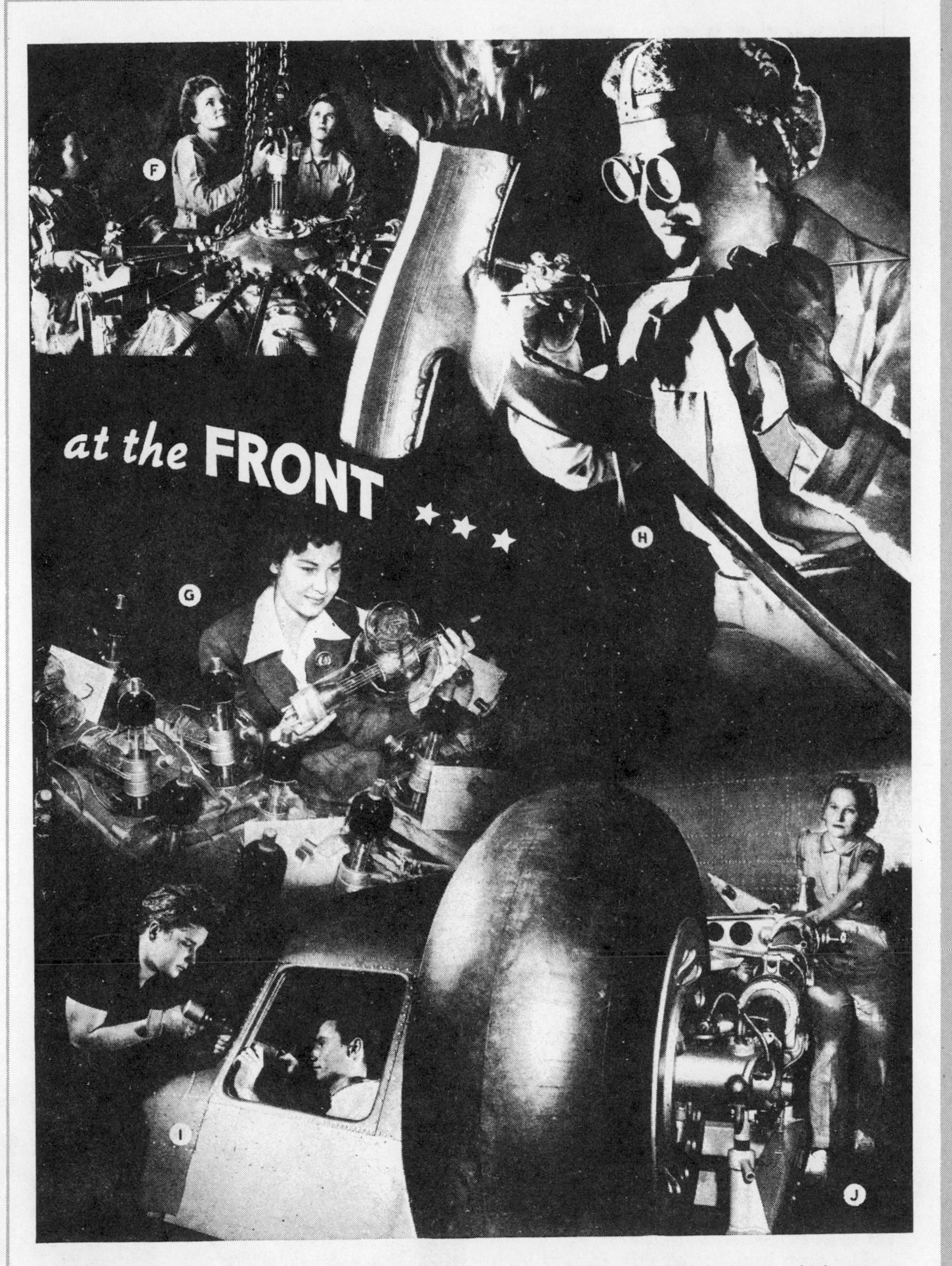

for planes, and the worker in D is making adjustments in the wheel well of an inner wing. Resembling machine gunners, are the inspectors (E) in a binocular assembly room. The women lowering an engine onto a block (F) are learning skills that will relieve men for military service. Inspecting high power radio transmitting tubes (G), welding a part of the exhaust system of a training plane (H), riveting (I), and jobs like rolling a landing gear onto a final assembly line (J), are performed by patriotic women.

The talents of women were particularly useful in the airplane, radio and precision-instrument factories. On some jobs they were better than men because of smaller and more dexterous fingers—a heritage from centuries of needlework. Glamour on the production line brought some problems to management—film star Veronica Lake was asked to change her long-locked hair-do after several women war workers had caught theirs in factory machinery

This article ushered in a new era in aviation, during which flight in the stratosphere at speeds first approaching, then surpassing the speed of sound, became feasible. Between 1945 and 1948 the speed of jet-propelled planes crept upward from 600 to 670 miles an hour. The F-86A Saber jets used by the United States Air Force during the Korean campaign exceeded 700 miles an hour

FLYING GAS JET

Above, tail view of Italy's jet plane of 1940. Below, one of four engines of the Constellation. By eliminating propellers, jet plane may add 100 miles an hour

THE FIRST fundamental improvement in flight since the Wright brothers attached an engine and propellers to a glider and rose off the ground 41 years ago is embodied in the jet propulsion airplanes with which the United States has been experimenting for the last year.

Odd as it seems, today's fastest conventional aircraft are nothing more than improved models of the original Wright plane. Modern aircraft are larger, vastly more efficient; yet they operate by the same means, air screws driven by internal combustion engines.

A jet-driven plane was decided upon by General H. H. Arnold and other Air Force officers "when present planes gave indications they had about reached the limit of performance obtainable by means of propellers," writes Capt. Ezra Kotcher of the A.A.F. Materiel Command in Air Force magazine. "The limit was imposed by the rapid falling off in the efficiency of the propeller when the effects of compressibility set in at extremely high speeds."

The drop in propeller efficiency at high speeds and in thin air have limited propeller-driven aircraft roughly to 500 miles per hour and 50,000 feet altitude.

Air compressibility, which becomes manifest at about the speed of sound, affects the propeller "long before the wings of a plane are affected," says Captain Kotcher, in Air Force. "The jet engine eliminates propellers. It will not eliminate the inevitable effect of compressibility on wings, but since the breakdown of flows occurs on a propeller long before it does on wings, it enables the plane designer to realize the difference in speeds between the points where the propeller is affected and where the wing is affected. This difference may be about 100 miles an hour for the immediate future."

In this country the first flights were made in a twin-

Artist's conception of possible appearance of America's jet plane, similar to Airacobra. In wing is schematic sketch of engine

engined jet plane built by Bell Aircraft, based in part on British developments. The experimental models have top speeds between 500 and 600 miles per hour. Pilots who have flown them can scarcely hear the weird noise of the exhaust and are impressed by the absence of vibration, the smoothness and ease of control. A jet propulsion airplane is simpler to fly than a primary trainer.

"The number of gadgets and dials are cut down considerably from the number in the conventional fighter plane," writes Captain Kotcher. "One throttle does all the work, forward to go, further forward for greater speed, back to slow down or stop. The aircraft is built low to the ground because there is no ground clearance to provide for the propeller."

But with little vibration to help tell him how his airplane is handling, a pilot has to dispense with "seat of the pants" flying and depend more on instruments. In fact, it was necessary to install a vibrator on the instrument panel of the Bell jet plane so that its pilots would be assured the instruments were not stuck.

For the time being, it appears that jet propulsion will be most valuable where high speed and fast acceleration are more important than economy and long range. Possibly the jet drive eventually will be so efficient it will replace propellers for all types of air travel.

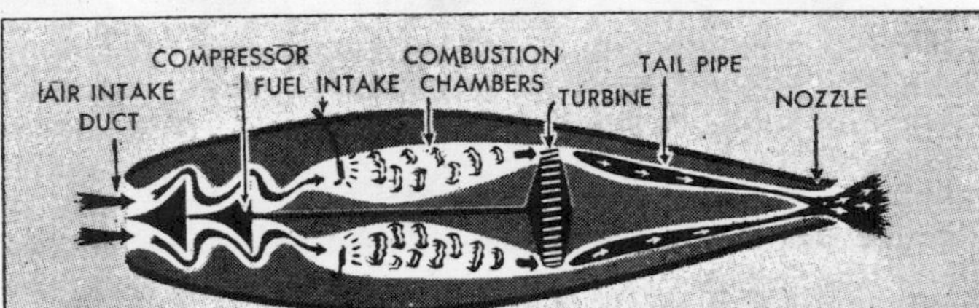

THERMAL JET: This formalized conception by a staff artist of Air Force magazine of a jet propulsion motor is not intended to illustrate mechanical workings or portray any specific engine design. In the thermal-jet system, oxygen is obtained from air which enters intake ducts and is sent by compressors into combustion chambers. Fuel is added to the compressed air and ignited. The resulting gases flow through a turbine, which drives the compressors, and from there to a tailpipe where they are nozzled down, attaining great speed and forming the propulsive jet

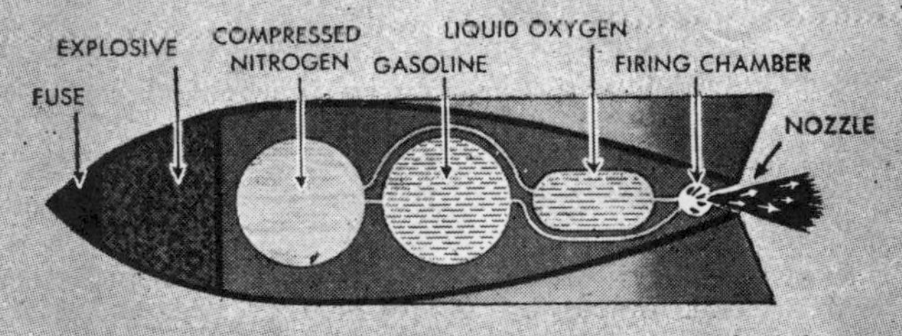

ROCKET: Both the thermal jet and rocket systems get their thrust from a rearward jet which forces the mechanism forward. The rocket contains all the elements needed for combustion. In the example above, compressed nitrogen provides pressure to force gasoline and liquid oxygen into a firing chamber where they ignite, and the resulting high-pressure, high-temperature gas escapes and sends the rocket forward. Many rockets use a relatively slow burning powder instead of liquid fuels. The powder contains the oxygen necessary for burning

Drawings by courtesy Air Force Magazine

It remained for rocket planes to attain real supersonic speeds. In 1951 a Navy rocket plane achieved a speed of more than 1300 miles an hour and reached a record height in the vicinity of 80,000 feet. The specific speed and height were not disclosed for security reasons

The tank was the No. 1 weapon in Europe, but the flamethrower was symbolic of the jungle fighting in the Pacific. The Germans introduced a flamethrower in 1915, but its range was only 70 feet, and its billowing flames could be as dangerous to the user as to the enemy if the wind shifted suddenly. Jellied gasoline proved the answer to this problem when the U.S. Chemical Warfare Service tested flamethrowers in 1942. The result was a weapon which could throw a cohesive rod of fire 60 yards at a speed of about 120 miles per hour

SIXTY-YARD FLASH

Mass demonstration of flamethrowers at a Chemical Warfare depot. Below, flamethrower on Bougainville routs Japs who defied bazooka

By Roderick M. Grant

IT ISN'T PRETTY, fighting with flames. But nothing in war is pretty, least of all the bark of a Jap machine gun from a timbered pillbox up ahead and the spatter of bullets against the log that shields you from immediate death in a rain-filled hole in the jungle.

The Marines had been pinned down long enough It was time to clean out that nest.

Two riflemen crept forward to right and left, keeping the narrow slit in the Jap pillbox covered. Between them the man with three tanks on his back and the "insect sprayer" in hand moved cautiously ahead. Now they had closed the range to 60 yards.

"Start your cooker!" someone shouted. There was a hiss of escaping gas under pressure and a jet of orange shot from the flamethrower. A two-second spurt corrected the aim, then a spurt of several seconds' duration arched through the jungle foliage right into the slot in the dugout. Inside, the jellied gasoline spattered and clung to the walls, flames leaped around the protective maze of timbers, and with a yell four Japs burst out of the pillbox and dropped, dying, at the exit. The rest were

Signal Corps photo
M1-A1 bores a hole through jungle on Munda, where numerous pillboxes were cleaned out. At left is the portable flamethrower

dead inside. The Marines resumed their advance.

The story was repeated at Munda and Bougainville, Tarawa and Kwajalein, Saipan and Guam. It was the same, with different settings, against the Germans in Italy. When the boys are stopped by a particularly tough pillbox that resists even direct shell hits, they call for the G. I. Hotfoot. That's Yankee for the M1-A1 flamethrower.

The "sixty-yard flash" below shows how the glowing jet of thickened gasoline can be aimed at distant target with great accuracy
Photo from Standard Oil Co. of N. J.

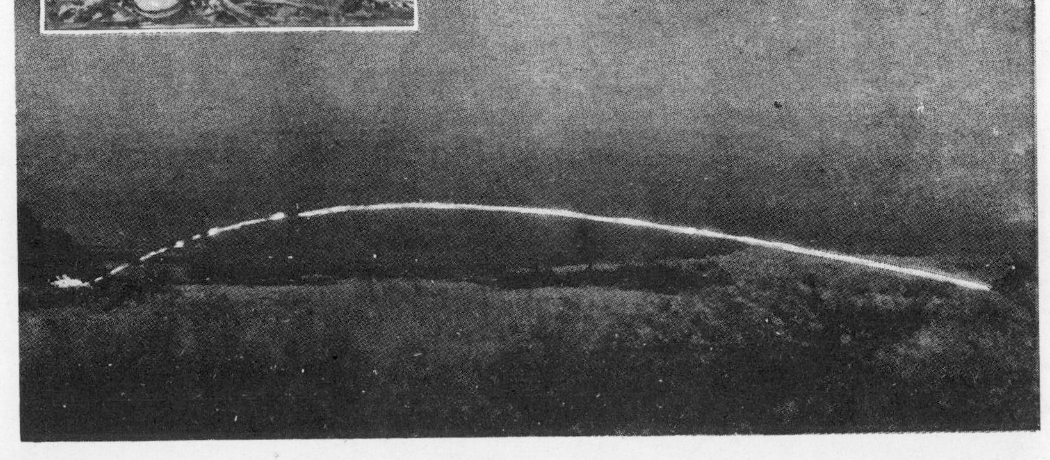

The flamethrower's hot tongue struck the target as a solid stream, then spattered and blazed with terrific heat. In the Pacific jungles, quick bursts were used to bore holes through thick underbrush for clean shooting by riflemen and machine gunners. Because the jelly could splash around corners, the man operating a flamethrower could often keep out of the range of enemy fire. Because the fire stream could penetrate into the narrowest slit or gun port the flamethrower was particularly effective against pillboxes

On June 6, 1944, almost two and a half years after Pearl Harbor, the Allies invaded the Normandy coast. On "D-Day plus five" 16 divisions had been landed from the invasion armada and 80 miles of coast line seized. Then began the huge task of unloading arms, supplies and reinforcements. The two artificial harbors each were designed to move above 12,000 tons of shipping and 2500 vehicles every day for the first 90 days after invasion

Popular Mechanics Magazine

REGISTERED IN U. S. PATENT OFFICE AND CANADA

WRITTEN SO YOU CAN UNDERSTAND IT

Vol. 83 JANUARY, 1945 No. 1

GANGPLANK to HITLER'S DOORSTEP

Cargo rolls from ships to floating harbor's pier, from which it will be transported to Omaha beach

By Wayne Whittaker

"ACH HIMMEL! It looks like Noah's Ark with the roof blown off and a Bofors mounted amidships!"

The eyes of German reconnaissance must have popped on D-day if they saw one strange segment of the invasion armada inching its way across the English Channel.

Aside from the ark-like ships, the like of which had never been seen on any sea, there were 200-foot floating monsters of steel, and long sections of what appeared to be bridges resting on queer-looking pontoons. All were being towed by tugs through the choppy waters at four knots.

Then, adding insult to mystery, Nazi reconnaissance might have spotted 60 decrepit freighters and warships heading toward the invasion coast. They looked out of place among the sleek invasion craft and modern warships, but they seemed to know where they were going.

Martial history was in the making, for the invasion forces advancing against the heavily fortified beaches of Normandy were bringing their own harbors with them. This feat, which has been called the eighth wonder of the world, will be recorded as one of the greatest military engineering achievements despite the fact that it was not an unqualified success.

The building of the prefabricated ports was one of the most closely guarded of invasion secrets. Everything pertaining to the project was in code. It was decided at the Quebec conference in 1943 that there should be two synthetic harbors—one for the British and one for the American forces—to be known as "Mulberries."

Each of the harbors was designed to move an estimated 12,000 tons of supplies and 2,500 vehicles per day for the first 90 days of fighting.

The plan for the ports was prepared by a joint committee of technical experts working under the Joint Anglo-American Chiefs of Staff, and the units were constructed in England and Scotland.

The general plan called for a system of breakwaters in the lee of which were to be piers with docking facilities for the rapid unloading of the big LSTs, Liberty ships and other craft. The requirements—breakwaters and piers—were conventional enough, but the units that formed them are the most revolutionary in the history of ports. The breakwaters consisted of three elements: concrete caissons ("phoenixes"), floating breakwaters, sunken ships ("gooseberries").

Tugs jostle the concrete caissons into position. Note antiaircraft gun mounted amidships. Below, aerial view before storm wrecked harbor

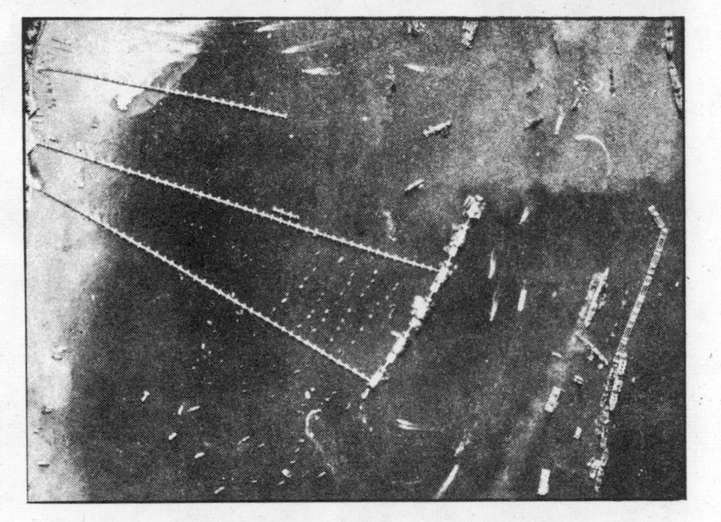

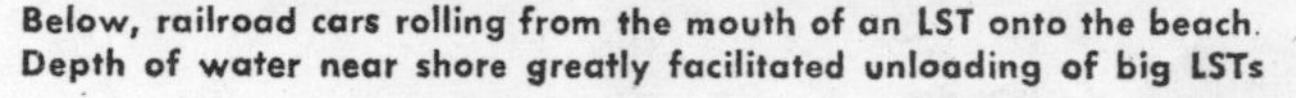

Below, railroad cars rolling from the mouth of an LST onto the beach. Depth of water near shore greatly facilitated unloading of big LSTs

Part of the breakwaters were formed by sinking 60 ships, including several antiquated battleships and cruisers. These were reinforced by floating concrete caissons, the largest of which had a displacement of 6044 tons. On the seaward side of the ships and caissons lay 200-foot floating steel breakwaters. A fleet of more than 150 tugs towed the 600 harbor units, altogether weighing more than a million tons, into place for assembly. One of the harbors was smashed by a terrible storm shortly after it was assembled off the French beach. This presented an almost disastrous supply problem for the men already ashore. The situation was saved by diverting troops for the speedy capture of the port of Cherbourg

Early in 1944 Adolph Hitler began boasting of a secret weapon, and in June the huge, cigar-shaped V-1's began falling on London. Because it was relatively slow (360 miles an hour) and flew on a straight and level course, the V-1 could be shot down rather easily. Late in 1944 the Nazi rocket-launching platforms began sending over V-2's, which reached 3000 miles an hour and had a maximum range of 200 miles. The V-1 was simply a pilotless airplane with a war head in the nose. It was driven by a pulse-jet engine. The V-2 was a real, rocket-propelled projectile

Popular Mechanics Magazine

REGISTERED IN U. S. PATENT OFFICE AND CANADA

WRITTEN SO YOU CAN UNDERSTAND IT

Vol. 83 FEBRUARY, 1945 No. 2

DEATH FROM THE STRATOSPHERE

Above, radio-controlled glider bomb is released from plane miles from target

WORST of all was the terrifying suddenness with which it struck. They couldn't see it coming. They couldn't even hear it—until too late. Without warning, the ground trembled as if from a local earthquake and a roaring blast beat on their ear drums, followed by an eerie, rumbling "whoosh." Most of the people were knocked flat but those close to the explosion were killed or mangled. Twisted fragments of metal littered the area and when the dazed survivors stumbled to the wreckage they found a deep crater, perhaps 30 feet in diameter, from which protruded the finned tail of a curious cylindrical missile the size of a small airplane fuselage

A shudder rippled through the onlookers. They knew then that the fantastic stratosphere rocket, another monstrous perversion of German science, had

CONTROLS
ALCOHOL
LIQUID OXYGEN
TURBINE AND PUMP
EXTERNAL CONTROL VANES
COMBUSTION CHAMBER AND VENTURI
INTERNAL CONTROL VANES
STABILIZING FINS

DIAGRAM OF V-2: (1) electric motor; (2) alcohol supply from pump; (3) air bottles; (4) radio guiding equipment; (5) central exploder tube; (6) nitrogen bottles; (7) pitch and azimuth gyros; (8) alcohol delivery pipe to pump; (9) hydrogen peroxide tank; (10) permanganate tank; (11) oxygen distribution from pump; (12) alcohol pipes for subsidiary cooling; (13) electro-hydraulic servo motors

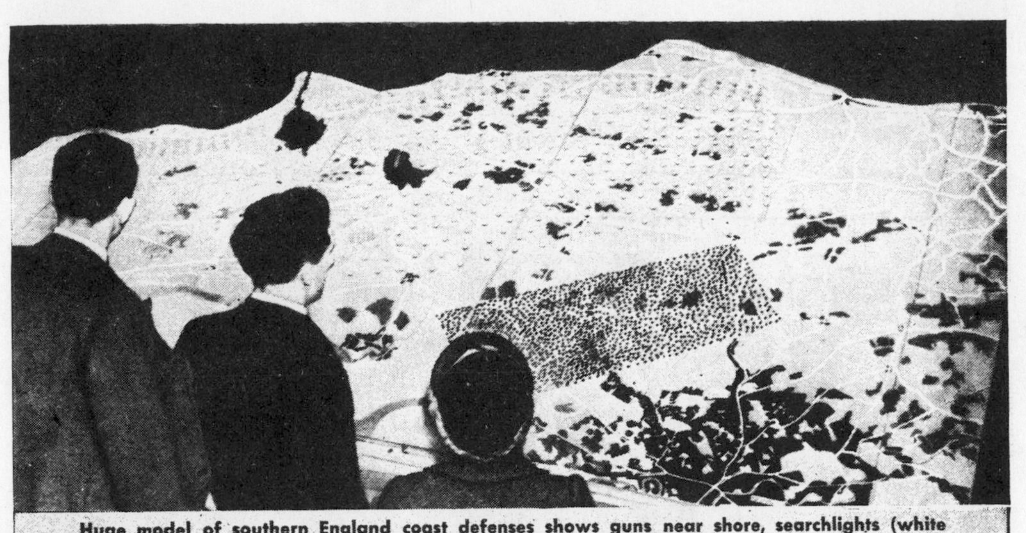

Huge model of southern England coast defenses shows guns near shore, searchlights (white dots), and balloon barrage (rectangle of black dots) which lie between London and the coast

paid them a lethal visit. It seemed to be the handiwork of demons—a wingless, self-propelled projectile which, fired into space at supersonic speeds, would plunge at random like a vengeful meteor upon a peaceful countryside or city.

To Allied scientists this new manifestation of indiscriminate warfare—known as V-2—is a "considerable technical achievement" but less destructive than the Nazis must have hoped it would be. True, numerous civilians were killed and wounded after the bombardment began to rain on England last autumn. And of the 1,100,000 English homes, hospitals, churches and schools reported damaged by "V bombs" since last June, many were victims of V-2.

But as to military effectiveness V-2 was regarded as no more destructive than V-1, the "buzz bomb" with wings. V-2 penetrates deep into the earth and thus concentrates much of its damage around its own self-made crater. V-1, which is cheaper and much less complicated to build, but carries the same amount of explosives (one ton), digs hardly any hole but scatters glass and shrapnel over a greater radius.

Recently, the Germans launched over the Western Front what is believed to be a new type of rocket. This barrage weapon has been called a V-1½ for it is said to combine features of both the V-1 and V-2.

The V-2 is the weirdest-looking of World War II's surprise weapons. It resembles a metal telegraph pole 46 feet long and five feet in diameter, and it behaves like a gigantic Roman candle gone berserk. Weighing 13½ tons at takeoff, it climbs upward to 70 miles above the earth before it starts its descent. When it strikes, it plows under more than half its length.

Artist's conception of portable launching ramp for V-2

After the war the United States confiscated a number of V-2's and employed some of the German scientists who made them. Research with these at White Sands, N. M., proved helpful in developing radio-guided rocket missiles, jet and rocket planes, and gained information about the outer limits of the atmosphere. Guided missiles can now be equipped with atomic war heads

Exploding with the force of 20,000 tons of TNT, the atom bomb blew open the door to a world of power beyond man's wildest previous dreams. Scientists figured one pound of hydrogen contained more than 400 billion trillion ergs of energy, or 11 billion kilowatt hours of electricity. The atoms in a glass of water could heat 100 million tons of water—the flow over Niagara Falls in four hours—from freezing to boiling. A shovelful of coal contained enough energy to work all the machinery in New York City for five years—a cigarette puff could run a tractor a year

Popular Mechanics Magazine

Registered in U. S. Patent Office and Canada

WRITTEN SO YOU CAN UNDERSTAND IT

Vol. 84 NOVEMBER 1945 No. 5

BRINGING THE ATOM DOWN TO EARTH

By Wm. F. McDermott

THERE were three atom bombs and four explosions: New Mexico, Hiroshima, Nagasaki and, the fourth and most shattering of all, the blast that plummeted the minds of untold millions into the strange new world of atomic energy.

The fact is that the dreaded but alluring atomic age is already here. Whole nations have grasped that fact almost with the speed of light. They may cringe before it—but they want it for its advantages and in spite of its dangers.

What does it portend for the future? Is a breath-taking revolution—industrial, social and even political—at hand? Has a new starting point in history arrived? Are science and invention, in unleashing unlimited power, about to turn the world upside down? Here's a prediction:

Within five years the first harnessing of the atom for peace will have been achieved, and within 10 years it will be the useful servant of man in a score of different ways.

Before we do any crystal-gazing, however, let's look at what some of the world's greatest thinkers and scientists, including several who were in on

Dr. Samuel K. Allison, head of the University of Chicago's new nuclear institute, inspects one type of atom smasher—a voltage multiplying unit

ATOMIC CHAIN REACTION

TWO NEUTRONS
TWO ELECTRONS
TWO PROTONS
SIMPLE HELIUM ATOM
U-235
TWO NEUTRONS RELEASED
FOUR NEUTRONS RELEASED
EIGHT NEUTRONS RELEASED
PARTICLE HURLED BY CYCLOTRON
NEUTRONS RELEASED BY SMASHING ATOM
COMPLEX U-235 ATOM CONTAINS 92 PROTONS, 143 NEUTRONS

Simplified version of atomic chain reaction which releases tremendous energy; not shown are unstable atoms formed by splitting U-235 which throw off gamma and beta rays as well as the "trigger" neutrons

the miracle of the atom bomb, have ventured to foresee about man's capture of this secret of the universe:

1894—H. G. Wells predicted world-wide use of atomic energy and the employment of atom bombs by 1954, saying that civilization would either destroy itself or adapt itself to a life as different as that of another planet.

1905—Einstein, declaring matter to be highly concentrated energy, calculated that 10 billion kilowatt-hours of energy are locked up in a pound of matter.

1926—Prof. James F. Morris, Massachusetts Institute of Technology, asserted that matter consists of "unthinkable amounts of

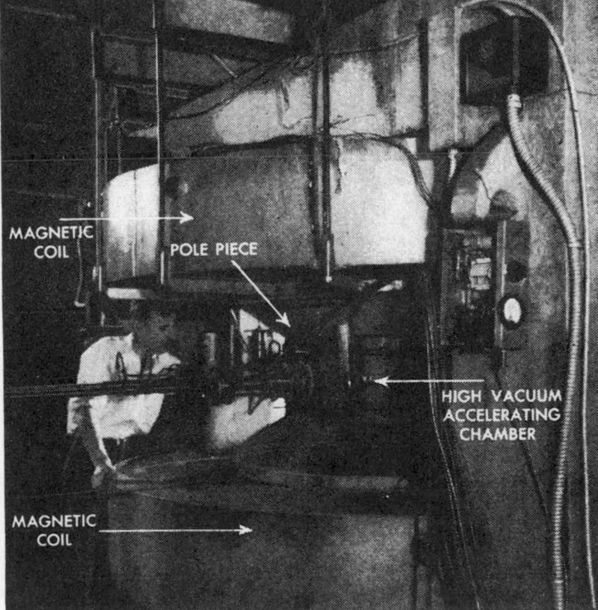

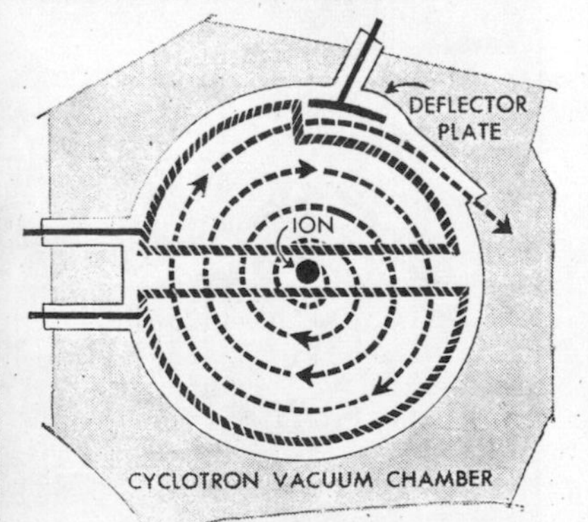

Diagram shows spiral path of ion in vacuum chamber of cyclotron at left; leaving chamber it is hurled at U-235

Stimulated by the new vision of power, both scientists and laymen made lavish predictions for the future use of atomic energy. Among the proposals: to blast gaps in the paths of forest fires, to make rain, to remove rock and shoals from ship routes, to dig canals, to lay bare the top of strip mines, and to blow the tops off mountains to make way for roads. The U.S. Navy made the most concrete approach with a research program designed to evolve atomic-powered ships

At this time none of the experts reckoned on the touchy international situation that was to develop—the cold war dropped a curtain over all atomic research, and undoubtedly sacrificed most civilian development to the demands for atomic military weapons. The Atomic Energy Commission has, however, given much direct aid to new medical research involving side effects of nuclear energy

bound-up energy," while Dr. Karl Schlessel, German scientist, forecast: "The time is not far distant when, with the liberation of the atom, man will forget there ever was such a thing as suffering or poverty."

1939—Dr. Arthur H. Compton, Nobel Prize winner, addressing the Association for the Advancement of Science, said that atomic power, long-sought goal of science, was nearer man's practical use than was even dreamed of a year before. This power, locked in the nucleus of the atom, is of such tremendous order that a minute quantity of it would be sufficient to transport a liner across the ocean or to fire a gun from Chicago to Berlin.

1940—Dr. R. M. Langer, California Institute of Technology, one of the leading scientists in the development of the atom bomb, predicted that atomic energy would "change the face of the earth," with Sunday driving in a propellerless plane 50 miles above the ground, with free power for everyone for all possible uses and with unimaginable convenience for everyone's pleasure.

Even before Pearl Harbor, the curtain was quietly drawn on atomic developments, but the most feverish experimentation in all history swung into full speed. Four years later, that curtain was literally torn to pieces with the crash of the bomb on Hiroshima. The unleashed power not only met every expectation, but seemed to give prophetic promise of the fulfillment of every amazing chronicle of what the release of atomic energy might mean to the future of mankind.

This is the target end of 90-ton atom smasher in Westinghouse research laboratory. Below, iron core of electromagnet built for cyclotron at University of California

Below, artist's conception of uranium engine adapted from 1941 issue of Popular Mechanics

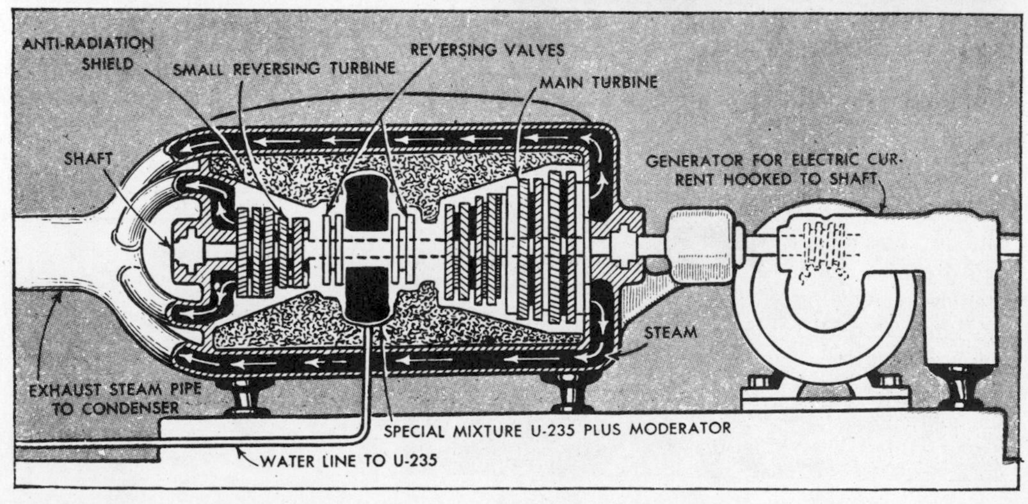

WRITTEN SO YOU CAN UNDERSTAND IT
VOL. 87 NO. 4

POPULAR MECHANICS

APRIL 1947

The House That Jacques Built

WITH THE HELP OF POPULAR MECHANICS

On page 105 we begin the inspiring story of how Jacques Brownson, young veteran of Aurora, Ill., met the housing shortage the American way—with fine craftsmanship and determination. He built his own home, the home planned for the average family by Popular Mechanics Magazine. It is a home you will want to build yourself. The full-color article in this issue introduces what we regard as one of the most important editorial projects in the history of this magazine. THE EDITORS

"The *Popular Mechanics* BUILD-IT-YOURSELF HOUSE strikes close to the heart of every American who has pounded a nail or put up a storm window. This attractive house is actually a blueprint for many a family's dream. The entire project of designing the house, building it and keeping a careful record of materials and requirements, and then giving this information to the public, is a truly unique and important achievement. Presented at this time of acute housing shortage, the house should have an enthusiastic reception. This is a practical approach to one of our greatest national problems. As governor of the state in which it was built, I congratulate the editors who conceived the project and the man whose craftsmanship translated the dream house into reality."

Dwight H. Green
GOVERNOR OF ILLINOIS

The GI's returned to find housing scarce and dear. The editors of Popular Mechanics *saw the need for houses that men with only ordinary ability with tools could build. They designed such a house, and to test its practicality, bought the materials for a young war veteran, Jacques Brownson. Jacques and his wife followed the plans and instructions and built their own dream home*

This is the house that Jacques built—six rooms with breezeway and garage. The cost of materials (Brownson did the labor) was $7000; the home was valued on completion at more than twice its building cost

THE BUILD-IT-YOURSELF HOUSE

The concrete-block house was the next PM *build-it-yourself housing project. Thousands of readers put these houses up all over the country after Henry M. Nehrbass, magazine staff artist, built the first one at a cost of $3650 in 1948*

THE CONCRETE-BLOCK HOUSE

In 1951 writer Tom Riley built the plywood ranch house. The cost of this modern, seven-room home with breezeway and two-car garage was $7450. With six rooms and carport, it could be built for $5000

THE PLYWOOD RANCH HOUSE

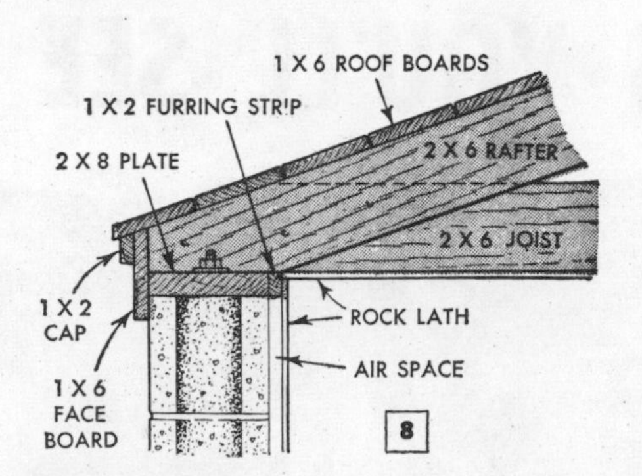

This sectional view and the photo at the right show the simplicity of the roof framing and the cornice. Rafters are spiked to the face of the joists and toe-nailed to a plate bolted to the top of exterior walls

plates which are placed on top of the blocks all around as in Fig. 7.

With the plates in place, the ceiling joists can be installed. These rest on a 2 x 4-in. plate bolted to the top of the main bearing partition, Fig. 9, and are lapped, spiked together and toenailed to both center and outside plates. Stock timbers (2 x 6 x 16s and 2 x 6 x 12s) are required for the joists which are spaced 16 in. on centers. When the joists are in place, they are cross-braced by bridging them with short lengths of 2 x 6-in. stock as shown in Fig. 9. A row of bridging is installed on each side of the

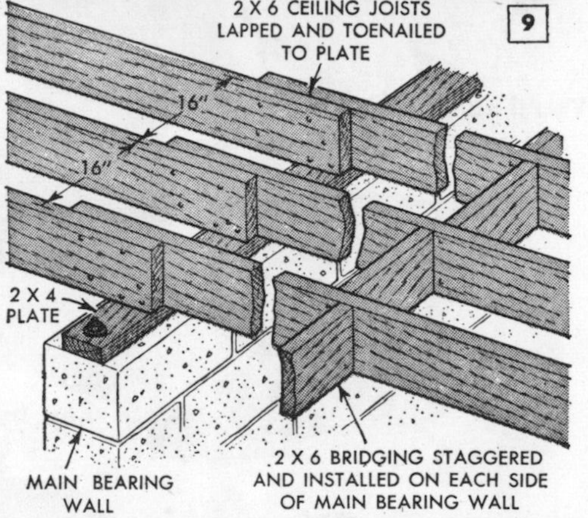

Ceiling joists rest on a plate bolted to the top of the main bearing partition. Ends are lapped, spiked together and toenailed to the plate. Bridging members are nailed between all joists to brace them

main bearing partition, the pieces being staggered to permit nailing.

Next come the rafters. Those in the center span of the house are raised first, using a 2 x 6-in. plank for a ridge board. These rafters are erected as if the house had a gable roof, spiking them to the face of the ceiling joists at the plate and into each other at the ridge board. With this section of the framing in place, a rafter is installed at each end, butting it against the end of the ridge-board plank. Then the long hip rafters are erected and short jack rafters are cut to fill in. The cornice around the roof consists of a 1 x 6-in. frieze board, which is nailed to the ends of the rafters as in Fig. 8. A 1 x 2-in. cap gives a slight overhang to the roof.

This is a typical page from a series of articles on building the concrete-block house. It shows how, with carefully planned photographs and scale drawings, each step of the building process is made intelligible to persons with little or no experience in carpentry. For each of the three houses illustrated on the preceding page, the Popular Mechanics Press has issued a book, with additional drawings and instructions, and full-size blueprints, to help others who want to build their own houses

Around the year 1800, Harvard University gave a degree—Doctor of Science. It was possible at that time for one man to encompass the entire field of science—natural, physical and abstract. Today a doctor's degree is attained in a highly specialized field within a field. The breeding rate of a single insect may be the topic of a doctoral thesis. A million scientific articles are written every year. Universal science, knowing no barriers of race or language, has developed what is called an "increasing function of time" by Pierre Auger, director of Unesco's Department of Natural Sciences. This means that the progress of science is not only accelerating, but also expanding. A graph of its expanse would look not like an ascending line, but a flaring trumpet bell

IN THE NEXT FIFTY YEARS

To those who have noted the technical progress of the last 50 years . . . watched the sky-cycle evolve into the jet plane . . . seen all the marvels of modern communication, transportation and engineering . . . these prophecies of science writer Waldemar Kaempffert do not seem as strange as similar ones made by Winston Churchill less than 20 years before. We have seen our ways of life change not once but several times in those five decades. And yet, in a sense, the change was just beginning. In the words of the circus side-show barker, "You ain't seen nothin' yet." What progress man had made was done with relatively simple mechanisms—the steam engine, dynamo, gas engine and turbine. On the threshold of the age of atomic and solar energy, nothing seemed out of the question for the future

. . . cook on a solar range

By Waldemar Kaempffert
Science Editor, The New York Times

WHAT WILL the world be like in A.D. 2000? You can read the answer in your home, in the streets, in the trains and cars that carry you to your work, in the bargain basement of every department store. You don't realize what is happening because it is a piecemeal process. The jet-propelled plane is one piece, the latest insect killer is another. Thousands of such pieces are automatically dropping into their places to form the pattern of tomorrow's world.

The only obstacles to accurate prophecy are the vested interests, which may retard progress for economic reasons, tradition, conservatism, labor-union policies and legislation. If we confine ourselves to processes and inventions that are now being hatched in the laboratory, we shall not wander too far from reality.

The best way of visualizing the new world of A.D. 2000 is to introduce you to the Dobsons, who live in Tottenville, a hypothetical metropolitan suburb of 100,000. There are parks and playgrounds and green open spaces not only around detached houses but also around apartment houses. The heart of the town is the airport. Surrounding it are business houses, factories and hotels. In concentric circles beyond these lie the residential districts.

Tottenville is as clean as a whistle and quiet. It is a crime to burn raw coal and pollute air with smoke and soot. In the homes electricity is used to warm walls and to cook. Factories all burn gas, which is generated in sealed mines. The tars are removed and sold to the chemical industry for their values, and the gas thus laundered is piped to a thousand communities.

The highways that radiate from Tottenville are much like those of today, except that they are broader with hardly any curves. In some of the older cities, difficult to change because of the immense investment in real estate and buildings, the highways are double-decked. The upper deck is for fast nonstop traffic; the lower deck is much like our avenues, with brightly illuminated shops. Beneath the lower deck is the level reserved entirely for business vehicles.

Tottenville is illuminated by electric "suns" suspended from arms on steel towers 200 feet high. There are also lamps which are just as bright and varicolored as those that now dazzle us on every Main

There has been a subtle change in the attitude of the man in the street toward technological development. The ranks of the skeptics—typified by those who were sure in the 1900's that the automobile would "never take the place of the horse"—are thin ranks today. Modern man has become conditioned to change, has come to expect it, to look forward to it, and most of all to prepare to adjust himself to it. He knows now that today's experiments in the research laboratories will concern him on some tomorrow

General Electric photo

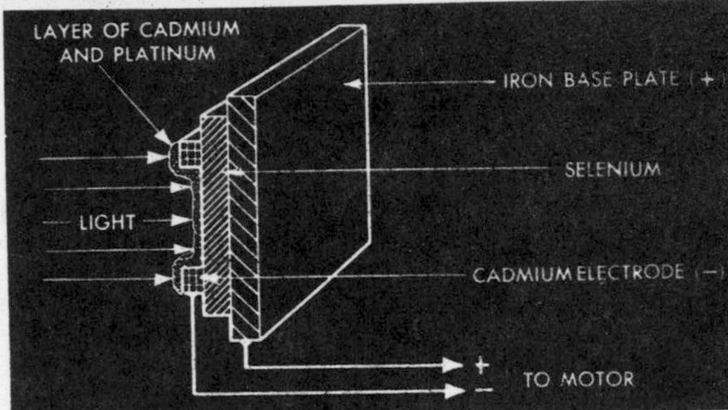

Top, Old Sol turns this electric motor. Drawing shows one of the motor's cells. Sunlight liberates electrons in selenium, which pass into cadmium-platinum plate to charge it negatively. Below, in another solar power plant the heat turns the motor

Smithsonian Institution photo

Street. But the process of generating the light is more like that which occurs in the sun. Atoms are bombarded by electrons and other minute projectiles, electrically excited in this way and made to glow.

Power plants are not driven by atomic power as you might suppose. It was known as early as 1950 that an atomic power plant would have to be larger and much more expensive than a fuel-burning plant to be efficient. Atomic power proves its worth in Canada, South America and the Far East, but in tropical countries it cannot compete with solar power. It is as hopeless in 2000 as it was in 1950 to drive machinery directly by atomic energy. Engineers can do no more than utilize the heat generated by converting uranium into plutonium. The heat is used to drive engines, and the engines in turn drive electric generators. A good deal of thorium is used because uranium 235 is scarce.

Because of the heavy investment that has to be made in a uranium or thorium power plant, the United States government began seriously to consider the possibilities of solar radiation in 1949. Theoretically, 5000 horsepower in terms of solar heat fall on an acre of the earth's surface every day.

Because they sprawl over large surfaces, solar engines are profitable in 2000 only where land is cheap. They are found in deserts that can be made to bloom again, and in tropical lands where there is usually no coal or oil. Many farmhouses in the United States are heated by solar rays and some cooking is done by solar heat.

The first successful atomically driven liners began to run in 1970 after the U. S. Navy had carried on many expensive, large-scale secret experiments. Outwardly the liners are not much different from the Queen Mary and Queen Elizabeth, but they have much more cargo and passenger space because it is no longer necessary to carry about 12,000 tons of fuel.

The metallurgical research that makes the gas turbines in the power plants and in the trans-Atlantic liners possible has influenced both civil engineering and architecture. Steel is used only

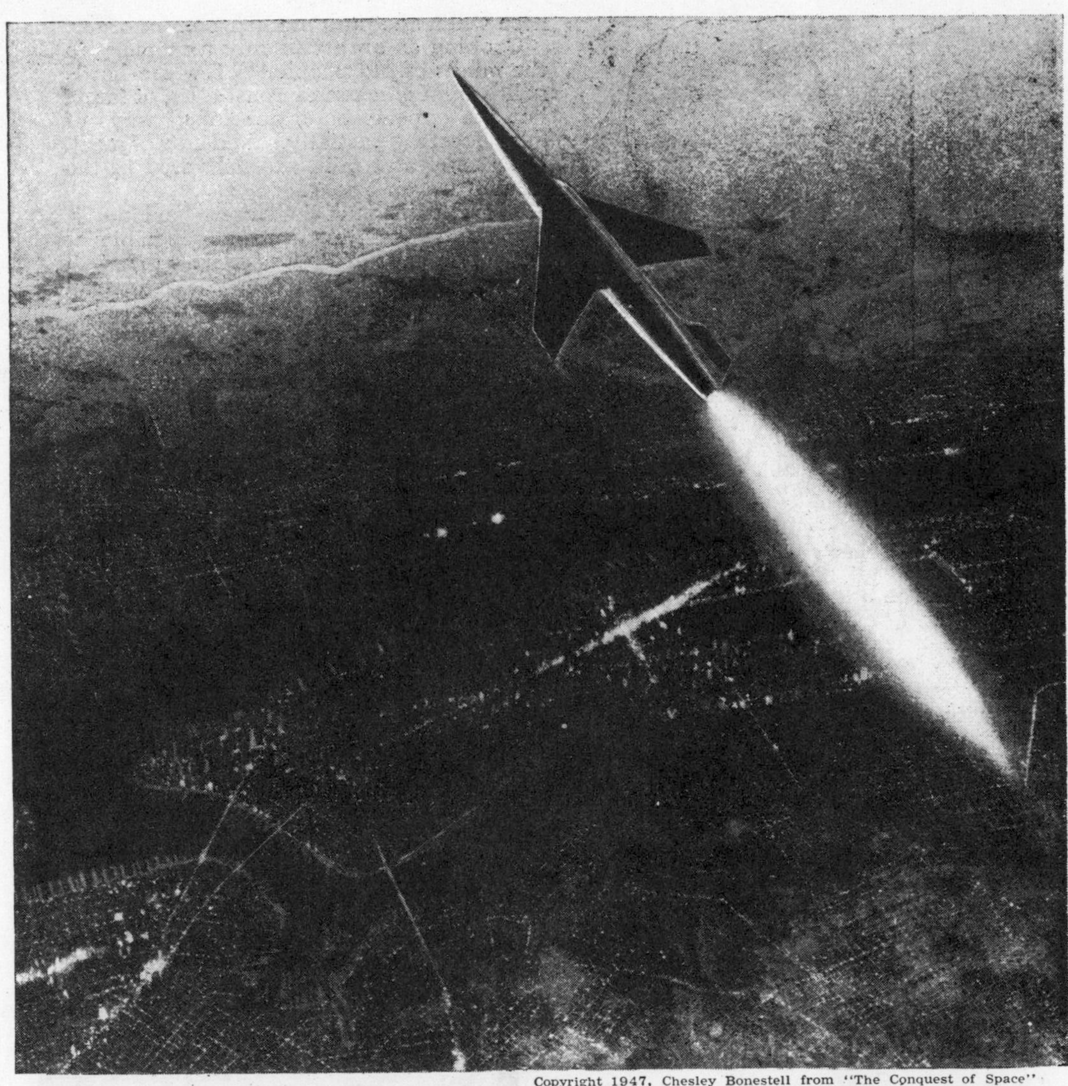

Copyright 1947, Chesley Bonestell from "The Conquest of Space"

In 2000, rocket passengers may arch through space from New York to San Francisco in less than two hours

In a democracy, under free enterprise, it was easy for the ordinary citizen to become conversant with and enthusiastic about the accomplishments of science. For it was the ordinary citizen who made some of the greatest contributions. It was he who proved the market and the testing grounds for the practical applications of scientific research. It was his whim, his preference, which forced the evolution of the automobile, the airplane, the modern house, the electrical appliances, the labor-saving machinery

for cutting tools and for massive machinery. The light metals have largely displaced it. Ways have been found to change the granular structure so that a metal is ultrastrong in a desired direction and weaker in other directions. As a result, the framework of an industrial or office building or apartment house is an almost lace-like lattice.

Thanks to these alloys, to plastics and to other artificial materials, houses differ from those of our own time. The Dobson house has light-metal walls only four inches thick. There is a sheet of insulating material an inch or two thick with a casing of sheet metal on both sides.

This Dobson air-conditioned house is not a prefabricated structure, though all its parts are mass-produced. Metal, sheets of plastic and aerated clay (clay filled with bubbles so that it resembles petrified sponge) are cut to size on the spot. In the center of this eight-room house is a unit that contains all the utilities—air-conditioning apparatus, plumbing, bathrooms, showers, electric range, electric outlets. Around this central unit the house has been pieced together. Some of it is poured plastic—the floors, for instance. By 2000, wood, brick and stone are ruled out because they are too expensive.

It is a cheap house. With all its furnishings, Joe Dobson paid only $5000 for it. Though it is galeproof and weatherproof, it is built to last only about 25 years. Nobody in 2000 sees any sense in building a house that will last a century.

Everything about the Dobson house is

As Waldemar Kaempffert points out in this article, many of the prophecies he makes here are already in process of development or in the testing stage. But their general application, and the form in which they make their final appearance, must await the inevitable "production lag"–the sort of lag that preceded the automobile, telephone, airplane, radio and television

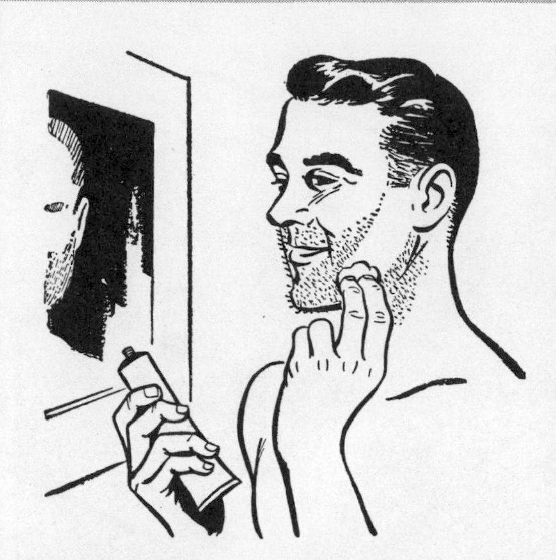

No more bouts with the razor for man of tomorrow. He'll whisk away whiskers with a chemical solution

synthetic in the best chemical sense of the term. When Joe Dobson awakens in the morning he uses a depilatory. No soap or safety razor for him. It takes him no longer than a minute to apply the chemical, wipe it off with the bristles and wash his face in plain water.

This Dobson house is not as highly mechanized as you may suppose, chiefly because of the progress made by the synthetic chemists. There are no dish-washing machines, for example, because dishes are thrown away after they have been used once, or rather put into a sink where they are dissolved by superheated water. Two dozen soluble plastic plates cost a dollar. They dissolve at about 250 degrees Fahrenheit, so that boiling-hot soup and stews can be served in them without inviting a catastrophe. The plastics are derived from such inexpensive raw materials as cottonseed hulls, oat hulls, Jerusalem artichokes, fruit pits, soy beans, bagasse, straw and wood pulp.

When Jane Dobson cleans house she simply turns the hose on everything. Why not? Furniture (upholstery included), rugs, draperies, unscratchable floors — all are made of synthetic fabric or waterproof plastic. After the water has run down a drain in the middle of the floor (later concealed by a rug of synthetic fiber) Jane turns on a blast of hot air and dries everything. A detergent in the water dissolves any resistant dirt. Tablecloths and napkins are made of woven paper yarn so fine that the untutored eye mistakes it for linen. Jane Dobson throws soiled "linen" into the incinerator. Bed sheets are of more substantial stuff, but Jane Dobson has only to hang them up and wash them down with a hose when she puts the bedroom in order.

Cooking as an art is only a memory in the minds of old people. A few die-hards still broil a chicken or roast a leg of lamb, but the experts have developed ways of deep-freezing partially baked cuts of meat. Even soup and milk are delivered in the form of frozen bricks.

This expansion of the frozen-food industry and the changing gastronomic habits of the nation have made it necessary to install in every home the electronic industrial stove which came out of World War II. Jane Dobson has one of these electronic stoves. In eight seconds a half-grilled frozen steak is thawed; in two minutes more it is ready to serve. It never takes Jane Dobson more than half an hour to prepare what Tottenville considers an elaborate meal of several courses.

Some of the food that Jane Dobson buys is what we miscall "synthetic." In the middle of the 20th century statisticians were predicting that the world would starve to death because the population was increasing more rapidly than the food supply. By 2000, a vast amount of research has been conducted to exploit principles that were embryonic in the first quarter of the 20th century. Thus sawdust and wood pulp are converted into sugary foods. Discarded paper table "linen" and rayon underwear

Already available is electronic stove which can prepare meal in 75 seconds. It may replace present ranges

General Electric photo

are bought by chemical factories to be converted into candy.

Of course the Dobsons have a television set. But it is connected with the telephones as well as with the radio receiver, so that when Joe Dobson and a friend in a distant city talk over the telephone they also see each other. Businessmen have television conferences. Each man is surrounded by half a dozen television screens on which he sees those taking part in the discussion. Documents are held up for examination; samples of goods are displayed. In fact, Jane Dobson does much of her shopping by television. Department stores obligingly hold up for her inspection bolts of fabric or show her new styles of clothing.

Automatic electronic inventions that seem to have something like intelligence integrate industrial production so that all the machines in a factory work as units in what is actually a single, colossal organism. In the Orwell Helicopter Corporation's plant only a few trouble shooters are visible, and these respond to lights that flare up on a board whenever a vacuum tube burns out or there is a short circuit. By holes punched in a roll of paper, every operation necessary to produce a helicopter is indicated. The punched roll is fed into a machine that virtually gives orders to all the other machines in the plant. The holes in the paper indicate exactly how long a reamer is to smooth the inside of a cylinder, just when a stamping machine is to pass a sheet of aluminum along to its neighbor with orders to punch 22 holes in indicated places. There are mechanical wrenches that obediently turn nuts on bolts and stop all by themselves when the bolts are in place, shears that know exactly where to cut a sheet of metal for a perfect fit.

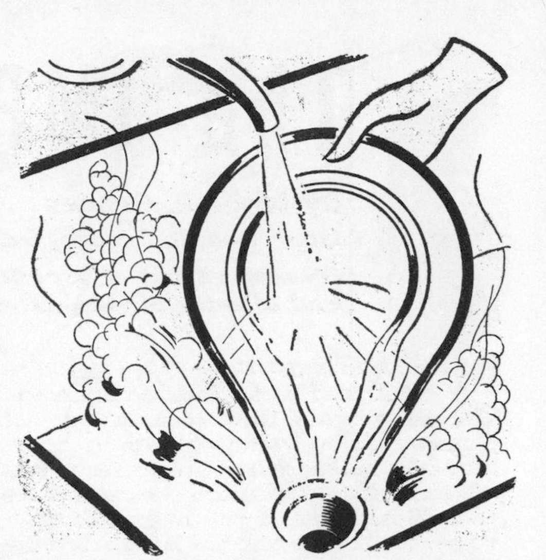

Housewives in 50 years may wash dirty dishes—right down the drain! Cheap plastic would melt in hot water

Inches-deep lake on roof already cools Southern homes and may become important air-conditioning method

Pomerance & Breines drawing

Thus the American dream continues to unfold. From Benjamin Franklin on, a part of the American heritage has been "Yankee ingenuity." Even Thomas Jefferson, who eyed industrial expansion with some apprehension, saw the need for technical progress, and wrote of the advisability of offering Europe's skilled artisans special inducements to immigrate to America. Today the average American's home contains more wonders than a king's castle in previous centuries. It appeared that man had just about mastered technology—it remained for him to solve his economic, political and moral problems

The IMPACT of the

By Leslie R. Groves
Lieut. Gen. U. S. Army Ret.
(Wartime Chief of Atomic Energy Commission and Director of Manhattan Project)

Men had barely come to appreciate the enigmatic threat of the A-bomb when behind it loomed the hydrogen bomb—a thousand times more powerful and many times more mysterious in its future possibilities. If the A-bomb could take man back to the Dark Ages, the hydrogen bomb might remove him from the face of the earth forever

MILITARY implications of the hydrogen bomb lead us far into the unknown. The limitations of the human mind do not permit such an excursion without reference to or guidance from proven facts. It is not difficult to understand the capabilities of a 16-inch gun if one is familiar with those of a 12-inch one; but it is not so easy to understand them if one's experience is limited to a brief acquaintance with a .22-caliber rifle. The destructive power of the atomic bomb, as it was exploded over Japan, and its influence on international affairs since then, gives us the foundation on which we can build our understanding of the hydrogen bomb.

I would like to emphasize first that no one really knows whether a hydrogen bomb can be designed and built; no one can say what effort would have to go into its manufacture; no one can be sure just how difficult it would be to deliver it on a target, nor exactly how great would be its power.

We do know, however, that the first atomic bombs were difficult to design and both difficult and expensive to manufacture. We know that although they were successfully delivered on enemy targets almost 2000 miles away from the take-off base, the enemy air defense was weak. We can say with certainty, that the single atomic bomb, model 1945, dropped on Hiroshima, not only effectively destroyed that city, but killed at least 70,000 Japanese and injured as many more. We also know that the radius of complete destruction of this bomb and of the bomb dropped on Nagasaki was about 1½ miles. Also, it is a fact that the development of the atomic bomb brought the war with Japan to a speedy conclusion, and that it thus saved thousands—possibly hundreds of thousands—of American dead and wounded.

Since V-J Day, the possession by the United States of the atomic bomb has greatly strengthened our international position, particularly with respect to Russia. This has enabled us to remain at peace and without the sacrifice of any of our American ideals.

When we try to anticipate the effects of weapons as powerful as the hydrogen bomb, we must face its possibilities calmly. We must assume that the hydrogen bomb can be made not only by us but by Russia; that it can be made at a not-too-excessive cost, giving due consideration to the economic capabilities of both nations; that it can be delivered on almost any target on the earth's surface; and that its power will be at least several times as great as that of the atomic bomb. And, possibly—if we are to give credence to recent news reports—it will be as much as 1000 times as powerful.

If we are to explore the problem of the hydrogen bomb intelligently, we must not limit ourselves to the strictly military implications in strategy and tactics, but we must consider the effects in the realms of international statesmanship and of diplomacy, or, as is the case today, in that of the conduct of the cold war.

Only a few years ago we hoped—and most of the world hoped with us—that the victorious conclusion of World War II would bring with it lasting peace. The more optimistic among us thought that there would never again be even the threat of conflict. While our desire for peace may be as strong as ever, today we are doubtful as to its certainty. We have seen that there is at large in the world community, one nation, Russia, which is bent on dominating all others. Treaties, promises and agreements mean nothing to the men in the Kremlin unless they are to their own immediate advantage. We are faced today with the certainty that only the strength of the United States of America stands between Russia and the fulfillment of the Russian dreams of mastering the world. To put it bluntly, we are now faced with the choice of either ultimately submitting to Russia or of maintaining a strong and effective military policy. Our military establishment must be of such strength that Russia will remain convinced of our ability to resist any aggressive action on her part vigorously and successfully.

The ultimate aim of all military operations is the destruction of the enemy's will or determination to fight or to continue his resistance. That aim was realized with the

Hydrogen Bomb

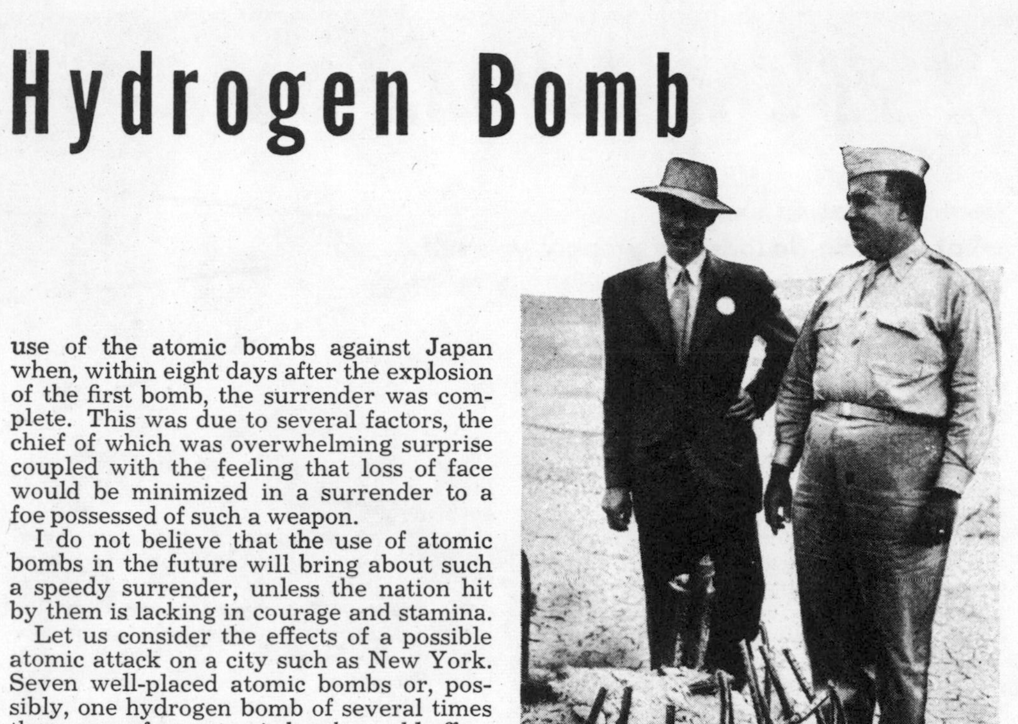

Lieut. Gen. Leslie R. Groves (right) confers with Dr. J. R. Oppenheimer at scene of atomic test blast

use of the atomic bombs against Japan when, within eight days after the explosion of the first bomb, the surrender was complete. This was due to several factors, the chief of which was overwhelming surprise coupled with the feeling that loss of face would be minimized in a surrender to a foe possessed of such a weapon.

I do not believe that the use of atomic bombs in the future will bring about such a speedy surrender, unless the nation hit by them is lacking in courage and stamina.

Let us consider the effects of a possible atomic attack on a city such as New York. Seven well-placed atomic bombs or, possibly, one hydrogen bomb of several times the power of one atomic bomb, could effectively destroy downtown Manhattan and all of New York's water-front facilities whether in Manhattan, in Brooklyn or on the Jersey shore. Any attack of such power would effectively destroy New York as a source of military and economic strength to our country. A hydrogen bomb of 1000 times the explosive power of the atomic bomb would extend this destruction farther into residential districts, would destroy more wealth and kill more people, but the military effect would not be much greater. A city like Washington would need only one hydrogen bomb to destroy it effectively as the seat of our government, instead of the three atomic bombs necessary to accomplish the same damage.

Since the conclusion of World War I, we have had with us the horrifying stories put out by the advocates of surprise aerial attacks. We have had pictured to us the thousands of bombing planes striking without warning other than that of strained international relations. And certainly no one has ever assumed that the relations would have to be more strained than those of recent years between Russia and ourselves. I believe that only behind an iron curtain could such attacks be prepared without some inkling of warning leaking out. Fortunately for us, and for those peace-loving nations which depend upon us for their protection from Russia's all-consuming desire for conquest, the iron curtain is still too far away to permit the mounting in the near future of any such large-scale attack. Today, it would even be difficult for Russia to make such a surprise attack with atomic bombs.

The first half of the 20th century has seen war change from being essentially limited to combat on the field of battle between military forces in uniform. We have seen the beginnings of modern total warfare. We would be closing our eyes to the inevitable if we did not realize that in future wars, if we are so unfortunate as to have them, all elements of the populations of the nations involved will be precipitated into the struggle. Our military strength has become so increasingly dependent upon industrial strength that everyone, regardless of age or sex, will become in effect a part of the war effort. No one who has read the news accounts of the recent trials behind the iron curtain, or of our troubles in Berlin, or of the Russian slave camps, can have any doubt but that the Soviet leaders would do anything they thought might be to their advantage.

The awesome A-bomb did have physical limits—the H-bomb had no theoretical limitations. A ton, or even 10 tons of heavy hydrogen—deuterium or tritium—might be used. The first A-bomb destroyed an area one mile in radius, and caused fire and flash damage to another two-thirds mile. A hydrogen bomb might destroy an area 10 miles in radius, or 300 square miles, and damage an area of 1200 square miles—about the size of Rhode Island

The question hovered in the back of everyone's mind: Would I survive an atomic bomb? The answer from science was discouraging: There was no real defense, no place to hide. There were, however, certain things that people could do . . . certain things they should know . . . for their protection in the event of an atomic attack

IF THE A-BOMBS BURST—

Here is what to expect, what you can do today to prepare yourself, what you can do then to survive

By Clifford B. Hicks

Part I

8:15 a.m., August 6, 1945. A single plane flies over the city. The only warning is a blinding flash of light. A ball of fire explodes in the sky, hanging there for a moment as it grows in size and fury. Then in a crackling instant the world's second atomic explosion races down to strike the earth at a spot called Hiroshima.

Sixty seconds later 70,000 Japanese are dead, caught above ground. The heart of the city has been blasted into rubble which still plummets down on the dead and dying.

10:15 a.m., January 2, 1950. A stenographer in Manhattan shrugs her shoulders over her mid-morning cup of coffee and says to her girl friend, "I'm tellin' you, there's nothing you can do to save yourself—just one bomb will wipe out New York. Me, I'm headin' for the country if things get worse."

At the same moment the sky above Chicago's Loop is split by a bright flash of lightning from a sudden winter storm. A nervous executive freezes in terror for an instant, then smiles sheepishly as he returns to the morning mail. But he can't help wondering whether the bomb would demolish his home and kill his family in a suburb 14 miles away.

Now, 4½ years after the atom bomb dropped toward its first target, the threat of a nuclear fireball hangs over every major American city. The residents of New York or Gary, Washington or San Francisco must

Japanese landscape: Main Street, Hiroshima, shortly after the first atomic air burst. Reinforced concrete withstood blast the best

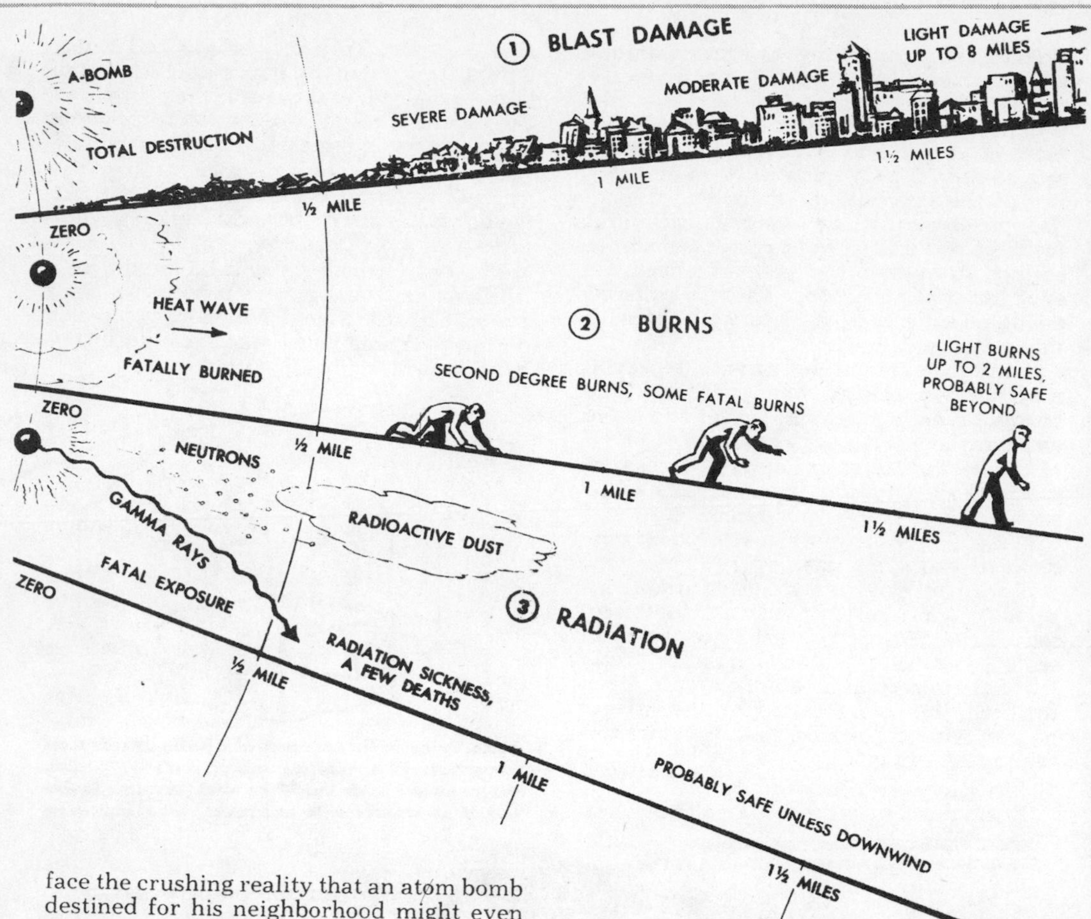

An A-bomb kills three ways—by blast, burns and radiation. About half the casualties at Hiroshima and Nagasaki were from blast. The burns were caused by heat flashing out from the bomb's center at a temperature of one million degrees centigrade. Afterward comes deadly radiation, of which there are three kinds. Gamma rays penetrate human tissues, but do not render surroundings radioactive. Neutrons cause death and radioactivity, but their effective range is shorter than gamma rays. The long-time effect of radiation is caused by radioactive dust which settles over the bombed area, making any movement dangerous until it is dispersed

Blast, burns and radiation cause all the casualties in an A-bomb burst. In diagram above, the legends show the effect of each of these three dangers at various distances from ground zero. Whether you live or die depends upon your location and protection

face the crushing reality that an atom bomb destined for his neighborhood might even now be winging its way across the curve of the world.

After Hiroshima, Americans soaked up the idea that they owned a superweapon. "There's no defense." Now, the Manhattan stenographer and the Chicago suburbanite shrug their shoulders in resignation. They are victims of a distorted belief that an entire city can disappear in a whiff of nuclear fission. If a bomb drops, the city dweller figures, there's little he can do to save himself or his family.

There are a great many things he can do. Hundreds of scientists, under guidance of the Atomic Energy Commission, have been groping into the unknown since 1945, working toward a realistic appraisal of the bomb. With full respect for the awesome power of the weapon, they have found that:

No big city will disappear in the burst of one Hiroshima-type bomb.

There is much less danger from radiation than originally supposed.

Shelters are effective. (In Nagasaki, a few hundred people who were in tunnels almost directly beneath the burst of the A-bomb are alive and healthy today.)

Underground shelters provide the best protection from atomic blast. Outside, the victim had best leap into a doorway and cover as much skin area as possible. The only real protection, of course, lies in the prevention of an atomic explosion in the first place. Nobody yet seems to have found exactly how to do this but there are plenty of ideas about it. Members of Congress, advocates of world government, the United Nations, and others including the Armed Forces and some earnest individuals are all desperately seeking an answer. The whole course of civilization may well depend on the degree of their success

At this stage not many American families will consider an Anderson shelter, or even a cave in the back yard. The next best bet is to prepare the strongest spot in the basement of your home or apartment building as a shelter. Likely this will be in one corner of the foundation, where you'll have the protection of two strong structural walls. If you don't want to pour a concrete ceiling, strengthen the joists overhead. Be sure the spot you choose has two exits, as a single exit can be clogged with debris if the building caves in.

Stock your chosen shelter with items you may need—a shovel, rope, jack for lifting beams, an ax, a hose, a flashlight and a fire extinguisher or container of sand. Get rid of fire hazards in your home. At Nagasaki, the heat wave ignited dry materials as far as 10,000 feet from ground zero.

Fix a screen or cloth inside your windows to stop flying glass.

Stock your shelter with medications, especially bandages for cuts and ointment for burns. Store some drinking water in sealed jars, as the water pressure likely will fade to zero in an atomic attack. Open food may be contaminated by the fall-out so keep enough canned food in your shelter to last you a few days.

When an alert sounds.

Don't use the telephone. Don't rush outside in panic. Turn off the gas and water where they enter the house and check the pilot lights to make sure they are extinguished. Pull the master electric switch. Then join your family in the shelter.

Lie down on your stomach against the wall. If you notice a sudden bright light, the bomb has burst. Immediately cross your arms over your head.

The only warning you'll have will be a brilliant flash of light, so bright you can't mistake it. Don't look! Whether you live or die may depend upon what you do in the next second.

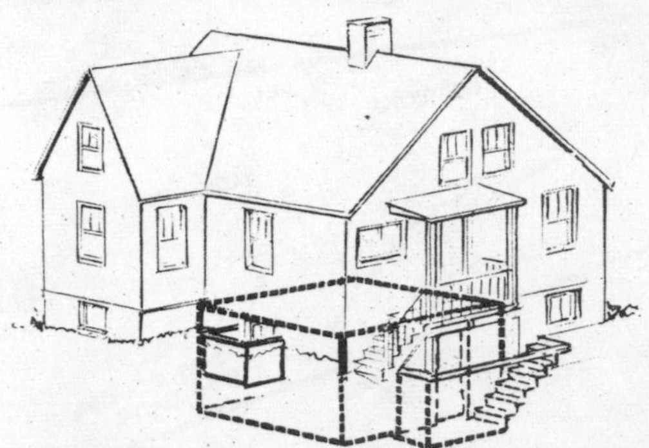

Bomb shelter in the basement of a home affords some protection. If a concrete ceiling can't be poured, the overhead joists should be strengthened. Shelter should be stocked with equipment, food and water

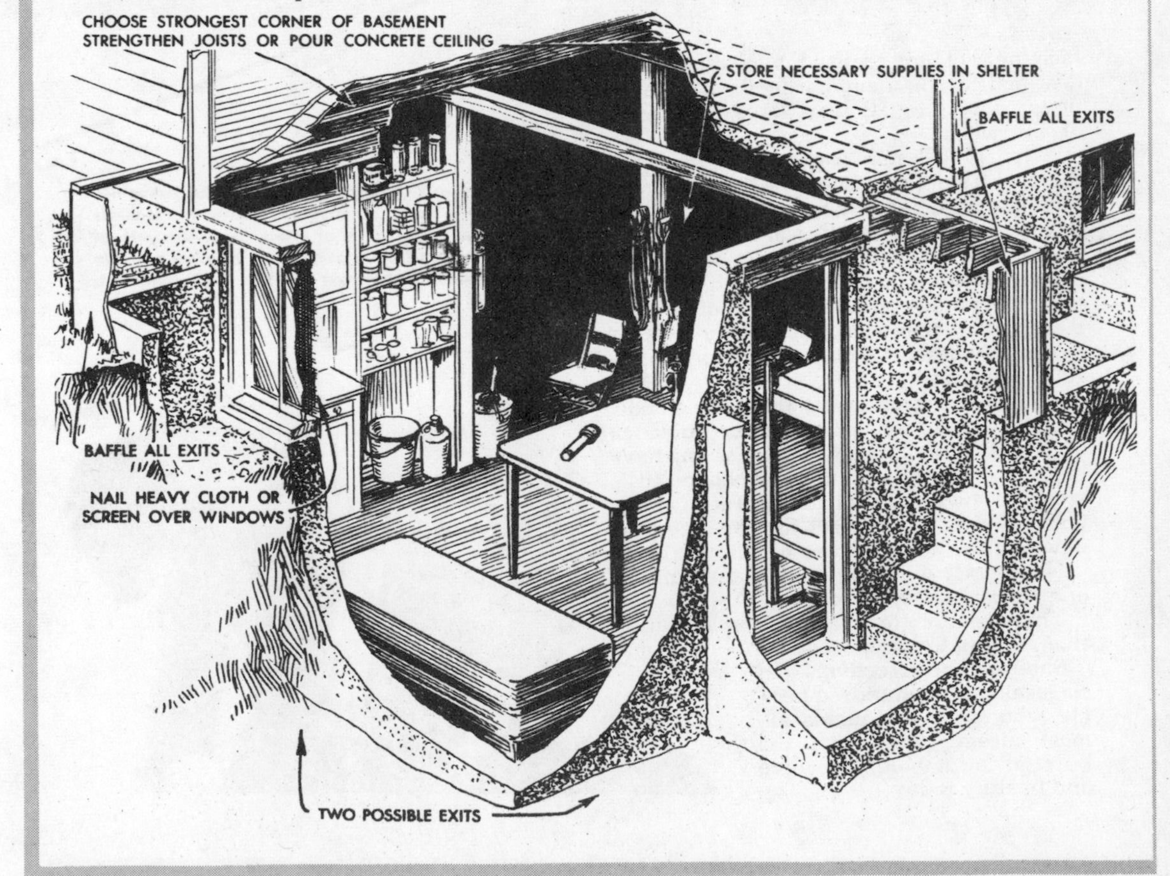